OUTLINES
OF ENTOMOLOGY

OUTLINES
OF ENTOMOLOGY

R.G. Davies

Emeritus Professor of Entomology
Imperial College, University of London

SEVENTH EDITION

London   New York
CHAPMAN AND HALL

First published in 1942 by Methuen and Co Ltd
Second edition 1944, third edition 1947
Fourth edition 1949
Fifth edition revised by O.W. Richards and R.G. Davies 1959
Reprinted 1961, reprinted with corrections 1967
Reprinted 1970, reprinted 1973
Sixth edition published in 1978 by Chapman and Hall Ltd
11 New Fetter Lane, London EC4P 4EE
Reprinted 1981,
Seventh edition 1988
Published in the USA by Chapman and Hall
29 West 35th Street, New York NY 10001

© 1988 R.G. Davies

Typeset in 10.5/12 Bembo by Photoprint, Torquay
Printed in Great Britain at the University Press, Cambridge

ISBN 0 412 26670 9 (Hardback)
ISBN 0 412 26680 6 (Paperback)

British Library Cataloguing in Publication Data

Davies, R.G. (Richard Gareth), 1920–
    Outlines of entomology. — 7th ed.
    1. Insects
    I. Title II. Imms, Augustus Daniel.
    Imms' outlines of entomology
    595.7

    ISBN 0–412–26670–9
    ISBN 0–412–26680–6 Pbk

Library of Congress Cataloging in Publication Data

Davies, R. G. (Richard Gareth), 1920–
    Outlines of entomology. — 7th ed. / R.G. Davies.
        p.   cm.
    Enl. ed. of: Outlines of entomology / A.D. Imms.
    Bibliography: p.
    Includes index.
    ISBN 0–412–26670–9. ISBN 0–412–26680–6 (pbk.)
    1. Insects. I. Imms, A. D. (Augustus Daniel), 1880–1949.
Outlines of entomology. II. Title.
QL463.D38 1988
595.7—dc19   88–10865
                                                         CIP

Contents

CONTENTS

Preface to the seventh edition

The present edition may be regarded as a descendant, much changed and greatly enlarged, of the late Dr A.D. Imms' *Outlines of Entomology*, first published in 1942. This went through three further editions without much change, but after the death of the original author a fifth, revised edition by Professor O.W. Richards and myself appeared in 1959 and a sixth in 1978. The book now appears in a considerably extended version in which I have tried to provide a more balanced introduction to the whole field of modern entomology by dealing with several aspects of the subject not discussed at all in previous editions. Thus, in addition to innumerable lesser changes in the sections on insect structure, function, development, classification and phylogeny, I have completely recast the earlier chapter on some important modes of life in insects. This now includes a far wider range of biological topics well exemplified by the insects and should, I hope, appeal not only to those already dedicated to entomology but also to others with more general biological interests. A completely new chapter on the biology of insect populations has also been added and may serve to indicate the debt which modern ecological theory owes to work on insect populations. It should hardly be necessary to apologize for introducing a certain amount of elementary mathematics into this account of a subject which is now among the most highly quantitative of biological disciplines. A third new section is that devoted to the biology of a selection of injurious insects and the principles that underlie modern integrated methods of pest management. The examples here are drawn from many parts of the world and should help to demonstrate the extent to which practical control of insect pests depends on an understanding of their biology. The book is now more fully illustrated, with most of the figures newly redrawn and relettered so as to make them more immediately intelligible. Lastly, a much larger classified bibliography aims at introducing more advanced students to the ever-increasing range of specialized publications on entomology.

R.G.D.
London, November 1987

1

Introduction

Insects are segmented animals with a relatively tough integument and jointed limbs. They breathe by air-tubes or tracheae, and the body is divided into head, thorax and abdomen. The head is the sensory and feeding centre, bearing the mouthparts and a single pair of antennae, perhaps homologous with the antennules of the Crustacea; compound eyes are usually present and often simple eyes or ocelli. The thorax is the locomotor centre, carrying three pairs of legs and usually two pairs of wings. The abdomen is the metabolic and reproductive centre; it contains the gonads and organs of digestion and excretion, and usually bears special structures used in copulation and egg-laying. When it leaves the egg, the young insect differs more or less extensively from the adult form and its development therefore involves some degree of metamorphosis.

The number of known species of insects is difficult to estimate, but certainly exceeds that of all other animals together. That approximately 900 000 different insects have been named and described is probably a conservative estimate. About 7000 new species are described each year and there is no doubt that the numbers yet to be discovered will exceed those now known. The single order Coleoptera, or beetles, alone consists of over 370 000 named species. Even the one family Curculionidae, or weevils, includes more than 60 000 known species, while the Carabidae, or ground beetles, number about 25 000 kinds.

This remarkable capacity for differentiation shown by insects does not lend itself to exact analysis, but it is of interest to consider some attributes which have probably helped the members of this class to attain their dominant position in the animal kingdom.

1. Capacity for flight. Most insects are not wholly confined to the ground and vegetation, but are also able to fly. The possession of wings provides a unique means of dispersal, of discovering their mates, of seeking food and of escaping from their enemies. Such a combination of advantages is not found elsewhere among invertebrate animals.

2. Adaptability. No other class of animals has so thoroughly invaded and colonized the globe as the Insecta. Their distribution ranges from

the poles to the equator; every species of flowering plant provides food for one or more kind of insect, while decomposing organic materials attract and support many thousands of different species. Very many are parasites on or within the bodies of other insects or of some very different animals, including vertebrates. The soil and fresh waters support their own extensive insect fauna. Great heat and cold are not impassable barriers since some species can withstand temperatures of about −50° C, while others live in hot springs at over 40° C or in deserts where the midday surface temperature may be twenty degrees higher than this. A few species live in what seem almost impossible environments; the larva of an Ephydrid fly, *Psilopa petrolei*, inhabits pools of crude petroleum in California, and some beetles have been reported from argol (containing 80% potassium bitartrate), opium, Cayenne pepper, sal ammoniac and strychnine.

3. Size. The relatively small size of most insects has many advantages. Each individual requires little food, so large populations may occupy small habitats that often also offer security from enemies. Thus, several leaf-mining larvae may develop in the tissues between the upper and lower epidermal layers of a single small leaf, a weevil will complete its life cycle in one small gorse seed, while a moderately-sized fungus will support very many beetles and fly larvae.

In fact, insects vary greatly in size, from minute Hymenopteran parasites about 0.2 mm long to forms like the bulky Goliath Beetle with a length of up to 120 mm. However, these are extremes, and both very large and very small insects suffer disadvantages which do not apply to the more numerous species of intermediate size. If a very small insect is wetted, the weight and surface tension of the encompassing water film soon exhaust its efforts to free itself. On the other hand, very large species are subject to a limitation imposed by their characteristic method of tracheal respiration. Oxygen passes along these breathing tubes by gaseous diffusion, and the physical law which this process follows is such that an increase in the size of an insect is not accompanied by a proportional increase in the rate at which oxygen can reach the tissues (p. 74). When an insect reaches a diameter of about 2 cm, therefore, its method of respiration is liable to incommode it and make it sluggish – a further increase in bulk would soon make it too inert to survive competition with other organisms. For such reasons the relatively gigantic forms which do occur, as among beetles, grasshoppers, water-bugs and fossil dragonflies, form a very small proportion of their own groups. Furthermore, even among large insects very few have a diameter of more than about 1–1.5 cm, though there may be a great extension in the length of the body or the area of flat, plate-like projections from it. Thus the giant stick insect *Pharnacia serratipes* is up to 260 mm long but retains a proportionately attenuated form. Some of the great fossil dragonflies of Carboniferous times had wings exceeding 60 cm in expanse but with typically slender bodies. The giant Noctuid moth *Erebus agrippina* has a wingspread of 280 mm, but its slender body is no more than 55 mm long, and the same applies to the giant Atlas moths and to Oriental butterflies of the genus *Troides*.

4. The skeleton. The skeleton of insects, like that of other arthropods, is an exoskeleton and has many features of great significance. It consists of hard regions – sclerites – separated by soft membranous zones, and therefore combines strength and rigidity with flexibility. It protects the insect mechanically, provides firm sites for the attachment of the muscles which move the body, acts sometimes as a mechanism for storing energy, and is invaginated in various ways to support some internal organs and to line the tracheae, parts of the gut, and a few other structures.

Its construction in the form of a series of jointed tubes surrounding the body and appendages gives the exoskeleton a much greater power of resistance to bending than the endoskeleton of a vertebrate. The two cases have been contrasted by the Russian writer Chetverikov. In Fig. 1, (a) represents a cross-section of an insect limb with its tubular exoskeleton while (b) and (c) are cross-sections through two vertebrate limbs, each with its axial endoskeleton. It is known from physical principles that the modulus of resistance to bending in a solid cylinder and in a hollow one is given by the formulae:

$$M = \frac{\pi D}{32} \quad \text{and} \quad M_1 = \frac{\pi(D_1{}^4 - d^4)}{32D_1}$$

where M and M_1 are the respective moduli and D is the diameter of the endoskeleton, while d and D_1 are the internal and external diameters of the exoskeleton. If, for the sake of argument, we take the case of $d = \frac{4}{5}D_1$ and compare figures (a) and (b), the cross-sectional areas of skeleton and muscle being the same in the two cases, then the formulae show that the limb with the solid axial endoskeleton will be nearly three times weaker than the one with the hollow exoskeleton. Further, it may be shown that to have the same strength as the exoskeleton of Fig. 1(a), an axial endoskeleton would take up 84% of the total diameter of the limb (Fig. 1c); under such conditions there would be little space left for musculature.

Because of its mechanical efficiency therefore, the insect skeleton combines great strength with lightness. Composed of an amazingly plastic material, it has lent itself to the most varied processes of evolutionary modification under the influence of natural selection. Increased deposition of cuticular substance has occurred in many ways and in adaptation to many different requirements. Especially to be noted are the immensely varied developments of form and size in the head and jaws; the growth of horns, spines and other processes; of bristles and of scales; of membranous wings and horny elytra; of stout fossorial legs; of needle-like ovipositors, and so forth. Furthermore, it is the exoskeleton which displays many of the structural characters that distinguish the many species of insects.

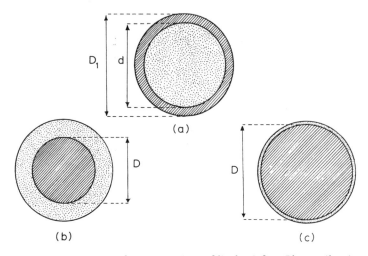

Fig. 1   Diagram of cross-section of limbs (after Chetverikov)
(a) Exoskeleton with internal diameter $d = \frac{4}{5}$ of external diameter D_1; (b), (c) endoskeletons. (Skeletons cross-hatched; musculature, etc. stippled.)

Because the exoskeleton is rigid and inextensible, the growing insect must shed it periodically. During this process of moulting the insect is somewhat vulnerable, but this disadvantage may be less real than it seems, for the sequence of moults is the basis on which have evolved the elaborate changes of form which occur in the life cycles of the higher insects and which have allowed the immature and adult stages to become adapted each to its own conditions of life.

5. Resistance to desiccation. Though some insects are aquatic or inhabit moist environments, the success of the class has depended to a considerable extent on an ability to survive under the relatively dry conditions of terrestrial life. The capacity of insects to resist desiccation and conserve water shows itself in many ways. The cuticle is provided with a thin layer of waxy material which greatly reduces transpiration from the surface of the body, and the openings of the tracheal system, known as spiracles, are provided with closing mechanisms or other devices which further reduce water loss, while permitting enough oxygen to enter. The principal excretory products of most insects are insoluble and therefore do not require a large volume of water for their

removal from the body in solution, while the terminal part of the alimentary canal reabsorbs water which would otherwise be lost in the faeces. Some insects living under unusually dry conditions depend to a considerable extent on the water produced when foodstuffs are oxidized within their bodies – the so-called metabolic water. Finally, in their reproductive behaviour, with internal fertilization and the habit of laying eggs whose impervious shell protects the developing embryo from desiccation, the insects are well adapted to terrestrial conditions.

6. Tracheal respiration. The characteristic tracheal respiratory system of insects tends to limit their size and requires modifications to offset this disadvantage and to restrict water loss. In other respects, however, tracheal respiration is very efficient, and the direct carriage of gaseous oxygen to within very short distances of the respiring tissues has enabled insects to evolve the very high rates of metabolic activity needed to achieve rapid flight. In fact, insect flight muscle is the most actively respiring animal tissue known, and the tracheal system shows several specially interesting adaptations to supply it with enough oxygen (e.g. p. 74). It is also worth emphasizing that though tracheal respiration probably arose and first evolved in terrestrial and aerial habitats, it has nevertheless been retained (though often with a closed tracheal system) in almost all of the insects that have returned to colonize aquatic environments secondarily. Only a relatively few very small insects are able to obtain enough oxygen by simple diffusion through their tissues.

7. Complete metamorphosis. The more highly evolved types of insect life-cycle entail a transition from the immature larval stages through a pupal phase into the winged, sexually mature adult (p. 106). This form of development, found for example in beetles, moths and flies, differs from the simpler, incomplete metamorphosis of, say, grasshoppers or cockroaches, in that it allows the larva and adult to exploit different food resources and occupy different ecological niches. Such a transition from larva to adult involves extensive anatomical, histological and functional changes, which occur mainly during the apparently quiescent pupal stage. The latter therefore represents an evolutionary innovation of great importance, as can be seen from the fact that insect species with a complete metamorphosis outnumber those with an incomplete metamorphosis by about ten to one and have successfully invaded a much greater range of habitats.

This short preamble reviews the more obvious factors that may have contributed to the success of the insects. It also helps to explain why they have persisted from pre-Carboniferous times with increasing diversity, far beyond that of any other class of animals. In the pages that follow the elementary features of insect structure and function are discussed. These are followed by a short account of development and metamorphosis, sections dealing with the classification and biology of the orders of insects, and an outline of their probable evolutionary history and relationships. Discussions of the principal modes of life of insects are then followed by an introduction to some aspects of insect ecology and to the biology and control of those species injurious to people, domestic animals and crops. Finally, a classified list of bibliographic references will enable the reader to pursue the main aspects of entomology in far greater detail.

2

Insect structure and function

THE INTEGUMENT AND ITS DERIVATIVES; COLORATION

The integument (Fig. 2). This consists of a cellular layer, the epidermis, with an outer non-cellular cuticle. The epidermis secretes the greater part of the cuticle and is responsible for dissolving and absorbing most of the old cuticle when the insect moults (p. 104) as well as repairing wounds and differentiating so as to determine the form and surface appearance of the insect. The cuticle forms the outer exoskeleton and is also present as a lining to the fore and hind intestine, to the tracheae and to other parts similarly formed by an ingrowth of the ectoderm or epidermis. Typically, it is composed of three layers:

1. The outermost layer, or *epicuticle*, less than 4 μm thick, consists mostly of a hardened protein, but also contains the waxes which are largely responsible for reducing water loss through the cuticle, as well as an outer 'cement layer'.

2. The *exocuticle* is a much thicker layer consisting mainly of chitin and proteins, the latter being 'tanned' by phenolic substances to produce a hard, brown material called sclerotin, which gives the cuticle its rigidity. The exocuticle is absent or reduced in the more flexible regions of the integument, and may be entirely absent from insects with a soft, thin cuticle.

3. The *endocuticle*, which is usually the thickest layer, also contains chitin and proteins, but the latter are not tanned and this part of the cuticle is therefore soft and flexible.

Both endocuticle and exocuticle consist of numerous laminae arranged approximately parallel to the surface and are traversed by very numerous pore canals, each of which may contain a thread-like cytoplasmic extension of the epidermis. Chitin, which makes up 25–60% of the dry weight of the cuticle, is a nitrogenous polysaccharide consisting of many acetylglucosamine residues joined end to end in long molecular chains. It is resistant to alkalis and dilute mineral acids, and can be detected by the van Wisselingh test: heating with concentrated potassium hydroxide at 160° C for 20 min converts it to chitosan which gives a rose-violet colour with 0.2% iodine in 1% sulphuric acid. In the cuticle the chitin forms ultramicroscopic fibres embedded in a protein matrix.

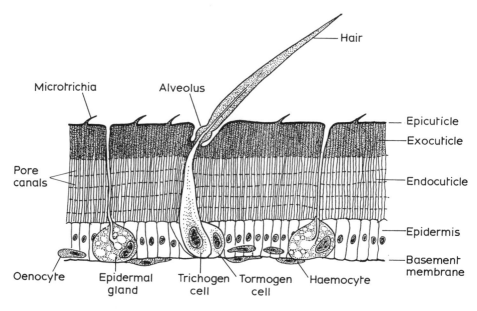

Fig.2   Integument of an insect, semi-schematic section.

Physiology of the cuticle. Many important physiological processes take place in the insect cuticle. These include the hardening and darkening of the exocuticle through sclerotization, with accompanying changes in mechanical properties; the waterproofing mechanisms that operate in the epicuticle; the temporary storage of energy in specialized cuticular regions and its release during locomotion; the surface phenomena involved in water repellence and adhesion to solid surfaces; and the permeability of the integument to oxygen, carbon dioxide, water and inorganic ions. The major structural and functional changes which occur in the cuticle during moulting and metamorphosis are also of great physiological interest, but are considered separately on pp. 104–13.

Sclerotin is formed when exocuticular proteins become 'tanned' through the linkage of adjacent protein chains by quinone or acetyl-dopamine molecules. These are formed in the integument by a series of enzymatically controlled reactions which, starting with the amino acid tyrosine, convert it first into *l*-dopa (*l*-hydroxyphenylalanine), followed by decarboxylation to dopamine and acetylation of the side-chain. The mechanical properties of insect cuticle can be studied by means similar to those used in investigating engineering structures. In this way it has been shown that the stress–strain relationships of cuticle entitle it to be regarded as a highly efficient skeletal material, comparable to bone and more effective than many artificial substances. A special cuticular protein known as resilin has a uniform three-dimensional configuration and behaves like rubber. It can be deformed readily, and when the deforming forces no longer act it will return to its original shape, thus imparting some elasticity to the cuticle. Blocks of resilin in the cuticle of the metathorax of fleas or near the wing-bases of other insects act as devices for the temporary storage of energy because of their deformability (see p. 27).

If the spiracles of an insect are occluded, very little water is lost through the cuticle by evaporation at normal temperatures. However, as the temperature is raised a relatively abrupt increase in transpiration occurs around a certain 'transition temperature' (which varies from 35 to 60° C according to species). This change is due to the disorganization of the epicuticular waxes which normally form a protective waterproofing film over the insect's body and thus play a major part in water conservation. Disruption of the layer by abrasion, experimentally or through the normal action of soil particles, may also lead to excessive water loss through the cuticle.

When a wax layer has formed on the outside of the cuticle, the insect's body becomes 'hydrofuge' and can no longer be wetted with water. This property of the cuticle enables some insects to walk or scull over the surface of ponds or streams, buoyed up, as it were, by the forces of surface tension. The cuticular hairs of some aquatic insects form a dense unwettable pile. This may also assist locomotion on the surface, as in the pondskaters (Gerridae), or it may allow an air bubble or air film to be trapped and used for respiration when the insect swims below the water surface, as in the backswimmers (Notonectidae). In mosquitoes special hydrofuge hairs ('palmate hairs') (Fig. 118d) may enable the larva to cling beneath the surface film, while the hydrofuge properties of the respiratory siphon enable it to be held in position to obtain access to atmospheric oxygen. The ability of many terrestrial insects to walk on vertical or overhanging surfaces is well known, and seems to depend on molecular forces between the cuticle and the substrate. In such cases the insect may have specialized adhesive hairs or flap-like pulvilli at the ends of the legs.

The relative impermeability of the cuticular surface to water does not hold for the finer branches of the tracheal system (tracheoles) which are freely permeable. Movement of water vapour along the larger tracheal trunks then leads to a substantial loss of water from the spiracles, which need to be provided with closing mechanisms (p. 68) if the insect is to survive outside humid environments. Many insects are also known to conserve water by absorbing it actively from the gut contents through the very thin cuticle lining the rectum. Most insects cannot absorb water from a saturated atmosphere, though a few have evolved the ability to do this through the lining of the rectum (flea larvae, *Tenebrio* larvae and, most effectively, the firebrat *Thermobia*). Waterproofing the cuticle of terrestrial insects has been accompanied by its low permeability to oxygen. The finer branches of the tracheal system are, however, increasingly permeable to oxygen, and this is especially true of the tracheoles. Many aquatic insects, such as the larvae of mayflies, dragonflies and Diptera, have a closed tracheal system into which oxygen diffuses through the cuticle of specialized gills, as well as through the general body surface. Carbon dioxide, unlike oxygen, can diffuse more readily through the cuticle, and much of it leaves the body through the tracheal walls and the surface cuticle.

The permeability of the cuticle to inorganic ions plays an important part in osmoregulation and excretion. Some aquatic insects, such as the larva of the alder-fly *Sialis*, have a cuticle that prevents the loss of sodium, potassium and chloride, thus helping the insect to conserve these physiologically important ions. In other cases the anal papillae of mosquito larvae, and even the gills of dragonfly and caddis-fly larvae, are able to absorb inorganic ions actively from the very low concentrations present in fresh water and so maintain an appropriate internal environment.

Integumentary processes. The surface of the cuticle bears two main types of outgrowths.

1. Rigid non-articulated processes; these include the microtrichia and spines. Microtrichia are minute, non-cellular, hair-like structures (Fig. 2) formed entirely of cuticle and often occurring in very large numbers on the wings of certain insects. Spines are large, hollow, heavily sclerotized, thorn-like processes of multicellular origin; they are well seen on the legs of cockchafers and dor-beetles (Scarabaeidae).

2. Movable articulated processes attached to the cuticle by a ring of articular membrane which may be sunk into a cuticular socket, or alveolus, or elevated on a tubercle; they include macrotrichia and spurs. Macrotrichia or setae (Fig. 2) are hollow extensions of the exocuticle and epicuticle. Each is secreted by the cytoplasmic outgrowth of a single modified epidermal cell, the trichogen cell, while the socket from which the seta protrudes is produced by another specialized epidermal cell, the tormogen cell. The following specially modified setae are known: (a) Clothing hairs which cover the general surface of the body and

appendages. These may be branched or plumose, as in the bees, or, when specially stiff, they form the bristles of, say, Tachinid flies. (b) Scales, such as occur in Lepidoptera and some Collembola, Diptera and Coleoptera. Essentially these are flattened setae, often with a striate surface and sometimes containing pigment. (c) Glandular setae, which serve as outlets for the secretions of epidermal glands; these include the silk-spinning hairs of Embioptera and the urticating hairs of some caterpillars, e.g. those of the Brown-tail Moth (*Euproctis chrysorrhoea*). (d) Sensory setae, which are more or less specialized in structure, and have one or more nerve cells at their base. They perceive various stimuli and are discussed further on p. 49. Spurs differ from setae in being thick-walled multicellular structures; they are often large and occur more especially on the tibiae of the legs.

Epidermal glands. These consist of one or more cells specially modified for the secretion of such materials as wax, lac and a variety of biologically important substances known as pheromones (p. 54) which influence the behaviour or development of other members of the species.

Apodemes. These are sclerotized cuticular ingrowths which collect-ively form the endoskeleton, providing sites for the attachment of muscles and sometimes supporting other organs (Fig. 13). They may be approximately tubular or flattened and, though the mouths of the invaginations sometimes persist, the apodeme usually becomes solid as the cuticle is laid down. The endoskeleton of the head is known as the tentorium (Fig. 3). It consists of paired anterior and posterior arms whose origins are visible externally as slit-like pits; the inner ends of the arms amalgamate to form the body of the tentorium, from near which a third, dorsal pair of arms often arises. The tentorium gives rigidity to the head capsule, provides attachments for muscles and supports the brain and oesophagus. The endoskeleton of the thorax (Figs 15 and 16) usually consists of dorsal phragmata, pleural apodemes and ventral apophyses. The abdominal segments and external genitalia may also bear apodemes (Fig. 11c).

Coloration. Insect colours fall into three groups: (a) those due to specific pigments (chemical colours); (b) those due to optical effects produced by special cuticular structures (physical colours); and (c) those produced by the presence together of pigment and colour-producing structures (combination or physicochemical colours).

Pigments may be present in the cuticle, the epidermis or the subepidermal tissues, and are substances, often of known chemical composition, which are coloured because they absorb some wavelengths of incident light and reflect others. The three most common groups of insect pigments are the melanins, the carotenoids and the pterines. The black or brown melanins of the cuticle are probably derived initially from the amino acid tyrosine by reactions in which the enzyme tyrosinase plays a part; the tyrosinase is generally distributed and melanic patterns depend on the localized occurrence of the tyrosine. The yellow or red carotenoids are characteristically synthesized by the plant on which the insect feeds; after ingestion, however, they persist with little or no alteration in the insect's tissues, either free or combined with protein. The pterines are a group of white, yellow, orange or red pigments that are chemically related to the purines; they are found in Pierine butterflies, wasps and other species.

Structural colours differ from pigmentary ones in several respects. They are altered or destroyed by physical changes in the cuticle, they disappear on immersion of the part concerned in liquids of the same refractive index as cuticle (about 1.55), they can be imitated by purely physical models and they cannot be bleached. Scattering, reflection and refraction of the light by particles which are large compared with the light wavelengths produce structural whites. Optical interference between reflections from a series of superimposed laminae of microscopic thickness produces the characteristic metallic or iridescent interference colours, such as those occurring in the wing scales of *Morpho* butterflies or in the diamond beetles *Entimus* and *Cyphus*. Diffraction colours, caused by the presence of closely spaced cuticular striae, are characteristic of some beetles.

Combination colours are much more common than purely structural ones. A structural blue may be combined with a yellow pigment to produce a brilliant green, as in some butterflies (*Troides*); or a pigmentary red in the walls of the wing scales of another butterfly, *Teracolus*, combines with a structural violet to give magenta.

SEGMENTATION AND BODY REGIONS

Segmentation. Though the cuticle forms a continuous investment over the whole body of an insect, it usually remains membranous and flexible along certain transverse infoldings, so that the body is divided externally into a series of segments separated by intersegmental membranes. This segmentation, which is a development of the even more complete metameric segmentation of the early embryo, also manifests itself in some internal organs. Thus, the body musculature, nervous system, tracheal system and heart all show, to varying degrees, a longitudinal repetition of parts. The cuticle of a segment or other region of the body may be further subdivided by sutures, a general term given to narrow membranous lines of flexibility, or to inflected

12

strengthening ridges (sulci), or to impressed lines of no obvious mechanical significance.

The body regions. The insect body consists of 20 primitive segments, all of which may be apparent in the embryo, grouped into three well-defined regions, or tagmata – the head, thorax and abdomen. The head is formed of six segments and an anterior non-segmental acron, all closely amalgamated to form a hard case, or head capsule. It reveals few indications of its segmental origin, apart from the possession of paired appendages. The thorax consists of three segments; each of these carries a pair of legs, and the second and third usually also carry the two pairs of wings. The thorax is connected with the head by the cervix, or neck, which is largely intersegmental in origin. The abdomen consists of 11 segments and a terminal non-segmental telson, but reduction and fusion in the anterior and posterior regions often results in only ten or fewer divisions being visible.

The divisions of a segment. In many soft-bodied larvae, such as those of blow-flies and other Diptera, the cuticle is membranous and each segment is a simple ring without division into separate areas. In most insects, however, a typical segment is divisible into four main regions; viz. a dorsal region (or tergum), a ventral region (or sternum), and, on either side, a lateral region (or pleuron). The cuticle of each of these regions may be differentiated into separate sclerites, in which case those composing the tergum are known as tergites, those of the sternum are termed sternites and those of the pleura are the pleurites.

The appendages. In the embryo each segment typically bears a pair of outgrowths or appendages which may be retained in post-embryonic life. An appendage is a jointed tube implanted in the pleuron of its side. Between two adjacent segments the cuticle is flexible and forms the articular membrane. Because of its jointed structure the whole or part of an appendage is movable by means of muscles. A typical insect appendage consists of a limb-base and a shaft. It is characteristic of the arthropod lineage to which the insects belong that their appendages are morphologically one-branched, or uniramous, structures; nothing comparable to the biramous appendages of the Crustacea occurs in the insects.

THE HEAD AND ITS APPENDAGES

The head-capsule. The exterior of the head is formed of several sclerites amalgamated to form a hard compact head capsule (Fig. 3). The dorsal region, or epicranium, is commonly divided by a bifurcating

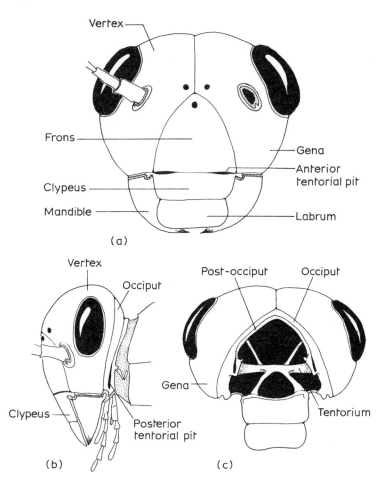

Fig. 3   Structure of the insect head–capsule
(a) Anterior view; (b) lateral view; (c) posterior view showing tentorium.

suture shaped like an inverted **Y**. This is the ecdysial cleavage line, sometimes known as the epicranial suture, its median part being the coronal suture and the two arms the frontal sutures. It is a line of thin cuticle along which the head-capsule of the immature insect breaks open at moulting. In the adult stage this is retained only in the more generalized insects; in specialized forms it is absent or replaced by an inflected strengthening ridge. The part of the head above the frontal sutures is the vertex; below them lies the frons, though the precise limits of the latter area are not easily defined. The frons usually bears the median ocellus and is bounded distally by a transverse epistomal sulcus (sometimes absent), which runs between the anterior tentorial pits.

Immediately anterior to the frons is the clypeus, to which the labrum, or upper lip, is hinged along the clypeo-labral sulcus. At the back of the head between the vertex and neck lies the occiput, while the side walls of the head, below and behind the eyes, are known as the genae; the latter may be separated from the facial part of the head by the frontogenal and clypeogenal sulci. At each side of the clypeus, where it adjoins the genae, is a facet with which the anterior ginglymus of the mandible articulates. Posteriorly each gena bears a cavity for the articulation of the mandibular condyle. The hind surface of the head is perforated by the occipital foramen, through which the nerve cord and the oesophagus enter the thorax. Separating the labium from the occipital foramen and lying between the genae, in some insects there is a median sclerite, or gula (Fig. 83d). Two main types of head occur, differing in the inclination of the long axis and in the position of the mouthparts. In the hypognathous type, well seen in cockroaches, grasshoppers and flies, the long axis is more or less vertical and the mouthparts ventral. In the prognathous type, prevalent in many beetles, the long axis is approximately horizontal and the mouthparts placed anteriorly.

Head appendages. These paired structures consist of the antennae, derived from the second embryonic head segment, and the mouthparts, which represent the appendages of the fourth, fifth and sixth segments.

The antennae are freely mobile segmented appendages articulated with the head in front of or between the eyes. They differ greatly in appearance in different groups of insects and are sometimes sexually dimorphic, being deeply pectinate in the males of certain moths and plumose in male mosquitoes and midges. The antennae are moved by extrinsic muscles usually arising from the tentorium and inserted on the base of the enlarged first segment, or scape. Intrinsic muscles arising in the scape are inserted on the pedicel, or second segment. The remaining divisions of the antenna together constitute the flagellum and are entirely without muscles except in the primitively wingless orders Diplura and Collembola. The antennae are sensory organs, well provided with olfactory and tactile receptors (pp. 49 and 52).

The mouthparts (Fig. 4) consist of the anterior jaws, or mandibles, followed by a pair of maxillae and a lower lip, or labium, the latter formed by medial fusion of paired maxilla-like structures. Arising from the floor of the mouth cavity is a median, non-appendicular, tongue-like lobe, or hypopharynx, whose body, or lingua, is supported by suspensory sclerites and, in primitive insects, bears a pair of small outgrowths, the superlinguae. The labrum is also closely associated with the mouthparts; its inner surface often bears gustatory receptors and is produced into a stylet-like epipharynx in the fleas. The mouthparts show great variation in structure, correlated with different

15

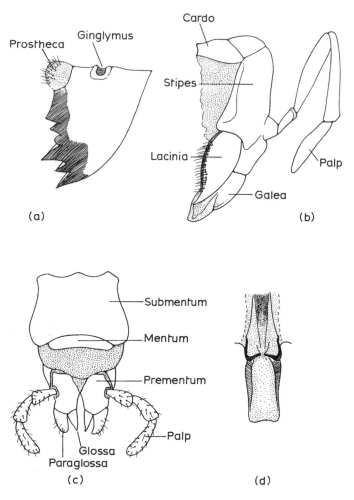

Fig. 4   Mouthparts of *Periplaneta americana* (after Snodgrass)
(a) Left mandible, anterior view; (b) right maxilla, posterior view; (c) labium, posterior view; (d) hypopharynx.

kinds of food and feeding mechanisms. Mandibulate mouthparts, used for biting and chewing, occur in most insects, but in the Hemiptera, sucking lice and some Diptera they are greatly modified for piercing the tissues of plants or animals and sucking up the contained fluids. In most Lepidoptera and some Hymenoptera the mouthparts are long haustellate structures which do not pierce but suck up liquids such as the nectar of flowers. Adult mayflies and some moths do not feed and have atrophied mouthparts.

The mandibles are stout and tooth-like in chewing insects, articulating with the head capsule at two points as described on p. 15. Each is moved by abductor and adductor muscles arising from the wall of the head. In the Hemiptera they are produced into long piercing stylets (p. 143) and in the Lepidoptera and most Diptera they are usually vestigial or absent. Each maxilla consists basally of a cardo, or hinge, which articulates with the head behind the mandible, and a more distal stipes. The latter bears two median endites – a lateral galea and a medial lacinia – and a lateral maxillary palp composed of several segments. The palp may be borne on a specially differentiated part of the stipes, known as the palpifer. Highly specialized maxillae occur in the Hemiptera, Lepidoptera, Diptera and some other orders.

The labium (fused second maxillae) shows clear indications of its paired origin. The basal postmentum (corresponding to the fused maxillary cardines) is often secondarily subdivided into submentum and mentum (Fig. 4). Distally lies the free prementum, which is often bilobed and represents the fused stipites. The prementum carries a pair of lateral segmented palps, sometimes arising from special lobes known as palpigers, and a median ligula. In insects with mouthparts that are more generalized the ligula consists of paired lateral paraglossae and medial glossae, corresponding respectively to the galeae and laciniae of the maxillae. The hypopharynx lies on the inner face of the labium; the common salivary duct opens near its base, and in some Diptera it is produced into a long stylet–like organ. Superlinguae occur only in some Apterygotes and in mayfly nymphs.

The cervix. The cervix, or neck, is the flexible region between head and thorax; it is largely intersegmental in origin, but may include parts of the labial segment and the prothorax. Paired plates, the cervical sclerites are usually present in the membrane of the cervix. The most important of these are the lateral cervical sclerites which act as a fulcrum between the head and the prothorax; distally they articulate with the occipital condyles of the head and proximally with the episterna of the prothorax. Muscles arising from the head and pronotum are inserted on the lateral sclerites to form a protractor mechanism of the head, the angle between the two lateral sclerites of each side being narrowed or widened according to the extent of the protraction.

THE THORAX, LEGS AND WINGS

The three thoracic segments are known respectively as the prothorax, mesothorax and metathorax, and are seen in their simplest form in the Apterygotes and many larvae, where they differ little in size or proportions. The acquisition of wings has led to greater specialization and the meso- and metathorax then become more elaborate and more intimately associated. The prothorax is best developed in such insects as the cockroaches and beetles, where its tergum forms a large shield; in higher insects it is often reduced to a narrow ring. The degree of development of the other segments depends on the condition of the wings. Where the fore and hind wings are very similar (as in termites or dragonflies) the meso- and metathorax are about equally developed; conversely, in the Diptera, where only the fore wings are used to propel the insect in flight, the mesothorax is much larger. In referring to the sclerites of the thorax, the segments to which they belong are denoted by the prefixes pro-, meso- and meta-; thus, the protergum refers to the tergum of the prothorax, and the mesepimeron to the epimeron of the mesothorax.

In many larvae and pupae and in the Apterygotes, the tergum of each segment is a simple, undivided, segmental plate or notum. This condition is retained in the prothorax of almost all adult Pterygote insects, but the meso- and metanota of winged forms are usually divided into three sclerites, the prescutum, scutum and scutellum (Fig. 5a). An additional intersegmental sclerite, the postnotum, is commonly also present and bears a phragma to which the dorsal longitudinal flight muscles are attached.

The pleuron possibly originated by modification of a primitive basal leg-segment or subcoxa, indications of which are seen in some Apterygotes and a few larval insects. In higher insects this region has become enlarged, flattened and fully incorporated into the thoracic wall, to which it gives rigid support (Fig. 5a). It is then divided into two main pleural sclerites, an anterior episternum and a posterior epimeron. These are separated by the pleural suture, or sulcus, marking the line along which an internal strengthening pleural ridge is inflected. In a wing-bearing segment the pleuron develops dorsal and ventral articular processes for the wing and leg, respectively. Both episternum and epimeron may be subdivided into upper and lower sclerites and a further small pleurite, the trochantin, is often present near the lower margin of the episternum.

The sternum (Fig. 5b) presents many modifications. The main segmental plate is often subdivided into presternum, basisternum and sternellum, the last two of these separated from each other by a suture which joins the apophyseal pits from which the endoskeletal invaginations arise. An intersegmental sclerite, the spinasternum or poststernellum, may also be visible, bearing a median internal spina. In higher insects the sternum is often less fully developed, or it may be fused with the pleura so that its boundaries are difficult to define. It is often greatly reduced in breadth and partly infolded between the legs, while the two sternal apophyses are often united on a common base to form a Y-shaped furca.

The legs. The normal insect leg (Fig. 5d) consists of five segments – the coxa, trochanter, femur, tibia and tarsus – and it ends distally in the pretarsus. An additional basal segment, the subcoxa, may – as indicated above – have given rise to the pleuron, but it is not recognizable as a separate, definitive leg segment. The coxa is the functional limb-base, articulating with the coxal process of the pleuron and sometimes also with the trochantin and sternum. The trochanter articulates with the coxa, but its attachment to the femur is fixed; it occasionally appears to be subdivided (e.g. Odonata and many parasitic Hymenoptera) but the distal piece really belongs to the femur. The femur is usually the largest segment, and in the hind leg of most Orthoptera it is still further

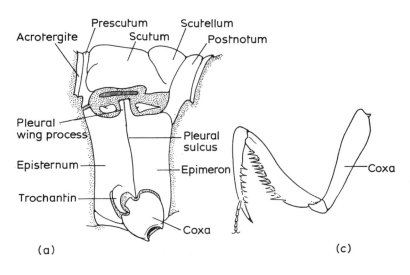

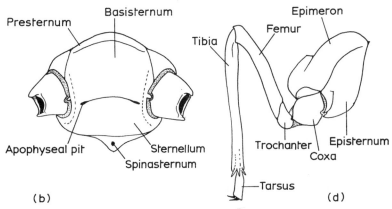

Fig. 5   Thorax and legs

(a) Lateral view of pro- and mesothorax (schematic); (b) sternum of a wing-bearing segment (schematic); (c) fore leg of a mantid (Dictyoptera: Mantidae); (d) hind leg of a cicada nymph (Hemiptera: Cicadidae).

increased in size to accommodate the tibial levator muscles used in jumping. The tibia is generally a slender shaft and the tarsus is often divided into two to five subsegments, or tarsomeres, though many larvae and some Apterygotes retain the primitive undivided condition. The tarsus often bears ventral pad-like structures, the plantulae or tarsal pulvilli. The insect leg ends in the pretarsus; in the Protura, Collembola and many larvae this is a simple claw, but in most insects there are paired claws (Fig. 6). The other pretarsal structures, not all of which are usually present together, include the internal unguitractor plate on which the flexor (retractor) muscle of the claws is inserted, the paired pulvilli which lie one under each claw, a median pad-like arolium and a median bristle, or empodium.

When used for walking, the legs conform to the description given above, but they are often modified structurally to perform other functions. Enlargement of the femur and special modifications of the musculature enable the hind legs to be used for jumping (e.g. grasshoppers, leafhoppers and fleas), while aquatic insects have swimming legs which are broad or fringed with specially long hairs (Fig. 118e). The praying mantids and some other predacious insects have raptorial fore legs, with elongate coxae, spinose femora and tibiae, and reduced tarsi (Fig. 5c), while some soil-inhabiting forms like the mole-crickets (Gryllotalpidae) have stout, spurred fossorial (digging) legs. In many male insects the legs are modified to hold the female when mating, e.g. the elongate fore legs of male mayflies and the apparatus of suckers on the fore tarsus of some male Dytiscidae.

Walking. When they walk or run, insects move the legs of each side in a stepping sequence which is basically similar in many species: the hind, mid and fore legs are moved forward one after the other. However, the phase difference between the stepping sequences of the right and left sides of the body differs from one case to another, so that a great variety of gaits can result. Some legs may step in pairs or there may be three legs in motion at any one time – two on one side and one on the other. It sometimes happens in this way that the insect is momentarily supported on a tripod formed of the fore and hind leg of one side and the mid leg of the other while the three remaining legs are in motion. However, this alternation of 'tripods of support' is not a constant feature of insect locomotion and other patterns of support occur, depending on the time-relations of the individual leg movements. The complicated set of co-ordinated leg movements seems to be controlled by a fundamental, overall pattern of activity in the central nervous system, monitored and modified as necessary by local reflexes involving each separate leg.

Many insects are able to climb and adhere to steep smooth surfaces because of the presence of adhesive organs on the legs. These are usually

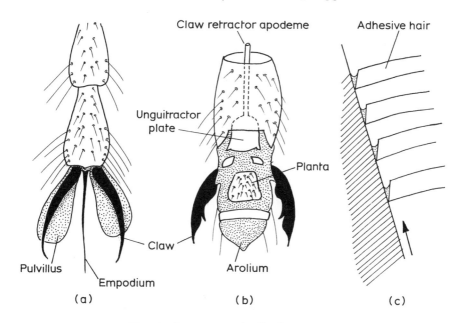

Fig. 6   Pretarsus and adhesive organs

(a) Pretarsus of *Asilus crabroniformis* (Diptera: Asilidae). (b) Pretarsus of *Apis mellifera* (Hymenoptera: Apidae) (after Snodgrass). (c) Apices of hairs from adhesive organ of *Rhodnius prolixus* (Hemiptera: Reduviidae) (after Wigglesworth); sliding movement up a steep surface in the direction of the arrow takes place readily; movement in the opposite direction is greatly hindered by surface forces, depending on the presence of a film of oily secretion beneath the obliquely truncate tip of each hair.

the plantulae of the tarsus and the arolium and pulvilli, but *Rhodnius* and its relatives have a special adhesive organ at the apex of the tibia. Though the physical basis of adhesion is uncertain, it may be due to surface molecular forces which operate when the extremities of the fine hairs clothing the adhesive organs are moistened by a glandular secretion and brought into contact with the substrate (Fig. 6).

Wings. Most adult insects have two pairs of wings, articulated by a complex group of sclerites to the two sides of the meso- and metathoracic terga respectively. However, the primitive Apterygotes are all wingless, representing an evolutionary stage which precedes the origin of these structures, while some Pterygote insects, such as fleas and lice or worker ants and termites, have lost their wings in the course of evolution from winged ancestors. The youngest developmental stages of insects have no wings, but their rudiments become apparent in later instars, two main types of wing development being recognizable. In the Exopterygote insects the wings arise as externally visible, projecting wing pads which gradually increase in size at each moult,

21

whereas in the Endopterygotes they undergo their early development concealed beneath the cuticle of the larva and first become visible externally in the pupa. Histologically, however, the two types of developing wing rudiments are very similar. They are flattened evaginations of the lateral margins of the meso- and metaterga, each of whose main surfaces consists of epidermis and basement membrane, the former secreting the cuticle which invests the wing once it comes to project externally. During development the upper and lower epidermal layers meet and fuse except along certain linear channels, or lacunae. Tracheae and nerves grow into the lacunae, blood circulates in them and they determine the course of the strengthening tubes, or wing veins, which eventually appear in the fully formed wing. At the moult into the adult the relatively small, fleshy wing rudiments are inflated to their full size by blood pressure and the epidermal cells atrophy, so that the adult wing consists of a thin double layer of cuticle supported by the more heavily sclerotized wing veins. The wing surfaces may be smooth or clothed with microtrichia (Fig. 2) or macrotrichia; or they may be partially scaled (mosquitoes) or wholly scaled as in Lepidoptera. A small scale-like sclerite, or tegula, overlaps the base of the fore wing in Lepidoptera, Hymenoptera and some Hemiptera.

In the more generalized insects the two pairs of wings are used in flight and are very similar in size and shape, though the posterior part of the hind wing is often enlarged to form a fan-like expansion, or anal lobe, which is delimited from the more anterior part of the wing by an anal furrow. In other insects one pair of wings – usually the fore wings – is specialized, often to protect the delicate hind wings. Thus, in the cockroaches, mantids, stick-insects and Orthoptera the fore wings are sclerotized, leathery tegmina; in the Heteroptera the fore wings are sclerotized over their basal half and are known as hemelytra, while in the earwigs and beetles they form hard sclerotized protective structures known as elytra, and are no longer used for flight. In the Diptera the hind wings are modified to form small vibrating organs known as halteres, which control equilibrium during flight and, in the more specialized flies, are largely concealed by the lobe-like calypters at the base of the fore wings. In many insects the fore and hind wings of each side are held together in flight by some form of coupling apparatus, so that they beat in unison. In many moths this apparatus consists of one or more stout bristles, the frenulum, which arises from the base of the hind wing and interlocks with a retinaculum on the underside of the fore wing. In the Hymenoptera a series of minute hooks, or hamuli, on the front margin of the hind wing engages with the reflexed hind border of the fore wing, in this way uniting the two wings of a side (Fig. 96d).

Wing venation. The complete system of wing veins is termed the venation. It is virtually constant for each species, and the various taxonomic groups often show characteristic venational features which are therefore of great importance in insect classification. Though many specialized kinds of venation are known, it has been possible to formulate a general system (Fig. 7) from which all others appear to have been derived. The homologies of veins within this scheme may frequently be decided on three main types of evidence.

1. That provided by the system of tracheae found in the pupal or nymphal wing pad. These often agree broadly in arrangement with the subsequent venation but retain other, more primitive, features which make them easier to identify than are the veins. 2. That provided by the venation of fossil insects or by comparative studies of the more primitive recent groups, thus revealing the connections between primitive, easily identifiable patterns and the more specialized kinds. 3. That due to the fact that in the more generalized fossil and recent insects the wings tend to be longitudinally folded, or plicate, with intervening furrows, e.g. Ephemeroptera. Veins found on the ridges –

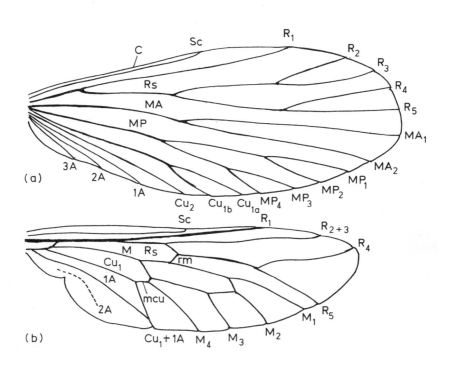

Fig. 7   Insect wing venation
(a) Hypothetical complete venation; (b) wing of a horsefly, *Tabanus* (Diptera: Tabanidae).

when the outspread wing is viewed from the dorsal side – are termed convex veins (denoted by +) and those in the furrows are concave veins (denoted by −).

It should be noted that none of the above three criteria are wholly satisfactory, and in some groups (e.g. Hymenoptera) the homologies of the wing veins are not established with certainty. Nevertheless, the system of terminology depicted for a hypothetical primitive system of wing veins in Fig. 7 is now widely accepted. It has largely replaced the older special systems of nomenclature, each applicable only to a particular group, though the latter still retain the advantage of convenience for some descriptive taxonomic purposes. Beginning from the anterior or costal margin of the wing, the first vein is the costa (C), which is unbranched and forms the wing margin. The subcosta (Sc) lies closely behind the costa and is usually undivided. The radius (R) or third vein forks into an anterior branch R_1 and a posterior branch, or radial sector (Rs), which divides into four branches, R_2 to R_5. The fourth vein, or media (M), forks into an anterior media (MA) which is typically two-branched but often completely absent, and a posterior media (MP or simply M) which is four-branched. The fifth vein, or cubitus (Cu), similarly divides into anterior and posterior branches. The anterior cubitus (Cu_1 or CuA) is typically two-branched and the posterior cubitus (Cu_2 or CuP) is undivided. Finally, a variable number of anal veins (1A, 2A, etc.) are present. Additional rigidity of the wing membrane is obtained by the development of a network of cross-veins between the veins. While these are numerous and variable in the Ephemeroptera and Odonata, in the higher orders they tend to become few and located at fixed positions of mechanical advantage. The main cross-veins and their symbols are the radial (r) from R_1 to Rs; the radio-medial (r-m) from R to M; the medial (m) from MP_2 to MP_3; and the medio-cubital (m-cu) from MP to Cu. The veins divide the wing area into cells, and the name of each cell is taken from that of the vein which forms its anterior border. Thus, the cell lying behind the main stem of the media is cell M, while a cell lying behind R_1 is cell R_1. Where two veins have fused the cell immediately behind is named from the posterior component; thus, when veins R_4 and R_5 coalesce the area behind is cell R_5.

The hypothetical venational pattern is most nearly approached in some Palaeozoic fossils. Among living insects the least departure from it is seen in the Ephemeroptera and some primitive Endopterygotes like the Trichoptera and Mecoptera. In most recent insects the media is represented only by MP, but the Ephemeroptera retain the primitive condition while in the Odonata and perhaps also the Plecoptera it is only MA which has been retained. In some orders, e.g. Neuroptera, specialization has taken place by the addition of subsidiary branches to the main veins, and in the Ephemeroptera there are many secondary intercalary veins lying between the main ones. More often, however, specialization occurs by reduction in the number of main veins and their branches and in some parasitic Hymenoptera, for example, the venation has atrophied entirely. A small, thickened, darkly pigmented area near the costal margin of the fore wing in many Hymenoptera and on both pairs of wings in Odonata is known as the stigma or pterostigma (Fig. 65).

Origin of wings. The tracheal gill theory claims that wings were derived from plate-like thoracic gills of the kind well shown on the abdomen of some mayfly nymphs. Being basally articulated with the body and already supplied with muscles and tracheae, it is claimed that they only required to become enlarged and adapted for flight. However, wings differ in their mode of development, and do not seem to be serially homologous with tracheal gills. The theory also involves the assumption that the ancestors of winged insects were aquatic, which is contrary to much evidence. The more widely accepted paranotal theory postulates that wings arose from lateral tergal expansions, or paranota, of the thorax. It is maintained that the prothoracic lobes of some of the most ancient fossil insects are organs of this kind which had persisted long after the paranota of the other thoracic segments had developed into wings. Paranotal expansions occur in positions characteristic of wings, not only on the thorax, but also on the abdomen in various arthropods; among insects they are seen in many larvae and also in *Lepisma*, where they contain tracheae recalling those of a wing pad. It is suggested that they became sufficiently large to function as gliding planes or to control landing in leaping insects. Later they acquired basal articulations which, along with the development of muscles, enabled them to become organs of independent movement. It is not improbable that at an early stage in their evolution wings were concerned more with sexual display or temperature regulation than with flight.

Flight mechanics. Insects fly at various speeds. These are often exaggerated, and probably no insects surpass the larger dragonflies which may move at about 10 m s^{-1}. The movements of the wings during flight are quite complex. The trajectory of the wing tip relative to the insect's body takes the form of an elongate figure-of-eight approximately oblique to the long axis of the body. During the downstroke – on which most of the propulsive force is generated – the wing is pulled downward and forward and its surface assumes a position in which the anterior margin is lowered in relation to the elevated posterior area. In the upstroke the wing is pulled upward and backward while its anterior margin now comes to lie relatively higher than the

25

depressed posterior area (Fig. 8). The result of these movements is that aerodynamic forces act on the wings in such a way as to maintain the insect in the air and propel it forwards. The movements of the wings are brought about through the activity of three sets of flight muscles: the direct, indirect and accessory indirect muscles. The direct flight muscles arise on the pleural and sternal regions and act directly on the base of the wing since they are inserted on the basalar and subalar sclerites or on the axillary sclerites. They are important in the Orthoptera, Dictyoptera, Odonata and Coleoptera, but elsewhere they are small and the main propulsive forces are developed by the powerful indirect flight muscles. These are arranged in two functional groups – a dorsal longitudinal set running between the phragmata of meso- and metathorax, and a dorsoventral set running from tergum to sternum. The traditional explanation of the mode of action of these muscles is illustrated in Fig.

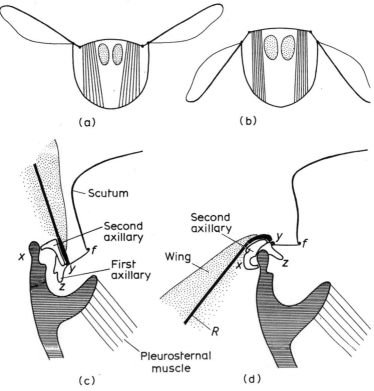

Fig. 8   Mechanism of insect flight

(a) and (b) illustrate the traditional theory of the mode of action of the indirect flight muscles. (c) and (d) are diagrammatic transverse sections through the base of the wing of *Sarcophaga*, showing flight movements (after Boettiger and Furshpan; see text for explanation: f, x, y and z are points referred to in text).

8a and b; contraction of the dorsoventral muscles lowers the tergum and elevates the wings (Fig. 8a) while contraction of the dorsal longitudinal muscles raises the tergum and depresses the wings (Fig. 8b). This is an oversimplified interpretation; the pterothoracic box consists of rigid and more flexible parts, and may be deformed in a complicated manner while elastic forces thus generated in the cuticle play an important role in moving the wings. Certain accessory indirect muscles, such as the pleurosternals and tergosternals, also influence flight movements by altering the relative position of moving parts or by changing the elastic properties of the pterothorax. In the fly *Sarcophaga* the mechanism of wing movement has been studied in detail and may be understood by reference to Fig. 8c and d, which show the changing relations between the scutum, the first and second axillary sclerites and the pleural wing process. When the wing is elevated (Fig. 8c), contraction of the dorsal longitudinals tends to force the edge of the scutum (f) laterally, but this force is resisted by the contraction of the pleurosternal muscles and little movement of the wing takes place. Another effect of the contracting dorsal longitudinal muscles, however, is to exert an upwardly directed force on the first axillary via a process of the scutellum (which articulates with the axillary at z). When this force becomes sufficient to carry the point y nearly to the line joining x and f, the elastic energy stored in the tergum is suddenly released through the rotation of the second axillary about the pleural wing process and the wing 'clicks' into the depressed position (Fig 8d). The contraction of the dorsoventral muscles then follows and this also has the effect of forcing the point f laterally; again, however, there is no appreciable movement of the wing until the force on z – now acting in a downward direction – reaches a critical value, when the wing suddenly clicks back to the elevated position.

Physiology of insect flight. The frequency with which the wings beat varies greatly in different insects. In a dragonfly there may be only 28 strokes per second and no more than 9 per second in a cabbage butterfly. On the other hand, the number of strokes per second is stated to be 180–200 in the housefly and the honey-bee and 280–310 in a mosquito; a few species even exceed these figures considerably. The necessary high rates of muscular contraction are only possible because of the peculiar physiological properties of some insect flight muscles which behave in an asynchronous manner. Such muscles are capable of contracting as a direct response to being stretched, and the frequency with which they undergo cycles of contraction and relaxation is therefore no longer limited by the relatively slow rate at which they receive nervous impulses. The more primitive, synchronously acting flight muscles occur in cockroaches, Orthoptera, Lepidoptera and dragonflies. In these insects the wing-beat frequency does not exceed

27

100 cycles per second and it is little affected when the tip of the wing is cut off experimentally, since it is determined within the thoracic ganglia. In those insects with asynchronous flight muscles, such as the Diptera, Hymenoptera and Coleoptera, removal of the wing tip increases the already much higher wing-beat frequency, since the operation reduces the inertia of the wing and therefore increases the frequency at which the wing–thorax system is resonant. Associated with this difference in the physiological properties of the two types of flight muscle are various histological features: the myofibrils of asynchronous muscle are more distinct, the isotropic bands are narrower, and the sarcoplasmic reticulum is greatly reduced (p. 35).

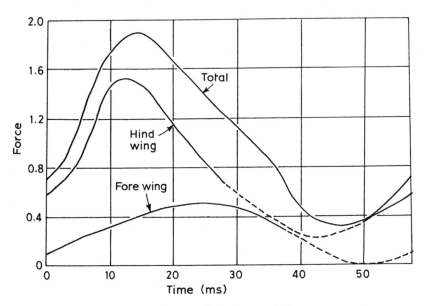

Fig. 9   Flight mechanics of the locust *Schistocerca gregaria*
(Orthoptera: Acrididae)

The curves show the lifting forces generated during one complete cycle of movement of the fore and hind wings, together with the total lift. Full lines denote downstrokes, broken lines refer to upstrokes; the force is measured in units equivalent to the weight of the insect.

The aerodynamic forces produced when air flows over the curved wing surface may be resolved into a vertical component (lift), which is opposed by the weight of the insect, and a forwardly directed component (thrust), which is opposed by the drag of the air on the insect's body. Careful measurement of these forces in a flying locust shows that the hind wings produce, on the average, much greater thrust and lift than the fore wings. The magnitudes of the two components also vary at different points in the cycle of wing movement (Fig. 9).

Most of the thrust is generated on the downbeat of the hind wing, but some also comes from its upstroke. More lift is also generated on the downstroke, but the upstroke of both pairs of wings makes an appreciable contribution. Thus, although the total lift and thrust both vary in rather complicated ways during the cycle, their net effect is to support the insect and move it forwards.

Free flight requires the regulation of the amount of lift and thrust, and this in turn is achieved as part of a co-ordinated system of nervous reflexes. Most insects begin to fly when their tarsi lose contact with the substrate (the tarsal flight reflex) and they then continue to fly while the flow of air over the head and antennae stimulates sensory receptors there. Further sense organs near the base of the wing or distributed along its veins then act rather like strain gauges embedded in the cuticle, and enable the insect to control the twisting of the wings during their beat cycle, to determine the plane in which the beat occurs and to vary the amplitude of the wing movement. By changing the amounts of lift and thrust, independently on the two sides of the body if need be, the insect can bring about deviations from straight and level flight. Many of these regulatory movements are produced by the action of small direct flight muscles, and the controlling mechanisms may also involve stimuli perceived by the visual organs. However, in insects like the locust the processes of regulation are superimposed on a centrally generated flight rhythm due to interneurons that are organized so as to stimulate alternately the antagonistic sets of longitudinal and dorsoventral indirect flight muscles. A highly specialized mechanism of flight control is provided by the modified hind wings, or halteres, of Diptera. These are small club-shaped structures composed of a relatively long stalk and a heavier, almost spherical head. They do not propel the insect, but they vibrate in an approximately transverse plane at the same frequency as the fore wings, and they act as gyroscopic organs of equilibrium during flight. While the insect is flying on a straight and level path, movements of the haltere are perceived by three groups of campaniform sensilla near its base. If the insect deviates from this flight path, then the inertia of the haltere leads to it tending to continue movement in its original plane of vibration. This modifies the pattern of deforming forces in the cuticle near the base of the haltere, and so changes the nervous output from the campaniform sensilla. The insect is thus enabled to monitor its deviation and manoeuvre accurately, even in complete darkness. Insects from which the halteres have been experimentally removed fly in a quite irregular and unstable fashion.

As in other muscles, the contractile machanisms of insect flight muscle depend on energy released in the hydrolysis of adenosine triphosphate (ATP). An external source of energy is needed to sustain this process and maintain flight for any length of time. Fats release more energy per unit weight than other reserve materials, and those insects which undertake long flights, such as locusts or migratory butterflies, use fats as their fuel. For the short flights of flies and bees, and even in the initial stages of locust flight, carbohydrates such as glycogen and the sugars obtained from nectar are more appropriate sources of energy, since they can be mobilized more rapidly. The intense metabolic activity of flight muscle requires an abundant supply of oxygen, which is transported to and through the muscle blocks by arrays of air-sacs and tracheae. These then branch repeatedly and the finest tracheoles enter the muscle cells and bring gaseous oxygen to within 5 μm of the mitochondria responsible for intracellular oxidative processes. The changes in thoracic shape which accompany flight movements also help to pump air through the air-sacs and tracheae, and this forced ventilation not only promotes the supply of oxygen but also helps to disperse some of the heat generated in the muscles.

THE ABDOMEN AND GENITALIA

The insect abdomen consists primitively of 11 segments and a terminal non-segmental telson. These 12 divisions are usually recognizable in the embryo, but the full complement is rarely seen in the postembryonic stages. Only the Protura retain a distinct telson and this order is also peculiar in showing anamorphosis – the newly hatched stage has eight segments and telson, but subsequent stages acquire another three segments which develop from the front of the telson. The Collembola also display an unusual condition; they have only six abdominal segments, both in the embryo and afterwards. Eleven segments may be recognized in the Archaeognatha, Zygentoma and most generalized Pterygotes, but in many specialized insects the first one to three segments may be reduced and the tenth and eleventh are inconspicuous and often fused together. It is sometimes convenient to distinguish the genital segments – the eighth and ninth in the female and the ninth in the male – from the pregenital and post-genital ones. When the eleventh segment is well developed it may be divided into a dorsal epiproct – the tergum – and a pair of paraprocts – the divided sternum (Fig. 11).

In the embryos of many insects each abdominal segment bears a pair of appendages, a varying number of which are retained in a reduced or highly modified condition in young and adult Apterygotes. Thus, in the Machilidae (Archaeognatha) many of the sterna bear a pair of plate-like limb-bases, or coxites, each carrying a style very like those on the coxae of the second and third thoracic legs (Fig. 62f). In the order Diplura the styles are present but the coxites are indistinguishably fused with the sterna, and it is probable that the definitive sterna of higher insects are almost all of this composite type. It is possible that the leg-like abdominal processes of caterpillars and some other immature stages are true segmental appendages, but the adult Pterygote insects only retain recognizable appendages on the genital segments – where they form the external genitalia discussed below – and on the eleventh segment. The appendages of the eleventh segment, the cerci, may be short and unjointed, or long and segmented; they are sometimes inserted between the epiproct and paraprocts (Fig. 11) but when the eleventh segment is atrophied they appear to arise from the tenth. In the Archaeognatha, Zygentoma and most Ephemeroptera the epiproct is prolonged into a median caudal filament flanked by the two similar cerci (Fig. 10a). The aquatic nymphs of the Zygopteran dragonflies also have three similarly situated processes which form flattened leaf-like gills (Fig. 66), but it is probable that the two lateral ones are outgrowths of the paraprocts rather than modified cerci. In many higher insects the cerci are absent.

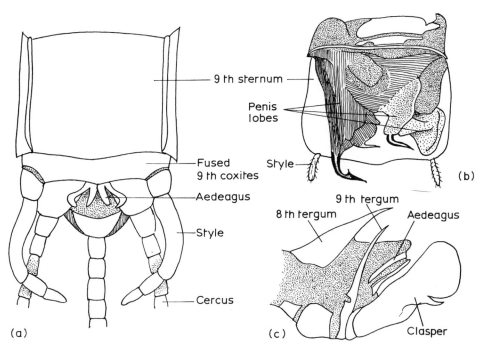

Fig. 10   Structure of male external genitalia
(a) Mayfly (Ephemeroptera), ventral view; (b) *Periplaneta americana*, dorsal view after removal of terminal abdominal structures (after Snodgrass); (c) Codling Moth, *Cydia pomonella* (Lepidoptera: Tortricidae), lateral view (after Snodgrass).

External genitalia. In both sexes these are usually said to be derived from highly modified abdominal appendages. Primitively, each genital appendage, or gonopod, may be regarded as consisting of a limb-base,

31

or coxite (gonocoxa), which bears an apical style (gonostylus) and has a long process, or gonapophysis, arising from its median basal region. Some or all of these parts may, however, be difficult to recognize in the adult insect, and though studies of the musculature and post-embryonic development provide much help, the homologies of the various structures which make up the external genitalia are not known with certainty in all orders of insects.

In the male the genital segment is the ninth abdominal one and its appendages typically form the genitalia. When complete these consist of (a) a pair of lateral claspers which grip the female in copulation and between which lies (b) the median aedeagus, or penis, which is flanked by (c) a pair of parameres. The penis is the intromittent organ of Pterygote insects; it bears the gonopore and develops by fusion of a pair of outgrowths from or behind the ninth segment. Only in mayflies and some primitive earwigs is it obviously paired in the adult (Fig. 10a). Parameres are present in many orders (e.g. Archaeognatha, Fig. 62); they are probably not always homologous, but in some cases they and the paired rudiments from which the penis develops perhaps represent the divided gonapophyses of the ninth abdominal segment. In the Archaeognatha the coxites and styles of the ninth abdominal segment resemble those of the pregenital segments and are not used for sperm transfer. However, in some insects such as the Ephemeroptera (Fig. 10a), the coxites and styles form functional claspers. Among other groups, where claspers as such are lacking, the coxites fuse indistinguishably with the ninth sternum to form the subgenital plate, or hypandrium, and the styles – if they persist – are small simple structures, e.g. some Orthoptera and the cockroaches (Fig. 10b). In the Lepidoptera the claspers (usually known as valves) probably represent only the styles, the coxites having become amalgamated with the sternum (Fig. 10c); it has, however, been claimed that the claspers of Lepidoptera, Mecoptera and primitive Diptera are parameres and are not homologous with the claspers of mayflies. Some orders, e.g. the Plecoptera and Coleoptera, have no recognizable traces of claspers, though in the former order – and in some other groups – the functional copulatory organs include structures which are not derived from the genital appendages. The male genitalia of related species and genera often differ considerably in detail and are therefore of great taxonomic value.

In the female the primitive condition of paired gonopores opening behind the seventh abdominal sternum is retained in the Ephemeroptera, but most female insects have only a single genital opening behind the eighth sternum. The paired appendages of the genital segments (eighth and ninth) then typically form the ovipositor, or egg-laying organ. In the Machilidae (Fig. 62) this consists of the two closely associated pairs of annulate gonapophyses, each arising from the base of the appropriate

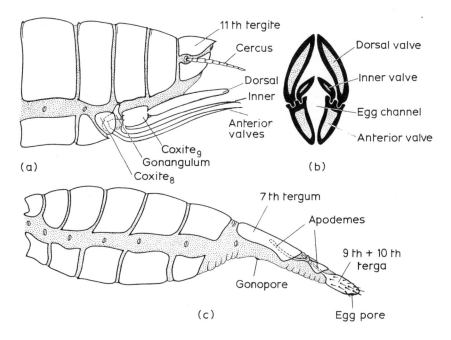

Fig. 11   Ovipositor and abdomen

(a) Diagrammatic lateral view of a generalized insect ovipositor. (b) Transverse section through ovipositor of a Tettigoniid, to show relative positions of valves. (c) Abdomen of *Lymantria monacha* (Lepidoptera: Lymantriidae), with terminal segments extended (after Eidmann).

unmodified coxite. Generally, however, the ovipositor consists of three paired valves associated basally with one or two pairs of small plate-like sclerites often formerly referred to as valvifers (Fig. 11). The anterior or ventral valves probably represent the gonapophyses of the eighth segment, though they are connected basally with a small sclerite (the gonangulum) thought to have been derived from part of the ninth coxite. The posterior or inner valves and the lateral or dorsal ones are, respectively, the gonapophyses and parts of the coxites of the ninth segment. The styles are absent and the extension of the ninth coxite that forms the dorsal valve is sometimes called the gonoplac by insect morphologists. In some Orthoptera all three pairs of valves are present, often interlocking by tongue-and-groove joints to form a rigid egg-laying organ (Fig. 11); in other Orthoptera the inner valves are rudimentary. In many Hemiptera and Hymenoptera the dorsal valves are softer separate structures which ensheath the effective ovipositor (formed from the other two pairs) when this is not in use. In all cases a space between the valves of the opposite sides forms an egg channel down which the eggs pass when being laid.

33

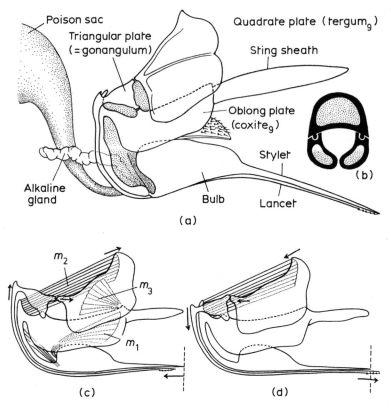

Fig. 12 Sting of honey-bee (*Apis mellifera*) (after Snodgrass)
(a) Sting and associated glands in lateral views; (b) transverse section through stylet and lancets; (c), (d) mode of action of sting; arrows indicate directions of movement of parts; see text for explanation.

In higher Hymenoptera such as the wasps and bees the ovipositor is no longer used for laying eggs, but has become modified to form a poison-injecting apparatus, the sting (Fig. 12). At rest this lies in a pocket within the seventh abdominal segment, from which it is exserted when in use. At the base of the sting are three pairs of plate-like sclerites – the quadrate, oblong and triangular plates. These articulate with each other as shown in Fig. 12 and represent, respectively, the ninth tergum, the ninth coxite and the gonangulum. The dorsal valves are soft, palp-like organs which arise from the posterior part of the quadrate plate and ensheath the protrusible shaft of the sting in the resting position. The shaft consists of the paired, barbed lancets (modified anterior valves) and the unpaired stylet (fused inner valves). At their bases the lancets are attached to the triangular plates while the stylet is expanded into a bulb-like structure from which the free proximal part of each inner valve runs to the anterior region of the corresponding oblong plate. Lancets and stylet are associated as shown in Fig. 12b, the lancets sliding to and fro along ridges on the ventral face of the stylet when the insect stings. The mechanism of stinging is as follows. First the basal apparatus is swung downwards on a pivot between the posterodorsal corner of the quadrate plate and the eighth tergite; meanwhile the shaft is depressed by the contraction of muscles which run from the oblong plate to the bulb of the stylet (Fig. 12c, m_1); finally the contraction of powerful muscles (Fig. 12c, m_2) running from the quadrate plate to the anterior part of the oblong plate causes the rotation of the triangular plate so as to push out the attached lancet. Retraction of the lancet is brought about through the action of a muscle (Fig. 12c, m_3) running from the quadrate plate to the posterior part of the oblong plate. The muscles on the two sides of the sting work alternately and, by successive acts of protraction and retraction, the lancets are driven more and more deeply into the victim's body, the stylet following the lancets into the wound. The poison which is injected into the wound is secreted by a pair of long thread–like glands in the abdomen. Their secretion accumulates in a large, ovoidal poison sac which opens at the base of the sting into the poison canal between stylet and lancets (Fig. 12b). In the honey-bee the poison contains a protein and certain enzymes which cause the tissues of the victim to produce histamine; this gives rise to the usual symptoms of a bee sting. The function of the so–called alkaline gland, which also opens at the base of the sting, is uncertain.

Among many insects, e.g. the Ephemeroptera, Plecoptera, Lepidoptera, Diptera and Coleoptera, there is no true appendicular ovipositor. However, in some members of the last three of these orders the posterior segments of the abdomen form a slender telescopic tube or oviscapt (Fig. 11) which acts as the functional ovipositor. It bears the opening of the egg passage distally, and enables the eggs to be laid in crevices or other concealed situations.

THE MUSCULAR SYSTEM

The muscles of insects, both skeletal and visceral, are striated in all cases, thus differing from those of vertebrates and many other animals. Even the delicate fibrillae of the heart wall and the muscle reticulum around the gut and other viscera are seen to be striated when suitably stained. Muscles are fibrous structures composed of many protein arrays, or myofilaments, arranged into myofibrils. These in turn are grouped into muscle fibres, each composed of fibrils embedded in a nucleated cytoplasmic matrix, the sarcoplasm. This may form a peripheral layer, the sarcolemma, or make up a central cylindrical core around which the myofibrils are arranged. Each myofibril consists of alternating light (isotropic) and dark (anisotropic) portions, giving the whole fibre its cross-striated appearance. The skeletal muscles are attached to the integument in various ways (Fig. 13). Sometimes they are connected with unmodified epidermal cells, but more often the latter are traversed at the site of attachment by tonofibrillae – intracellular filaments which are closely associated with the myofibrils and sometimes appear continuous with specially differentiated regions of the overlying cuticle. The more powerful skeletal muscles are often attached to special

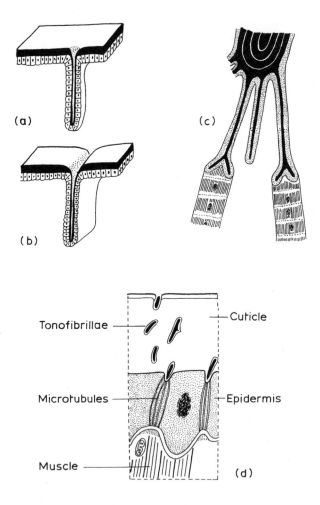

Fig. 13   Skeletomuscular structures

(a) An apodeme; (b) a phragma; (c) unicellular apodeme with attached muscle fibres (after Snodgrass); (d) ultrastructure of muscle attachment to integument (after Caveney).

cuticular ingrowths which may take the form of tubular or rod-like apodemes (Fig. 13a) or flat plate-like phragmata (Figs 15 and 13b).

Some insects are able to raise weights that are heavier than their own bodies or can leap relatively great distances, and this has given rise to the popular idea that their muscles are far more powerful than those of vertebrates. However, the insects' performance must be considered in relation to the size of their bodies. The power of a muscle varies with its cross-sectional area, i.e. with the square of a linear dimension, but the volume (and hence the mass) of the insect's body varies as the cube of a linear dimension. Consequently, other things being equal, the relative muscular power must increase as the size of the animal diminishes. The absolute power of a muscle, on the other hand, is the maximum load it can raise per square centimetre cross-section, and this tends to be a little less in insects than in vertebrates. In most physiological properties there are no great differences between insect and vertebrate muscles, and the biochemical changes accompanying contraction are essentially similar in the two groups though there are some interesting adaptive differences. Insects flying for long periods can sustain intense metabolic activity in their flight muscles without incurring an appreciable 'oxygen debt'. This completely aerobic metabolism is accompanied by an unusually high rate of ATP production and high rates of fuel consumption (p. 29). In insects that can fly actively the flight muscle mitochondria are very numerous, very large and provided with very densely folded cristae, thus supplying a large surface area for the rapid exchange of metabolites between the oxidative mitochondrial enzyme systems and the general muscle cytoplasm. As mentioned on p. 27 the very rapid wing movements of some insects depend on a special mechanism whereby the flight muscles, which are arranged in antagonistic sets, can contract as a direct response to being stretched. They are thus able to undergo repeated cycles of contraction and relaxation with a frequency far greater than that with which they could be stimulated by motor nerve impulses.

Myology

The following account enumerates the main skeletal muscles of a generalized insect, almost all of which are paired because of the bilateral symmetry of the body. Each muscle is attached at one end – its origin – to a stationary or almost stationary part of the exoskeleton and at the other end – its insertion – to the part which is moved. So far as the segmented appendages are concerned, the muscles may be extrinsic or intrinsic. Extrinsic muscles arise outside the limb, are inserted near its base, and are mainly concerned with its movements as a whole. Intrinsic muscles have their origins and insertions within the limb, and effect movements of individual segments or parts. The various muscles may be named from their sites of origin and insertion – as when one speaks of a pleurocoxal muscle – or by reference to their functions, e.g. the tibial levator. The latter system is probably the most generally useful, though it may lead to confusion when studying muscle homologies, since small differences in position may lead to important changes in function. Muscles whose contraction causes forward and backward movements of a limb in the horizontal plane are known as promotors and remotors respectively. Levators and depressors respectively raise or lower an appendage in the vertical plane, e.g. the levator muscles of the antenna raise that appendage. Flexors draw one part towards another (e.g. a leg segment towards the adjacent one) while the antagonistic extensors move them apart. In some cases, depending on the spatial relations of the part concerned, the terms flexor and extensor are synonyms of depressor and levator. Adductors draw an appendage towards its fellow of the opposite side of the body, whereas abductors move the two apart. Finally, rotators bring about turning movements of a limb or part.

The head muscles. The chief muscles of the head and its appendages are as follows (Fig. 14):

1. The cibarial and pharyngeal dilators run, respectively, from the clypeus to the dorsal wall of the cibarium and from the frons to the pharynx. One or both may operate the sucking pump of specialized insects (e.g. Hemiptera, Dytiscid beetle larvae).

2. Labrum. The paired anterior labral (levator) arises on the frons and is inserted on the anterior face of the labrum. A pair of posterior labrals (depressors) has the same origin, but inserts on the posterior surface of the labrum; each runs lateral to the corresponding anterior labral.

3. Antenna. Inserted on the base of the scape are the extrinsic antennal muscles – a levator and depressor – both arising from the tentorium. The only other antennal muscles in most insects are the intrinsic muscles of the scape, mainly levators and depressors of the flagellum, which arise within the base of the scape and insert on the base of the pedicel. However in the Diplura and Collembola, intrinsic muscles are present in each flagellar segment except the last.

4. Mandible. A powerful adductor arises dorsolaterally on the wall of the head and is inserted by a strong apodeme on the inner basal margin of the mandible. A smaller abductor arises external to the adductor and is inserted on the outer basal angle of the mandible.

5. Maxilla. The rotators of the cardo arise from the dorsal wall of the head and are inserted on the cardo, while adductor muscles inserted on the cardo and stipes originate from the tentorium. The cranial flexor of the lacinia is a long slender muscle arising from the occipital region of the head. On the stipes there originate the stipital flexor of the lacinia,

the flexor of the galea and the levator and depressor of the palp. The individual palp segments may contain intrinsic palp muscles.

6. Labium. The extrinsic muscles of the labium are the dorsal and ventral premental muscles; these arise from the tentorium and are inserted, respectively, on the distal and proximal boundaries of the prementum. A pair of median premental muscles arises on the postmentum or submentum and is inserted on the proximal margin of the prementum. The glossae, paraglossae and palps are moved by muscles arising in the prementum and corresponding to the stipital muscles of the maxilla. The cranial flexor of the lacinia has no counterpart in the labium.

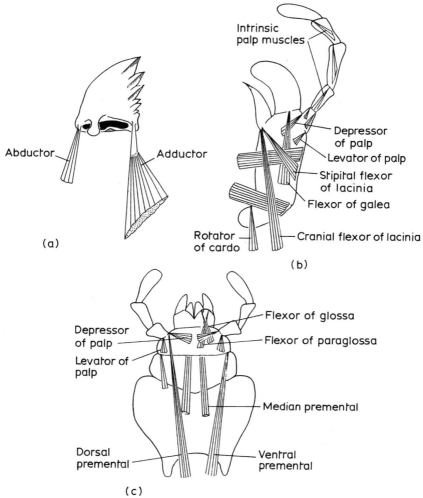

Fig. 14 Muscles of head and appendages of an Orthopteroid insect
(a) Mandible; (b) maxilla; (c) labium.

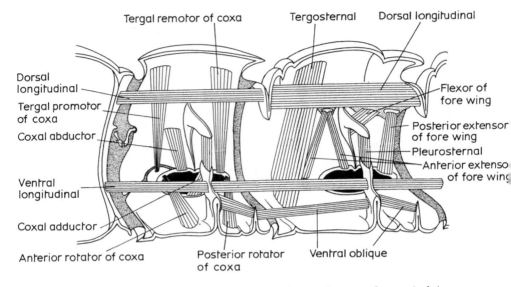

Fig. 15   Internal lateral view of pro- and mesothorax of a typical insect, showing musculature.

The thoracic muscles. These muscles (Figs 15 and 16) include the following:

1. Dorsal longitudinal, attached to successive phragmata; these are best developed in the wing-bearing segments, where they form the main depressors of the wings. In apterous insects and in those with weak flight these muscles are more or less reduced or wanting. In the prothorax they are smaller and attached to the occipital region of the head.

2. Ventral longitudinal; these extend from one sternal apophysis to another. In the prothorax they pass to the head, where they are inserted on the occiput or the tentorium.

3. Ventral oblique, consisting of anterior and posterior series that arise from the sternal apophysis and are attached to the spina of the segment in front and behind, respectively.

4. Dorsoventral or tergosternal muscles which act as the main levators of the wings and are therefore antagonistic to 1. They are wanting in the prothorax and reduced in flightless insects. The two series 1 and 4 are known as the indirect wing muscles because their insertions are not upon the wing bases. The next group, 5, includes what are commonly termed the direct wing muscles (see pp. 26–7) on account of their attachments being very near to or on the wing bases.

5. Pleural muscles which include (a) the anterior extensors of the wing arising from the pleuron and the coxal margin and inserted on the

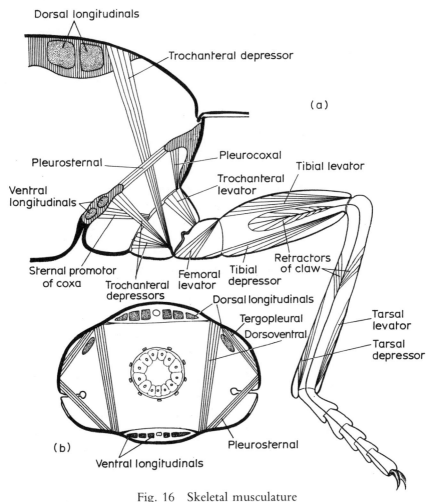

Fig. 16   Skeletal musculature
(a) Transverse section through thorax, showing intrinsic and some extrinsic muscles of leg; (b) transverse section through abdomen.

anterior pleural (basalar) wing sclerite, beneath the wing base; (b) the posterior extensor of the wing, whose origin is on the margin of the coxa of its segment and the insertion on the posterior pleural (subalar) wing sclerite, beneath the wing base; (c) the flexor of the wing, which arises from the pleural ridge and is inserted on the wing base. A further group of accessory indirect wing muscles runs from the tergum or sternum to the pleuron. Their action braces the thoracic exoskeleton or modifies its elastic properties during flight.

6. Leg muscles, which consist of extrinsic (Fig. 15) and intrinsic (Fig. 16) series. The extrinsic series is concerned with movements of the

leg as a whole. Arising from the tergum and inserted on the trochantin and coxa, respectively, are the promotor and remotor of the coxa; these muscles effect forward and backward movements in the horizontal plane. An abductor and an adductor of the coxa bring about up-and-down movements of the leg and arise from the pleuron and sternum, respectively. Anterior and posterior rotators of the coxa, of sternal origin, effect partial rotation of the limb. Finally, the depressor of the trochanter (Fig. 16) represents a group of muscles with origins on the tergum, furca and ventral margin of the coxa. When the articulation between the femur and trochanter is fixed, this muscle acts as a depressor of the leg.

The intrinsic series consists of several muscles. The levator of the trochanter, which arises from the base of the coxa, is inserted into the base of the trochanter. As in the case of the depressor, this muscle moves the leg as a whole where the femoro-trochanteral joint is fixed. The only muscle moving the femur is the levator of the femur, which arises ventrally on the trochanter and is attached to the dorsal tip of the base of the femur: it is wanting in the hind legs of locusts and crickets. The cavity of the femur is largely occupied by the levator and depressor of the tibia. A single muscle, the retractor of the claws, has points of attachment on the femur and tibia, and its long tendon is inserted on the unguitractor plate of the pretarsus. Its action is to pull the claws downward and towards the tarsus, the protraction of the claws being effected by the elasticity of their basal supporting parts. Originating in the distal half of the tibia are the levator and depressor of the tarsus; their insertion is on the dorsal and ventral borders, respectively, of the base of the first tarsomere.

The abdominal muscles. The absence of legs and wings greatly simplifies the myology of the abdomen, but there are special muscles associated with the ovipositor and male genitalia. The principal abdominal muscles include the following (Fig. 16b):

1. Dorsal longitudinals, whose origins and insertions are on the intersegmental folds. They form a series along each side of the heart.
2. Ventral longitudinals, which are the counterparts of 1 and lie on each side of the ventral nerve cord.
3. Dorsoventrals, which are mostly tergosternal in their attachments. They either lie within their segments of origin or cross from one segment to the next. They function as compressors of the abdomen and are of importance in respiration (p. 75).
4. Pleurals, including tergopleural and sternopleural series; in some insects they function as dilator and occlusor muscles of the spiracles.

THE NERVOUS SYSTEM

The tissue of the nervous system of insects consists of two main types of cells: the nerve cells or neurons and the non-nervous, irregularly branched, interstitial cells forming the neuroglia. The neurons, which are grouped together in nerve centres, or ganglia, are greatly attenuated cells derived from ectoderm and specialized for the rapid conduction of the electrochemical nervous impulses. Each neuron consists of a cell body with its nucleus, and one or more nerve fibres, or axons. According to the number of axons a neuron is described as unipolar, bipolar or multipolar. The axon often has a side-branch, or collateral, and both end in delicate branching fibrils – the terminal arborization. Each axon is enclosed in a nucleated coat – the neurilemma – and though there is no thick myelin sheath of the kind found in vertebrates, the cytoplasm of the axon is surrounded by a thin layer of fat-like material.

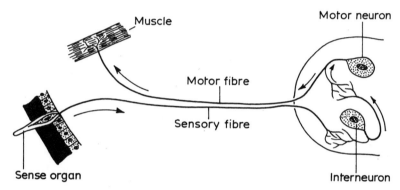

Fig. 17   Diagram of the reflex mechanism of an insect, showing left half of ganglion and its nervous connections.

Three kinds of neurons occur commonly: the sensory, motor and association neurons, the last of these also known as interneurons. A fourth type is represented by neurosecretory cells with special endocrine functions (p. 87). The sensory neurons are associated with the sense organs and lie near the integument; they are never found within the central nervous system, as in vertebrates. Each sensory neuron is usually bipolar. The distal process is adapted to respond to a particular kind of stimulus while the long axon (which develops as an outgrowth of the cell body) ends ultimately in an arborization within a central ganglion (Fig. 17). Fibres from neighbouring sensory neurons may be grouped together to form a sensory (afferent) nerve. The motor neurons always lie within the ganglia; they are mostly unipolar and their axons may be grouped together to form motor (efferent) nerves. These pass mostly to

43

the muscles, where the axons terminate in minute conical endplates or in fine branches on or within the muscle fibres. The interneurons, with their processes, form links between the sensory and motor neurons as shown in Fig. 17. The resulting junctions between the arborizations of adjacent nerve cells are known as synapses. The terminal branches of the two neurons are not usually in actual contact at a synapse; each nerve impulse which arrives there causes the temporary release of a transmitter substance which then activates the adjacent neuron, so ensuring transmission of the impulse across the synapse. Acetylcholine appears to be the principal neurotransmitter substance in the central nervous system, and its production and disappearance are controlled, respectively, by the enzymes choline acetylase and acetylcholine esterase. Other compounds – glutamic acid, γ-amino butyric acid (GABA), octopamine, dopamine and 5-hydroxytryptamine (serotonin) – are also present in the neuropile and can act as transmitters, though their exact role is not fully understood. Similar processes of chemical transmission occur at the neuromuscular junctions, where motor axons end. Here glutamic acid has been shown to be the transmitter for excitatory axons, while GABA is released at inhibitory endings and octopamine at the junctions between muscle and those axons which modulate the activity of the other motor endings.

The nervous system consists of the central nervous system, the visceral nervous system and the peripheral sensory nervous system.

The central nervous system. This is composed of a double series of nervous centres, or ganglia, joined together by longitudinal and transverse tracts of nerve fibres. The longitudinal tracts of fibres are the connectives (see Fig. 18) and serve to unite a pair of ganglia with those in front and behind. The transverse fibres, or commissures, unite the two ganglia of a pair. While there is usually a pair of ganglia in almost every segment in the lower insects (Fig. 18a), varying degrees of fusion occur in the higher groups (c and d). Also, the members of a pair are often so closely amalgamated that they seem to form a single ganglion. The connectives are separate and distinct in the more primitive insects, but often are so closely approximated that they appear as a single longitudinal cord (Fig. 18d).

The ganglia of the central nervous system are mainly formed of peripheral aggregations of nerve cells enclosing a central mass of nerve fibres (the so-called neuropile). Each lateral nerve has two roots. The fibres of the dorsal root arise from motor cells situated dorsolaterally in a ganglion and the sensory fibres, composing the ventral root, end in terminal arborizations on the ventrolateral aspect of the ganglion. The interneurons lie, for the most part, between the dorsal and ventral roots. Externally the ganglia and nerves are invested with a sheath, or

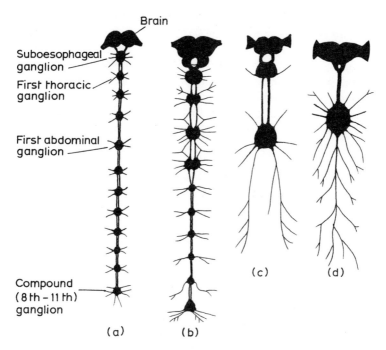

Fig. 18   Representative insect nervous systems
(a) *Japyx* (Diplura: Japygidae); (b) *Blatta* (Dictyoptera: Blattidae); (c) giant water bug, *Belostoma* (Hemiptera: Belostomatidae); (d) housefly *Musca* (Diptera: Muscidae).

neurilemma, secreted by a superficial layer of cells, the perineurium, which controls differences in the ionic composition of the blood and the nervous tissue. The central nervous system is divisible into the brain and the ventral nerve cord.

The brain (or supra-oesophageal ganglia). The brain (Figs 18 and 19) lies just above the oesophagus and is formed by the amalgamation of the ganglia of the presegmental acron and the three most anterior head segments. They develop very unequally and give rise to the protocerebrum, the deutocerebrum and the tritocerebrum. The protocerebrum forms the greater part of the brain, and represents the ganglia of the preantennal segment and the acron; it innervates the compound eyes and ocelli. Laterally this region is expanded to form the optic lobes which contain the elaborate system of nerve cells and fibres linking the visual cells of the eye with the centres of the protocerebrum. Their degree of development is correlated with that of the eyes. Within the protocerebrum are the 'mushroom bodies', composed of vast numbers of small interneurons whose axons are grouped together into stalk-like bundles. The size and complexity of these bodies corresponds in a

45

general way with complexity and specialization of behaviour. The deutocerebrum is formed by the ganglia of the antennal segment; it is chiefly composed of the antennal lobes and innervates the antennae and their muscles. The tritocerebrum is formed by the third pair of segmental ganglia, and lies beneath the antennal lobes. It is poorly developed, owing to the absence of the second antennae in insects, and its function is to innervate the labrum and the fore intestine. Its component ganglia are far apart and are joined by the postoesophageal commissure.

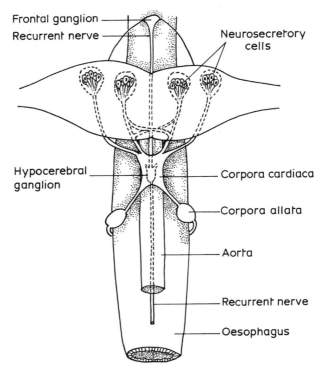

Fig. 19   Brain and stomatogastric nervous system (schematic).

The brain contains a few motor neurons concerned with antennal movements, but its main functions are those of sensation and co-ordination. It is responsible for maintaining the general tonus of the skeletal muscles, it controls the local reflexes which are mediated by the thoracic and abdominal ganglia, and it exerts an inhibitory action on centres in the suboesophageal ganglion. Experimental removal of one side of the brain reduces muscle tonus on that side and so results in circus movements towards the uninjured side. Removal of the whole brain allows the suboesophageal ganglion to excite the locomotor centres, and so causes the insect to walk restlessly in response to slight stimuli.

The ventral nerve cord. The ventral nerve cord (Fig. 18) is a median chain of segmental ganglia lying beneath the alimentary canal. It is joined to the tritocerebrum by the para-oesophageal connectives. The first ventral nerve centre is the suboesophageal ganglion, formed by the fusion of the fourth to sixth neuromeres of the mandibular, maxillary and labial segments. It gives off paired nerves supplying their respective appendages. There follow three thoracic ganglia and, at most, eight ganglia in the abdomen. The first abdominal ganglion often fuses with that of the metathorax, and the end ganglion of the chain is always a composite centre formed by the fusion of at least three neuromeres. In some groups of insects extensive fusion of the ventral ganglia occurs, especially in the Hemiptera and higher Diptera (Fig. 18c and d). In extreme cases all the ventral ganglia (including the suboesophageal) are amalgamated into a large compound ganglion from which nerves run to all parts of the trunk. The thoracic ganglia innervate the legs and wings, while each abdominal ganglion shows considerable autonomy and functions to some extent as a local centre for its segment. A complicated set of reflex acts such as oviposition can be carried out by a living isolated abdomen when suitably stimulated, provided the last ganglion and its nerves are intact.

The visceral nervous system. The principal component of the visceral or sympathetic nervous system is known as the stomatogastric system (Fig. 19), which is formed by ingrowth of the dorsal part of the stomodaeum. It includes, first, a median frontal ganglion lying just anterior to the brain. This ganglion seems to exert an effect on the ionic concentrations of the blood; it is joined by bilateral connectives to the tritocerebrum and gives off a recurrent nerve that ends in the hypocerebral ganglion. Behind the brain there are also paired corpora cardiaca that are joined to the protocerebrum and the hypocerebral ganglion. The corpora cardiaca exert important endocrine functions, and closely associated with them are further paired endocrine glands, the corpora allata (p. 87). A single or paired ventricular ganglion is linked to the hypocerebral ganglion. The stomatogastric system contains both motor and sensory fibres, and innervates the heart and fore intestine.

The ventral sympathetic system consists of transverse nerves associated with each ganglion of the ventral cord; these supply the spiracles of their segment. Arising from the last abdominal ganglion are splanchnic nerves that innervate the reproductive organs and the hind intestine.

The peripheral sensory nervous system. This is composed of a fine network of sensory cells and their axons lying beneath the integument. The nerve cells have branched distal processes that end in the epidermis itself. The axons combine and enter the paired segmental nerves of the ventral cord. This system is perhaps homologous with the nerve net of the lower invertebrates. Among insects it is best developed in soft-skinned larvae.

THE SENSE ORGANS AND PERCEPTION

Sensory perception is achieved by means of structures termed receptors or sensilla. These take various forms and are situated at the peripheral endings of the sensory nerves. In many cases – the tactile receptors, for example – they are scattered in distribution, whereas in the eyes and tympanal organs they are aggregated, often in large numbers. In their least modified form receptors closely resemble ordinary body hairs and only differ in being connected with the nervous system. The components of a simple type of receptor (Fig. 20a) are the cuticular or external part with its trichogen or formative cell, together with a bipolar sense cell. The latter lies in or just beneath the epidermis and its distal process penetrates the trichogen cell to enter the cavity of the cuticular part of the receptor. In many cases a tormogen or membrane cell is also present. Various types of receptors are evidently derived from this simple trichoid structure. They are characterized by the form of the cuticular parts and may be basiconic, placoid, campaniform, coeloconic, etc., that is, peg-like, plate-like, dome-like or in pits. Receptors of a different kind are the ommatidia or components of the eyes, and the chordotonal receptors of the tympanal organs.

Not all the receptors have yet had functions ascribed to them with certainty, though their probable role may sometimes be inferred from their structure and position. Further information has been gained by studying the reactions of insects in which receptors, or parts of the body bearing them, have been removed or coated, for example, with impermeable substances. Electrical methods of recording impulses in the sensory nerves, or even within the receptor cells, provide more exact physiological knowledge of their functions. However, in many cases the minute size of the sensilla and the fact that several kinds often occur in close proximity makes their investigation difficult.

The following classification of receptors is convenient:

1. mechanoreceptors, e.g. of touch, tension and balance
2. auditory organs, perceiving sound
3. chemoreceptors, perceiving odours and tastes
4. temperature and humidity receptors
5. photoreceptors or visual organs

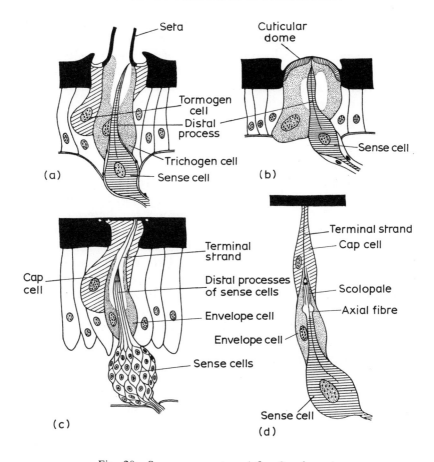

Fig. 20   Sensory receptors (after Snodgrass)
(a) Sensory hair; (b) campaniform sensillum; (c) placoid sensillum; (d) chordotonal sensillum.

The majority of these are exteroceptors, perceiving stimuli which arise outside the insect. However, some mechanoreceptors serve as proprioceptors, i.e. they respond to internal stimuli resulting from changes in the position of the body or its parts.

Mechanoreceptors. These are excited by stimuli which temporarily deform the cuticle in or near the sensillum; three main types occur. In the articulated sensory hairs (Fig. 20a) movement of the hair in its socket produces impulses in the sensory nerve fibre. Such sensilla mediate the sense of touch or perceive currents of air or water. When grouped together in the form of 'hair plates' near the joints of an appendage they act as proprioceptors, since they are then stimulated

49

when one segment of the limb moves against its neighbour. The campaniform sensilla (Fig. 20b) consist of minute circular or oval dome-shaped areas of thin cuticle, each of which is in contact internally with the rod-like terminal process, or scolopale, of a sensory nerve cell. When movement of the body causes stresses to develop in the adjacent cuticle, the scolopale is displaced up or down and so stimulates the neuron to discharge impulses in the sensory fibre. Campaniform sensilla are thus essentially proprioceptors, and are commonly found in groups near the joints of the legs and palps and at the bases of the wings and halteres. The chordotonal sensilla (Fig. 20d) occur singly or grouped in many parts of the body of insects. In the grasshopper *Melanoplus*, for example, Slifer found 76 pairs of chordotonal organs, each composed of one or more of these receptors. A chordotonal sensillum consists of a long cap cell attached to the integument, an envelope cell and a sense cell. The envelope cell surrounds the distal process of the sense cell, whose apex is prolonged into a terminal fibre that is fastened to the cuticle. At the apex of the sensory process is a sense rod, or scolopale, of complex structure. A delicate axial fibre arises in the sense cell and traverses the scolopale to end in its deeply staining cap or apical body. Any displacement of the scolopale, it would appear, excites the sense cell through the axial fibre. Very often chordotonal receptors are attached at both their ends to the integument, and it is probable that they are proprioceptors sensitive to changes of tension in the muscles. Intramuscular proprioceptors not unlike those of vertebrates have been found in some insects, but these appear to be less important as proprioceptors than the chordotonal and campaniform sensilla.

Specialized organs of equilibrium occur in some insects; they depend on the presence of one or more of the above types of mechanoreceptors. The halteres of Diptera, for example (pp. 29 and 159), which are concerned with the maintenance of equilibrium in flight, are provided basally with specially arranged groups of campaniform sensilla. These register the alterations in cuticular stresses at the base of the vibrating haltere when the insect changes its direction of flight. In the second antennal segment (pedicel) of almost all insects lies Johnston's organ. This is formed of chordotonal sensilla attached distally to the articular membrane at the base of the flagellum, and thus perceives the latter's movements. In the Chironomidae and Culicidae, where the organ is highly developed and has very many sensilla, the pedicel is specially enlarged to accommodate it.

Auditory receptors. Sound waves transmitted through the air are perceived by specialized organs which respond to very small displacement of their cuticular parts and are thus related to the mechanoreceptors described above. In male Culicidae, Johnston's organ acts as a sound receptor, since the densely plumose flagellum of the antenna is moved by the sound waves, while auditory hairs, not very different in structure from the tactile ones, occur on the cerci of cockroaches and crickets. But the most specialized sound receptors are the tympanal organs (Fig. 21c and e) such as occur on each side of the first abdominal segment in the Acrididae (short-horned grasshoppers) or on the proximal part of the fore tibiae in Tettigoniidae (long-horned grasshoppers) and Gryllidae (crickets). Comparable organs are found also in cicadas and many moths. In all cases they have an essentially similar structure. A delicate external cuticular membrane, the tympanum, overlies a tracheal air-sac and is therefore able to vibrate freely when sound waves impinge on it. The movements of the tympanum then stimulate the chordotonal sensilla attached to it. The tympanal organs of Orthoptera are most sensitive to sounds with frequencies between about 5000 and 20 000 Hz, while those of moths are sensitive to ultrasonic frequencies. In some cases it has been demonstrated that the responses in the tympanal nerves are related to the frequency with which the amplitude of the sound is modulated; the fundamental frequency of the 'carrier wave' is important

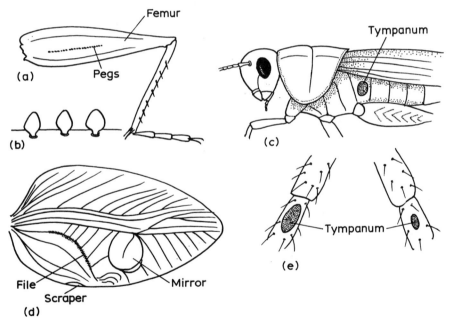

Fig. 21   Sound-producing and auditory organs

(a) Hind leg of an Acridid grasshopper showing row of stridulatory pegs on inner surface of femur. (b) Three pegs at higher magnification. (c) Lateral view of an Acridid showing tympanal organ on first abdominal segment. (d) Fore wing of male cricket, *Acheta*, showing stridulatory file and scraper. (e) Outer and inner views of tympanal organ on fore tibia of cricket (*Acheta*).

only in that it must fall within the auditory range of the insect. The latter therefore distinguishes sounds which differ in the rhythmic variations of intensity which make up the pattern of amplitude modulation; in this respect it differs greatly from man, who relies mainly on differences in pitch (frequency), though some degree of pitch discrimination is also found in insects.

Correlated with the ability of many insects to perceive sounds is their ability to produce noises and therefore to communicate with each other over relatively great distances. The sounds are produced in various ways. Thus, the familiar stridulation of many short-horned grass-hoppers is caused by rubbing the inner surface of each hind femur – which bears a row of minute pegs – against a thickened vein of the adjacent closed tegmen (Fig. 21a and b). In the crickets (Fig. 21d), each tegmen bears a rasping organ, or file, and a hardened area, or scraper, the file of one tegmen working against the scraper of the other, throwing into vibration the specialized resonating areas of the tegmen. In the long-horned grasshoppers there is a similar mechanism, but the file is only functional on the left tegmen and the scraper on the right one. Male cicadas have a pair of drum-like tymbals at the base of the abdomen, and loud sounds are produced when the 'head' of the drum is repeatedly moved in and out through the frequent action of powerful muscles, rather in the way that sounds can be made by pushing the lid of a tin can in and out. In all the above cases sound production is confined to or predominates in the males, the sounds may have relatively elaborate patterns, they display amplitude modulation and their characteristics are recognized by other members of the species through the auditory organs. A given species may produce more than one kind of song, and at least some of these play an important role in attracting or stimulating the female in courtship. Many other insects produce sounds by a great variety of means, but are not equipped with specialized auditory organs; in these cases the sounds may be defensive or of unknown significance.

Chemoreceptors. In this category are the receptors for smell and taste. In terrestrial insects the olfactory sense is stimulated by low concentrations of the vapours of volatile substances, while the gustatory sense perceives relatively high concentrations of the stimulant in aqueous solution. Whether a comparable distinction holds good for insects living in wet environments is not clear.

The olfactory receptors are found mainly on the antennae and less often on the palps. Each receptor possesses cuticle which is at least partly very thin and perforated by minute pores, and which is usually innervated by a group of bipolar neurons whose distal processes have a ciliary ultrastructure. The various different structural types of receptors have been classified as trichoid, basiconic, coeloconic and placoid (Figs 20c and 22). They are usually scattered over the surface of the organ bearing them, but are sometimes grouped in pits to form a definite olfactory organ (e.g. on the antennae of Muscid flies). The receptors may be more numerous in the male, and in *Apis*, for example, the last eight antennal segments of males bear about 30 000 placoid sensilla, compared with 6000 in the workers and 2000 in the queens. The sense of smell plays an important part in the life of insects, since many behavioural and developmental changes are caused by pheromones. These are highly specific, volatile substances usually perceived through the olfactory sensilla after having been secreted by other members of the same species and they are discussed separately below. Many female insects are attracted by smell to sites suitable for egg-laying and the development of the newly hatched young, while some phytophagous insects are attracted to their host-plants by the smell of the essential oils there.

The gustatory receptors are probably basiconic or trichoid. They occur on the surfaces of the pre-oral food cavity and mouthparts, on the antennae of some Hymenoptera and the tarsi of many Lepidoptera, Diptera and honey-bees. The Red Admiral butterfly (*Vanessa atalanta*) can, with its tarsal receptors, distinguish between distilled water and an M/12 800 solution of sucrose, a sensitivity over 200 times that of the human tongue. In general there are wide differences in the taste thresholds of different substances with a given species and for different

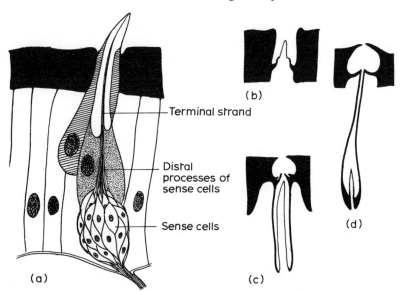

Fig. 22 Cuticular sensilla

(a) Basiconic sensillum; (b) coeloconic sensillum; (c), (d) two types of sensilla ampullacea. Only the cuticular structures are shown in (b), (c) and (d).

species with the same substance. Solutions of sugars and dilute solutions of acids and salts are usually preferred to distilled water, while more concentrated solutions of acids, salts, esters, alcohols and amino acids are usually rejected. Detailed investigations have shown that in some insects the individual sense cells of a single gustatory sensillum respond specifically to particular substances, some reacting to sugars, others to salts or to water.

Insect pheromones. A pheromone is a chemical substance secreted and released by some members of a species and affecting the behaviour or development of other members of the same species after they have perceived the stimulus through their olfactory senses. As such, pheromones are one class of semiochemicals, or substances which convey information between living organisms through the olfactory system. They may be distinguished from those other semiochemicals which act between different species, such as kairomones, which attract exploiting species like parasites or predators, and allomones, which are advantageous to the species producing them (e.g. by deterring other species that compete for the same environmental resource). In certain cases a single substance may act as a pheromone, kairomone or allomone, depending on the circumstances. Insect pheromones are single, relatively simple substances of considerable chemical diversity; they are very highly specific and show high biological activity, exerting their effects at very low concentrations. In some cases a pheromonal effect depends on the presence of two or more separate, but usually related, chemicals in the secretion. Pheromones may be involved in two rather different kinds of process. Some induce almost immediate, short-term behavioural responses, as in the attraction of males to an unmated female, while others initiate long-term, irreversible physiological or developmental changes such as sexual maturation or the differentiation of the various forms of a polymorphic species. Pheromones are often the only special stimuli required to induce relatively simple stereotyped forms of insect behaviour, and several distinct pheromonal mechanisms may be involved successively in each of the component parts of a more complex behaviour pattern. It is convenient to divide pheromones into about seven groups, depending on the kind of behavioural or developmental response they provoke: sex pheromones; aggregation pheromones; epideictic pheromones, causing dispersal or spacing-out of individuals; alarm pheromones; recruitment or trail-marking phero-mones; maturation pheromones; and the pheromones of social insects. A few examples of these are discussed briefly below.

The best-known sex pheromones are the sex attractants released by many female Lepidoptera to bring males into their immediate vicinity. These are known from over 100 species, and many have been intensively investigated, as in the silk moth *Bombyx mori* and the Gypsy Moth *Lymantria dispar*. Their effects are often due to more than one substance: *Bombyx mori*, for example, secretes a mixture of bombykol (*trans*-10,*cis*-12-hexadecadienol) and bombykal (the corresponding aldehyde), while the Pink Bollworm moth *Platyedra gossypiella* produces two different isomers of hexadecadienyl acetate. In general these sex attractants are produced by epidermal glands in the female abdomen, and they form a plume of scent that floats downwind. Males use this to orientate to her (anemotaxis) and fly upwind, often for considerable distances, until they approach her. Here they land and begin a mating display, such as wing-fanning or the protrusion of 'hair-pencils'. These are eversible tufts of glandular hairs which may produce further so-called aphrodisiac pheromones that induce the female to mate. A good example of this is provided by the abdominal hair-pencils of the male Queen butterfly *Danaus gilippus* which, after it has orientated to a female visually, releases pyrolizidine alkaloids that act as pheromones. In some insects it is the male which produces the sex attractant, as in the wax-moth *Achroia grisella*, whose males release *cis*-11-octadecenal and *n*-undecenal which help the female to locate them. Aggregation pheromones are perhaps best known from the Scolytidae (bark-beetles), among which many different and complicated mechanisms have been found. *Dendroctonus brevicomis* females colonize the host tree and bore into it. They then release a pheromone, *exo*-brevicomin, which with myrcene (a terpene from the host), attracts males and females. These males then produce another pheromone, frontalin, which enhances the activity of brevicomin and myrcene, so increasing the rate at which aggregation occurs on the host tree. Finally the inhibitory pheromones verbenone and *trans*-verbenol are released by males and/or females and stop the process of aggregation, thus limiting the extent to which each tree is colonized.

An alarm pheromone, *iso*-amyl acetate, is secreted by honey-bees which have been disturbed or injured, inducing other bees near them to sting their attacker. Among aphids, *trans*-farnesene may be released from the cornicles when they are attacked by predators, and this also acts as an alarm pheromone, causing nearby aphids to disperse and escape. Many ants and termites can secrete relatively persistent trail-marking pheromones, usually from epidermal glands in their abdomen; workers which have found a food source lay down a trail as they return to the colony, thus recruiting further workers which follow the trail to the food. Such trails remain active for times that vary from a few minutes to a few days, and they may be composed of short-chain organic acids, terpenoids or alkaloids, according to species. Among the pheromones which cause more pronounced physiological or developmental changes is that secreted by sexually mature Desert Locusts

(*Schistocerca gregaria*) and which accelerates the maturation of younger males. The 'queen substance' produced by queen honey-bees (*Apis mellifera*) consists mainly of 9-oxo-*trans*-2-decenoic acid and the corresponding 9-hydroxy compound. It controls several important processes in the social life of the bees, inhibiting the development of worker ovaries and the tendency of workers to construct cells for rearing queens, as well as acting as a sex pheromone that attracts males to a virgin female on her nuptial flight. Because they show high biological activity and specificity and can sometimes be manufactured easily, pheromones are likely to play an increasingly important part in insect pest control.

Temperature and humidity receptors. Temperature receptors may occur on the antennae, maxillary palps and tarsi, though relatively little is known of their structure and physiology. A few insects are known to respond to radiant heat, but more often it seems that convective transfer of heat in the air is the effective stimulus. Blood-sucking and ectoparasitic insects may in this way detect the presence of their warm-blooded hosts, while insects given the opportunity of moving freely in an experimental temperature gradient tend to congregate in a zone representing their temperature preference.

Many insects react to differences in atmospheric humidity, either by showing a preference for certain humidities or by orienting themselves to the vapour from a distant source of water. Basiconic, trichoid and placoid sensilla mediate these responses, but their mode of action is not known.

Photoreceptors. Photoreceptors in insects are of two kinds: ocelli or simple eyes, and compound or faceted eyes. Typically both kinds of eyes are found in the same insects, but either or both may be absent.

Ocelli. The most obvious distinction between an ocellus and a compound eye is the presence of a single corneal lens in the former, whereas in the compound eye there are many. Ocelli fall into two classes: the dorsal ocelli of imagines and nymphs, and the lateral ocelli of most Endopterygote larvae.

Dorsal ocelli are typically three in number, arranged in a triangle, either on the frontal region of the head or on the vertex (Fig. 3). That the median ocellus of the group was originally paired is shown by its bilateral form in some insects and by the double nerve roots. The dorsal ocelli are innervated from the ocellar lobes of the brain which are located in the protocerebrum between the mushroom bodies. Structurally an ocellus consists of a biconvex lens beneath which is a transparent corneagen layer which overlies the sensory elements, or retinulae (Fig.

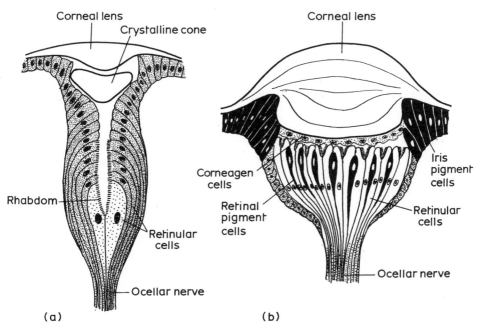

Fig. 23   Sections through two types of ocelli
(a) Lateral ocellus of larva of *Dytiscus* (Coleoptera: Dytiscidae) (after Günther); (b) dorsal
ocellus, schematic (after Weber).

23). A retinula is composed of a group of visual cells whose contiguous regions are specialized to form a more or less rod-like rhabdom, with each cell produced into a fibre of the ocellar nerve. Between the retinulae and around the margin of the lens there are usually pigment cells.

Little is known of the function of dorsal ocelli. Their structure shows that they are incapable of any but the crudest kind of image formation, but they probably perceive changes in light intensity. In some insects the response to light received through the compound eyes is more acute and lasting when the dorsal ocelli are in their normal condition than when painted over with an opaque substance. Evidence of this kind suggests that the ocelli and compound eyes interact in mediating the insect's response to light, but the ocelli seem to be more than simple 'stimulatory organs' and the interaction between eyes and ocelli may sometimes be antagonistic.

Lateral ocelli have no general uniformity of structure and may occur singly (sawfly larvae) or in groups (larvae of Lepidoptera and other orders) on either side of the head. They are innervated from the optic lobes of the brain, and when the larva undergoes metamorphosis they are replaced by compound eyes. In Lepidopterous larvae they have a structure recalling an ommatidium of a compound eye: a corneal lens, often with a crystalline cone, overlies a group of visual cells forming a retinula that secretes a central rhabdom. In the larvae of sawflies, and of some beetles, their structure is similar to that of a dorsal ocellus and consists of a number of retinulae in association with a single lens. Lateral ocelli are able to perceive movements of objects in their vicinity, besides being responsible for orientation to light, and perhaps for some appreciation of colour.

Compound eyes (Fig. 24). Compound eyes are the principal visual organs and are characterized externally by the cornea or investing cuticle, being divided into facets or lenses, usually hexagonal in form. Each facet is part of a separate visual structure, or ommatidium. The number of facets (and therefore of ommatidia) in a compound eye ranges from over 20 000 in some dragonflies to 12 000 or more among Lepidoptera and 4000 in *Musca*, while in the workers of certain ants they may be reduced to fewer than a dozen. The cornea is formed of transparent cuticle and is shed at each moult. It is produced by two epidermal cells which form the corneagen layer. Between the latter and

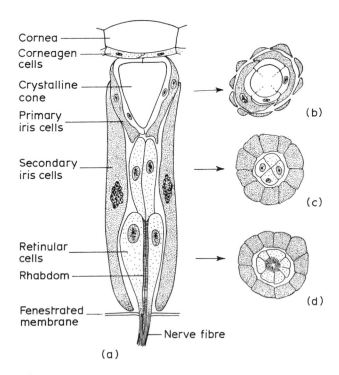

Fig. 24 Diagram of generalized ommatidium of a compound eye
(a) Longitudinal section; (b)–(d) transverse sections at indicated levels.

the visual cells is a group of four transparent cone cells which either contain fluid or secrete a body known as the crystalline cone. The retinula is composed of a group of usually seven pigmented visual cells which are collectively modified where they are in contact to form an internal rhabdom. The ommatidia are isolated from their fellows by pigment cells arranged in two groups: one group surrounds the cone and forms the primary iris cells, whereas the other surrounds the retinula and forms the secondary iris cells.

In general the compound eyes can perceive something of the form, movement and spatial location of external objects and detect some differences in the intensity and colour of light falling on them. The formation of an image is accounted for by the mosaic theory of vision. Light rays from external objects are focused on to the rhabdoms by the cornea and cones in such a way that each rhabdom is stimulated by a very small zone of light from that part of the visual field which it subtends. The small zones will normally differ in intensity and together they give rise to an erect image composed of light and dark spots, rather like a newspaper photograph. The process by which light rays are focused on to the rhabdoms is very complicated; it differs from one insect species to another and depends on whether the eye is in a light- or dark-adapted state. The many possible mechanisms have not yet been investigated sufficiently to allow simple modern generalizations, but the classical work of Exner distinguished two principal methods of image formation (Fig. 25). In eyes which form an apposition image (Fig. 25a), each ommatidium is optically separated from its neighbours by dense pigment. Each rhabdom is therefore stimulated only by light rays focused through the dioptric unit (cornea and cone) immediately above it, and any rays which cannot be focused on to this rhabdom are prevented by the pigment from stimulating adjacent ones. In the so-called 'clear zone eyes', on the other hand, there is a more or less wide, pigment-free gap between the inner ends of the cones and the outer ends of the rhabdoms, at least in the dark-adapted condition. In such eyes image formation seems to occur by several different methods, one of which involves the formation of a superposition image. Here pigment does not separate adjacent ommatidia, with the result that light rays can be brought to a focus on a given rhabdom after passing through the dioptric units of several adjacent ommatidia, as shown in Fig. 25b. The superposition image is less distinct, but brighter, since less light is wasted through absorption by pigment. This type of eye is therefore often found in nocturnal or crepuscular insects, while diurnal insects usually form an image by apposition. However, in some species migration of the pigment enables the eye to function in either way, depending on the light intensity, so that the phenomenon of adaptation occurs (see the right-hand side of Fig. 25b). The clear zone may also be

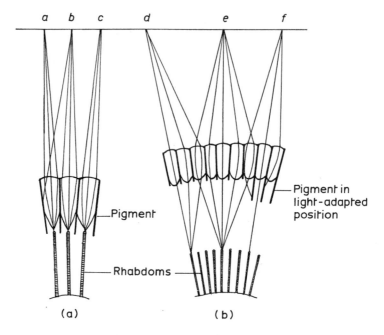

Fig. 25 Diagram showing classical theories of image formation by
compound eye

(a) Eye forming apposition image; (b) eye forming superposition image. *a–f* are luminous
points with the course of the rays emitted by them; at the right side of (b) the migration
of pigment into the light-adapted position results in an apposition image – all rays except
those entering the central facet are intercepted (after Kühn).

crossed by crystalline tracts which guide light within an ommatidium
from the cone to the rhabdom.

Though insects readily detect the movement of objects, the acuity of
their vision is much less than that of man. It depends, among other
things, on the number and angular separation of ommatidia in the eye,
but it is too low to make accurate recognition of form possible.
Perception of form is, in fact, an elaborate process and the honey-bee's
ability to distinguish between static patterns of different complexity
seems to depend on the changes of stimulation which occur as the image
passes over the retina of the moving insect. Some, but not all, insects
have colour vision, though different species may distinguish between
different sets of colours, and many insects are known to perceive
ultraviolet radiation, which is invisible to man. By training honey-bees
to associate certain colours with the presence of food, it has been found
that they distinguish between six 'colours'. One of these is in the
ultraviolet, others correspond to our violet, blue, blue-green and
yellow, while the last is 'bee purple', a mixture of yellow and

ultraviolet. They do not discriminate between the different hues within these 'colours'. A number of insects are able to perceive the plane of vibration of polarized light; honey-bees foraging for nectar under a partially clouded sky use this faculty for direction finding.

ALIMENTARY CANAL, DIGESTION AND NUTRITION

The alimentary canal

The alimentary canal (Fig. 26) is divided into three regions: the fore intestine that arises in the embryo as an anterior ectodermal ingrowth (stomodaeum); the hind intestine that arises as a similar posterior ingrowth (proctodaeum); and the mid intestine, stomach or ventriculus, formed as an endodermal sac (mesenteron) connecting the two. These differences in embryonic origin result in marked histological differences in the structure of the mid intestine compared with either of the other regions. The fore and hind intestine, being ingrowths of the integument, resemble the latter histologically and are lined with cuticle.

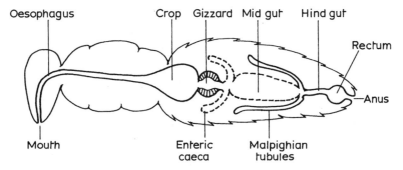

Fig. 26   Diagram of the digestive system of an insect

The regions of ectodermal origin are represented by full lines and those of endodermal origin by broken lines. Note, however, that the Malpighian tubules arise from an undifferentiated zone between the rudiments of the mid and hind gut.

Pre-oral food cavity. Strictly, this is not part of the alimentary canal, but it may conveniently be discussed here. In insects with simple biting mouthparts and a hypognathous head it is the space bounded in front by the inner surface of the labrum, behind by the labium, and laterally by the mandibles and maxillae. The hypopharynx (p. 17), which arises near the base of the labium, lies within this cavity and partially divides it into an anterior cibarium and a posterior salivarium. The cibarium is provided with dilator muscles which arise on the postclypeus and in some insects with specialized feeding habits (e.g. Hemiptera) it forms the cibarial sucking pump. The salivarium receives the common duct of the labial glands. These normally secrete saliva and in the Hemiptera the salivarium is modified into a salivary syringe which helps to inject saliva into the plant or animal on which the insect is feeding. In Lepidopterous larvae, where the labial glands secrete silk, the salivarium forms the silk regulator.

Fore intestine. This begins with the pharynx, a relatively narrow tube which leads back from the pre-oral food cavity and is equipped with dilator muscles arising from the frons. In some insects, such as the Lepidoptera and Hymenoptera, the pharynx may participate in the formation of a sucking pump. Posteriorly the pharynx passes into the oesophagus. This may be a simple tube leading into the mid intestine, or it may be expanded at some point to form a crop. The latter may be a simple dilatation of the posterior part of the oesophagus (Fig. 28) or, as in the blowfly and most Lepidoptera, it is a lateral diverticulum connected with the oesophagus by a narrow tube, illustrated in Fig. 29. The crop acts mainly as a food reservoir, from which the food is transferred to the mid intestine as required, but some digestion may also take place there. The fore intestine is separated from the mid intestine by the cardiac sphincter, and at this region it is often modified to form a muscular proventriculus or gizzard, which varies greatly in its development. Its main function is that of a sieve occluding the passage of food if not in a sufficiently divided state. Well-developed in many chewing

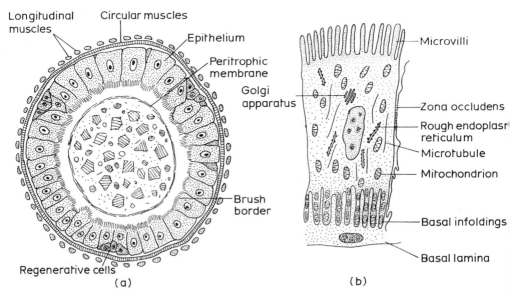

Fig. 27   Mid intestine
(a) Diagrammatic transverse section; (b) ultrastructure of a single midgut epithelial cell.

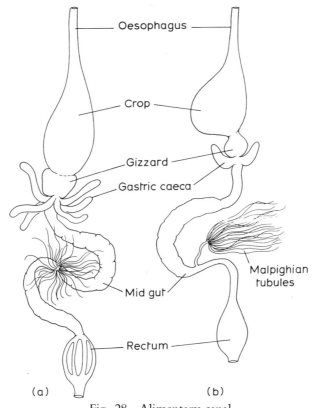

Fig. 28   Alimentary canal
(a) *Periplaneta americana* (Dictyoptera: Blattidae); (b) *Nemobius sylvestris* (Orthoptera: Gryllidae).

insects, in sucking insects it is little more than a valve. In the cockroach and in some Orthoptera and Coleoptera it has powerful radial teeth and circular muscles, and serves the additional function of crushing the larger food particles.

Histologically, the fore intestine consists of a cellular layer which secretes the cuticular lining and is covered externally with a basement membrane. Outside the latter is a coat of longitudinal muscle fibres overlaid by circular fibres.

The mid intestine. This is composed of a layer of large epithelial cells bounded externally by a basement membrane. On their inner aspect these cells usually show a striated border (Fig. 27) composed of large numbers of microvilli. A layer of minute circular muscle fibres and external longitudinal muscles is present. The superficial area of the mid intestine is increased not only by the microvilli but also, in many insects, through the development of outgrowths or caeca that vary in size and

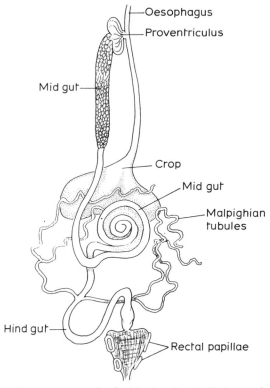

Fig. 29 Alimentary canal of a bluebottle, *Calliphora* (after Lowne)

number (Fig. 28). A third method of achieving the same result is by the folding of the epithelial layer to form crypts; all methods may occur in the same species. The epithelial cells of most insects usually appear to be of one kind, although individual cells may be in different phases at a given time. Secretion and absorption are therefore thought to take place by the same or similar cells. The method of secretion may be (a) merocrine, in which the cells discharge their products through the striated border without undergoing any drastic changes; and (b) holocrine, which is less prevalent, but occurs in Orthoptera and is characterized by the disintegration of the cells during the process. Larval Lepidoptera and Trichoptera are unusual in having a second type of midgut epithelial cell, the 'goblet cell', with a large central vacuole. Between the bases of the epithelial cells are small groups of replacement cells which divide and provide new epithelial cells (Fig. 27).

In most insects and their larvae the food is separated from the epithelial lining by the peritrophic membrane (Fig. 27) which forms a thin, colourless tube projecting backwards into the hind intestine. It is composed partly of chitin, and is supposed to protect the epithelial cells from abrasion. This explanation agrees with the absence of mucous cells that might otherwise perform this function. Also, the membrane is absent or greatly reduced and diffuse in many, but not all, insects that imbibe fluid food, such as Hemiptera, adult Lepidoptera and numerous blood-sucking forms. The peritrophic membrane is shed through the anus with the faeces. It is usually formed as a secretion from the surface of the mid-intestinal epithelium, but in some insects it is extruded in tubular form by an annular press formed from part of the cardiac valve. It is permeable to digestive enzymes and the products of digestion.

In the larvae of most Plannipennian Neuroptera and Apocritan Hymenoptera the capacious mid gut is closed posteriorly until the end of larval life; communication with the hind gut is then established and the accumulated stomach contents pass out.

The hind intestine. This is sometimes divisible into a narrow anterior tube or ileum, a colon, and a wider end region or rectum, which opens exteriorly at the anus. Histologically the hind intestine consists of the same layers as the fore intestine, but the cuticular lining is thinner and the circular muscles are present both external and internal to the longitudinal layer. In many insects the cellular layer of the rectum becomes greatly thickened to form six longitudinal pads, or rectal papillae. An important function of these papillae is the maintenance of the proper salt and water balance by absorption from the contents of the rectum (see p. 84). A pyloric sphincter separates the stomach from the hind intestine and close to the junction of these two regions there are outgrowths known as Malpighian tubules (p. 82). These vessels are the principal organs of excretion and are slender blind tubes lying in the haemocoel where they are freely bathed in blood. They vary greatly in number, ranging, for example, from 30 to 120 in Orthoptera and from four to six among many Endopterygota; in the Aphididae and the Collembola these organs are wanting. Each tubule is composed of large epithelial cells resting on an external basement membrane; outside the latter there are commonly muscle fibres. The inner margins of the cells show a striated border resembling that of the mid gut, and there is no cuticular lining.

Salivary glands. These are paired glands which discharge their secretion into the pre-oral food cavity, where it mixes with the food as this is being taken in. Usually these organs are labial glands which originate as paired invaginations of the ectoderm in close association with the developing labial rudiments. Their main ducts fuse to form a common outlet discharging on or near the hypopharynx. In many insects the cuticular lining of the ducts is spirally thickened as in tracheae. In caterpillars the labial glands are converted into silk-producing organs and their salivary functions are assumed by the mandibular glands.

Digestion

Before it can be absorbed by the mid gut, the insect's food usually has to be broken down into simpler soluble substances, such as the monosaccharide sugars and amino acids. These changes are accomplished with the assistance of digestive enzymes secreted by the salivary glands and mid-gut epithelium, digestion occurring in the crop and mid gut. Three main groups of enzymes have been found in insects: (a) the carbohydrases, which catalyse the breakdown of complex carbohydrates to simple sugars. The amylases of the saliva and mid gut act on starch, while the glycosidases of the mid gut control the breakdown of the complex sugars like maltose, sucrose and lactose; (b) the lipases, which catalyse the breakdown of fats; and (c) the proteases, which are responsible for the digestion of proteins. The endopeptidases act on proteins or peptones, converting them to polypeptides, while the exopeptidases complete digestion by breaking down the peptides into amino acids.

In *Glossina* and some other blood-sucking insects the proteases are abundant, but the carbohydrases are almost absent. On the other hand, in butterflies and moths – which feed mainly on nectar – almost the only enzymes present are the invertases which hydrolyse cane-sugar. No plant-feeding insects can digest lignin, and most cannot even make use of the cellulose in their diet. Of those insects which can utilize cellulose, a few species secrete cellulose-splitting enzymes (e.g. Cerambycid beetle larvae); more commonly, however, the breakdown of cellulose is accomplished by symbionts living in the gut. These may be bacteria, as in some Scarabaeid larvae, or Protozoa, as in the wood-feeding cockroach *Cryptocercus* and the more primitive termites. While the symbionts are present, such termites can live for long periods on pure cellulose, but they soon die if deprived of the Protozoa experimentally (e.g. by exposing the insects to 36° C for 24 h or to an oxygen tension of 3–4 atm). The Protozoa are not transmitted directly to the progeny and are lost at each moult with the other contents of the gut. Newly hatched or newly moulted termites acquire a new protozoal fauna by feeding on material exuding from the anus of other members of the colony.

Nutrition

The basic nutritional requirements of a number of species are now known in biochemical terms. Carbohydrates are the main source of energy, though proteins and fats may also be oxidized for this purpose.

The amino acid requirements of a few species are known in detail, and it has been shown that some amino acids are essential for growth and development. Most insects require an external source of valine, arginine, histidine, tryptophan, leucine, *iso*-leucine, lysine, methionine, phenylalanine and threonine. The diet must also include certain vitamins; different species have different needs, but a sterol and many of the B-complex vitamins are usually essential. In some cases these vitamins are not consumed in the food but are manufactured within the insect by symbiotic micro-organisms. These may live in the gut, e.g. the yeast-like *Nocardia rhodnii* of *Rhodnius*, or they are lodged in special cells, or mycetocytes (Fig. 30), which are sometimes grouped into organs known as mycetomes. Micro-organisms of the latter kind are known from many insects and are often transmitted from the mother to her progeny via the eggs; the insects may die rapidly when deprived of their micro-organisms, but their true physiological role has been established only in a few cases.

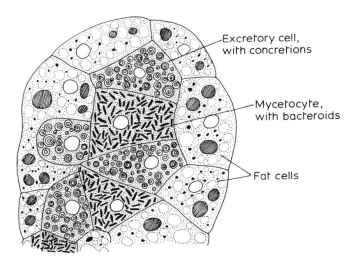

Excretory cell, with concretions

Mycetocyte, with bacteroids

Fat cells

Fig. 30 Lobe of fat-body from *Blatta orientalis* (Dictyoptera: Blattidae) (adapted after Gier)

THE RESPIRATORY SYSTEM

In almost all insects respiration takes place by means of internal tubes known as tracheae, which convey oxygen directly to the tissues. These tubes ramify over and among the various organs, and in insects with an open respiratory system they communicate with the atmosphere through one or more pairs of respiratory apertures, or spiracles. Some aquatic and endoparasitic insects have a closed tracheal system. In these there are no open spiracles, and oxygen either diffuses into the tracheae over the greater part of the cuticle or passes in mainly through the integument of special respiratory outgrowths known as gills or branchiae. In all cases the respiratory organs are derived from the ectoderm; the tracheae are developed as tubular invaginations and the gills arise as outgrowths. Histologically both types of organ consist of a thin layer of cuticle, an epidermal layer and usually a basement membrane, all of which are continuous with similar layers of the general integument.

The spiracles. The spiracles are paired openings usually situated on the pleura of the meso- and metathorax and along the sides of the abdomen. In generalized insects such as Orthoptera and in some larvae there are ten pairs of spiracles, two pairs being thoracic and eight pairs abdominal in position. However, reductions in this number are very frequent. In those cases where prothoracic spiracles occur their presence on this segment is apparently due to migration from behind in the course of evolution. Although spiracles are wanting in most Collembola, a single pair is present on the neck in some Sminthuridae. In the Diplura some Japygidae carry four pairs of thoracic spiracles, two on the mesothorax and two on the metathorax.

Many structural types of spiracles occur; the simplest are found in some Apterygotes, where they are merely openings into the tracheal system, surrounded by a simple rim or peritreme, but not provided

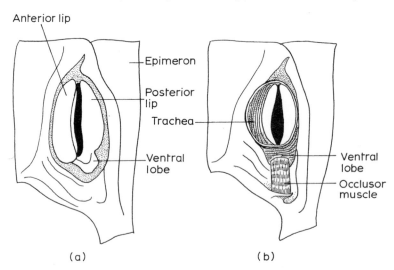

Fig. 31   Metathoracic spiracles of a grasshopper *Dissosteira* (Orthoptera: Acrididae)
(a) Outer view; (b) inner view. (After Snodgrass.)

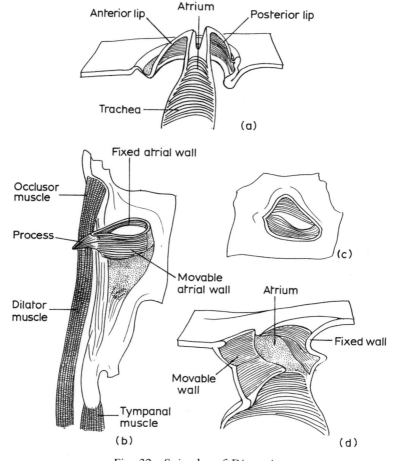

Fig. 32   Spiracles of *Dissosteira*
(a) and (d) Sections through metathoracic and first abdominal spiracles; (b) inner; (c) outer view of first abdominal spiracle. (Adapted from Snodgrass.)

with mechanisms for regulating the size of the aperture. More usually the spiracular opening leads into a chamber, the atrium, at the base of which is the tracheal orifice. The passage of air into and out of the tracheae is usually regulated by a spiracular closing mechanism, of which two main types occur: (a) An external closing apparatus, such as is well shown in the thoracic spiracles of a grasshopper (Figs 31 and 32a), consists of two movable lip-like sclerites united by a ventral lobe. The lips open through their own elasticity but are closed by the contraction of an occlusor muscle which arises from a process near the coxal cavity. (b) The internal closing mechanism may take many forms. That shown in Fig. 32 (b, c and d) has no external lips, but one wall of the atrium is movable while the other is fixed. The movable wall is

69

prolonged into a process to which are attached the occlusor and dilator muscles. Contraction of the former causes the movable wall to close the tracheal aperture, while the antagonistic dilator opens it. Spiracles of the second type often have the atrial wall produced into interlacing branched hair-like processes, or trabeculae, forming a filtering apparatus. This device allows the free passage of air, while the entry into the atrium of foreign particles or water is prevented. Provision of this kind is common in Lepidopteran larvae. In larvae of the bluebottle (*Calliphora*) and other Diptera there is no closing apparatus. The anterior spiracles consist of short lobes perforated at their apices, and the posterior spiracles have three openings guarded by trabeculae (Fig. 92e and f).

It should be noted that the spiracles, in addition to their respiratory function, are the apertures through which the old tracheal linings are drawn out when the insect moults, and that they are also a major site of water loss. The latter disadvantage is partially overcome by the closing mechanism or the atrial processes of Dipterous larvae, but these in turn have necessitated the evolution of special devices for withdrawing the tracheal linings at ecdysis.

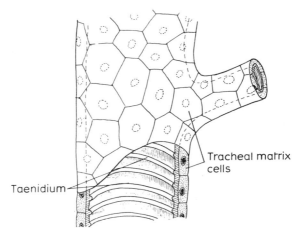

Fig. 33   Portion of a trachea (highly magnified)

The tracheae. The tracheae when filled with air present a silvery appearance. They are lined by cuticle continuous with that of the body wall. This lining has a characteristic striated appearance due to thread-like ridges which run helically around the inner circumference, and which form the so-called spiral thread, or taenidium (Fig. 33). Continuity of the spiral is often interrupted and a new spiral then begins. The function of this spiral thickening is to keep the tracheae distended and thereby allow the free passage of air. Externally there is a layer of polygonal cells that secrete the cuticular lining. When a trachea is

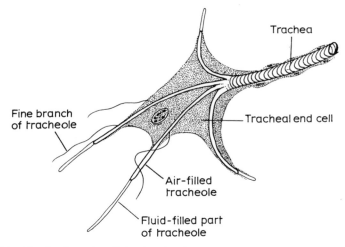

Fig. 34   Tracheal end cell in head of mosquito larva, *Aedes aegypti* (after Wigglesworth)

followed in its branching it finally enters a stellate end cell (Fig. 34) and there divides into tracheal capillaries, or tracheoles. These are less than 1 μm in diameter and their taenidia are so delicate that they are visible only under the electron microscope. The tracheoles end in the tissues in various ways. In the gut and salivary glands they ramify and pass between the cells without penetrating them. In the fat-body and rectal papillae, however, they may enter the cells, while in the flight muscles there is a network of intracellular tracheoles.

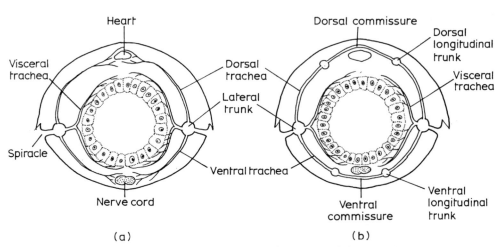

Fig. 35   Diagrammatic transverse section of an insect abdomen, showing two types of tracheal system
(a) With lateral longitudinal trunks; (b) with dorsal and ventral trunks and commissures.

71

In *Campodea* and some other Apterygotes the tracheae arising from each spiracle remain unconnected with those from the others. Elsewhere a more efficient system of longitudinal and transverse (segmental) connecting tracheae has been evolved. In a typical segment (Fig. 35) three principal tracheae arise from the main longitudinal trunk near the point where the spiracular trachea joins it. These tracheae are: (a) a dorsal trachea, supplying the dorsal muscles and heart; (b) a visceral trachea passing to the gut, fat-body and gonads; and (c) a ventral trachea which supplies the ventral musculature, nerve cord and, in the thorax, the legs and wings. Secondary longitudinal trunks (dorsal, visceral and ventral) may also be developed (Fig. 35b).

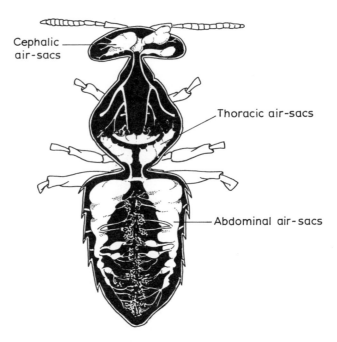

Fig. 36   Tracheal system of a worker honey-bee, *Apis mellifera*, viewed from dorsal side (after Snodgrass)

The air-sacs. In many insects thin-walled sac-like dilations or air-sacs occur in large numbers. The walls of these are usually extremely delicate in structure and devoid of any special thickening (Fig. 36). In the cockchafer (*Melolontha*) and in grasshoppers (Acrididae) air-sacs are present in large numbers as dilations of the smaller tracheae. In the housefly (*Musca*), in many other Diptera and in bees the main tracheal trunks are dilated to form extensive air-sacs, especially in the abdomen. Air-sacs are mainly developed in swiftly flying insects, and one of their functions is to provide increased ventilation for the tracheal system. They respond very rapidly to the increase and decrease of pressure resulting from respiratory movements, and consequently greatly augment the volume of air inspired and expired with each movement. Periodic compression of the thoracic air-sacs and tracheae also enables oxygen to be pumped into the actively respiring flight muscles.

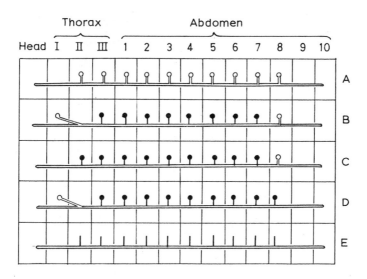

Fig. 37   Types of tracheal system
(A) Holopneustic; (B) amphipneustic; (C) metapneustic; (D) propneustic; (E) apneustic (all spiracles absent). Open tracheae are indicated by double lines, stigmatic cords by single lines; open spiracles are indicated by open circles, closed spiracles by full (black) circles.

Types of tracheal system. Several types of tracheal system are recognized, depending on the number and position of the open, functional, spiracles (Fig. 37). The holopneustic type of system has all ten pairs of spiracles open, the peripneustic type has all but a few open, and the amphipneustic type has only the first and last pairs open. In propneustic and metapneustic systems the first or last pairs, respectively, are the only open ones, while the apneustic type has no functional spiracles, respiration occurring through the general body surface or gills. The tracheal systems with few or no open spiracles are found in aquatic and endoparasitic insects. In all the foregoing types the non-functional spiracles are closed or reduced to minute scars, and each is connected to the longitudinal tracheae by a solid stigmatic cord. The latter helps to anchor the tracheal system in position and serves to pull out the old tracheal linings when the insect moults. If, in the ensuing instar, the non-functional spiracle is to be replaced by an open one, the new spiracular trachea – which forms around the stigmatic cord –

remains tubular; otherwise it shrivels to form a new stigmatic cord. In some insects one or more pairs of spiracles have disappeared completely and the tracheal system may lose much of its originally metameric nature. Such systems may be referred to as hypopneustic (e.g. some Coccoidea).

Respiration. In the smaller or less active terrestrial insects oxygen passes along the tracheal system, from the spiracles to the finer tracheoles, by the process of gaseous diffusion. This is possible because of the difference in partial pressure of oxygen between the atmosphere and the tracheolar endings, where the gas is constantly being removed by the respiring tissues. Surprising though it seems, a difference in partial pressure of only 2–3 mmHg is adequate to supply by diffusion all the oxygen that some insects require. A similar process, in the reverse direction, would also account for the removal of carbon dioxide. However, the latter diffuses through insect tissues much more readily than oxygen does, so it is likely that much of it – perhaps 25% – is eliminated through the tracheal walls and the cuticle of the body surface rather than through the spiracles. The walls of the tracheoles are more permeable to oxygen than the other parts of the tracheal system are, and it is therefore through these fine branches that the tissues receive most of their oxygen supply. There is usually some liquid in the endings of the tracheoles, but in active muscular tissue the rise in osmotic pressure which accompanies contraction results in the absorption of this liquid. Air can then penetrate further along the tracheoles, increasing the rate at which oxygen will diffuse into those tissues which are in great need of it (Fig. 38).

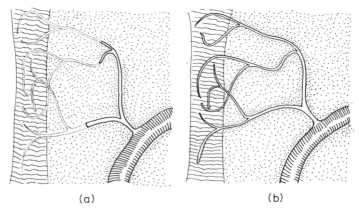

(a)   (b)

Fig. 38   Tracheation of a muscle fibre (semi–schematic, after Wigglesworth)
(a) Muscle at rest with terminal parts of tracheoles (shown dotted) containing fluid.
(b) Muscle fatigued, with air extending far into tracheoles.

The physical law governing the diffusion of oxygen along the tracheal system is such that large or very active insects would not receive enough by this means alone. Diffusion is therefore supplemented in these insects by ventilation of the tracheal system through respiratory movements. Expiration is effected by various muscles of the abdomen, whose contraction flattens the body in Orthoptera and Coleoptera, while among Hymenoptera and Diptera telescopic movements of the abdominal segments result. Inspiration is usually effected by the elasticity of the body segments as they regain their original shape. Most of the tracheae are circular in cross-section, and are therefore compressible only with difficulty, but they are readily extensible in the direction of their long axis. The main tracheal trunks are often oval in cross-section and are readily compressed while the air-sacs are even more prone to collapse. By alternately compressing and dilating the main tracheae and air-sacs, respiratory movements therefore bring about mechanical ventilation of the larger tubes. In some insects it is known that there is a directed air flow in the tracheal system. Among the Acrididae in particular it has been shown that the first four pairs of spiracles can remain open while the remaining six pairs are closed and vice versa, with the result that the former serve for inspiration and the latter for expiration. In larvae of the beetle *Dytiscus* it has been estimated that the tracheal system is emptied during strong expiration of nearly two-thirds (64 mm^3) of its total capacity (107 mm^3), the remainder being changed by diffusion.

Respiratory activity is regulated by the opening or closing of the spiracles (diffusion control) and, in those insects with ventilation, by variations in the intensity or frequency of respiratory movements (ventilation control). In each segment of the body the muscular contractions responsible for these changes are governed by a primary respiratory centre situated in the corresponding ganglion of the ventral nerve cord. Further co-ordination and control is exercised by the so-called secondary respiratory centres of the brain (diffusion control) or thorax (ventilation control). Lack of oxygen or accumulation of carbon dioxide stimulates these centres and results in the opening of the spiracles or the initiation of ventilatory movements.

Because the tracheal system conveys oxygen into or close to the respiring tissues, the blood of insects plays only a small part in respiration, and its oxygen capacity is apparently no greater than can be accounted for by simple solution. Exceptions to this are the aquatic larvae of some Chironomid midges, known as blood-worms, whose plasma contains haemoglobin in solution. However, the haemoglobin is such that it only transfers oxygen to the tissues when the partial pressure of oxygen is very low. It therefore appears to be an adaptation enabling the larvae to survive in the poorly oxygenated conditions which they sometimes have to endure.

Respiration in aquatic insects. Some aquatic insects have an open tracheal system and obtain oxygen from the atmosphere through one or more pairs of functional spiracles. In others the tracheal system is closed and oxygen diffuses into it from the water through part or all of the integument. Those forms with an open tracheal system show varying degrees of specialization. In the larvae of some Culicidae and Syrphidae, for example, the posterior spiracles are situated on siphon-like processes which penetrate the surface film and so make contact with the atmosphere. Again, in larvae and pupae of a few species of Coleoptera and Diptera (e.g. *Donacia* and *Taeniorhynchus*) the spiracles are placed on pointed processes which can be inserted into the air-containing cavities of submerged aquatic plants. Many Coleoptera and Hemiptera (e.g. *Dytiscus* and *Notonecta*) have aquatic adults which, when they submerge, carry air-bubbles trapped beneath the elytra or on other parts of the body. These air stores are in contact with open spiracles, and oxygen is drawn from them. They also act as 'physical gills' which extract dissolved oxygen from the water. This function depends on the invasion coefficient of oxygen between water and air being three times that of nitrogen. It follows that, as the partial pressure of oxygen in the bubble falls, further oxygen diffuses into it from the water faster than the nitrogen of the bubble diffuses out. In this way far more oxygen can be extracted from the water than was originally present in the bubble. Ultimately, however, the slow dispersal of nitrogen causes the bubble to grow smaller and it must therefore be renewed repeatedly by the insect ascending to the surface. However, a few insects, like the Hemipteran *Aphelocheirus*, have evolved a method of 'plastron respiration' in which a thin film of air – the plastron – is held against the body by special hairs or other cuticular processes in such a way that it cannot decrease in volume. It therefore functions as a permanent physical gill, and such insects, although they have an open tracheal system, can remain submerged throughout life, extracting all their oxygen from the water.

In some insects with a closed tracheal system the integument is very thin and overlies a network of fine tracheal branches. Oxygen then diffuses in from the water over most of the body surface, e.g. larvae of *Chironomus* and *Simulium*. In other species the body wall is produced locally into tracheal gills – thin-walled outgrowths which are well supplied with tracheae – and much of the respiratory exchange is restricted to these organs. They may be filamentous or lamellate, and occur on various parts of the body, e.g. the abdomen in nymphs of mayflies and Zygopteran dragonflies (Figs 64 and 66) and the thorax of some stonefly nymphs. The body wall adjacent to a spiracle may be produced into a 'spiracular gill'; insects so equipped can respire in air or under water. In Anisopteran dragonfly nymphs the gills occur on the inner walls of the hind gut – the so-called rectal gills – and water is repeatedly drawn in and expelled through the anus. A few aquatic insects, such as some Dipterous larvae, possess structures known as blood gills or anal papillae (Fig. 118a). These are small tubular out-growths of the body, usually near the anus, with few or no tracheae. They were formerly regarded as respiratory organs, but are now thought to be more concerned with absorbing inorganic salts from the water and so regulating the ionic composition and osmotic relations of the blood.

Respiration in endoparasitic insects. These insects live immersed in the body fluids of their host and therefore show respiratory adaptations which resemble those of aquatic insects. In some, such as the larvae of Tachinid flies, there is an open metapneustic respiratory system and the parasite perforates the integument of its host or one of the tracheal trunks. By inserting the spiracular region of the body into the opening thus formed it can draw on a supply of atmospheric oxygen. In others, such as the early larval instars of many parasitic Hymenoptera, the tracheal system is absent or filled with liquid, and oxygen diffuses into the blood from the body fluids of the host. In the older larval instars a closed tracheal system is present and oxygen diffuses through the integument, which is provided with a network of subcutaneous tracheae. Some endoparasitic larvae bear tail-like or vesicular out-growths which are known in a few species to act like gills (Fig. 115c); in a few others, however, they are not especially concerned with respiration, and in most cases their physiology has not been studied.

THE CIRCULATORY SYSTEM AND ASSOCIATED TISSUES

The body cavity in insects is a haemocoel which contains the circulating blood. All of the organs and tissues are bathed with this liquid and perform their functions through exchanges with it. The haemocoel in the majority of insects is divided into sinuses by fibromuscular septa or diaphragms (Fig. 39). The dorsal diaphragm is the septum most constantly present; it extends across the abdominal cavity just above the alimentary canal, and in this way divides the haemocoel into a dorsal or pericardial sinus, containing the dorsal vessel, and a very large visceral sinus representing the remainder of the body cavity. In some insects there is also a ventral diaphragm stretching across the abdominal cavity above the nerve cord and thus demarcating a ventral or perineural sinus. Pairs of aliform muscles arise from the abdominal terga and spread out fanwise over the dorsal diaphragm.

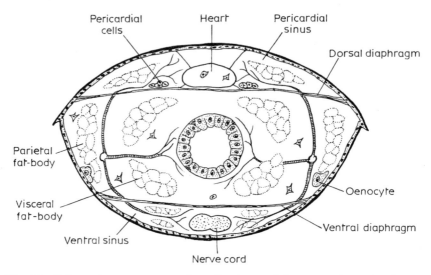

Fig. 39   Schematic transverse section of an insect abdomen to show circulatory system and fat-body

The dorsal vessel (Fig. 40). This is the main conducting organ of the circulatory system and is divided into the heart and the aorta. The heart is a muscular contractile tube situated in the median line of the pericardial sinus just above the dorsal diaphragm. It is held in position by fibrous strands connected to the body wall and the diaphragm. As a rule, the heart is a narrow continuous vessel whose sides are perforated with vertical slit-like openings, or ostia. The margins of the ostia may be prolonged inward to form valves which prevent the return of blood from the heart into the pericardial sinus. In other cases the heart shows a series of dilations or chambers, usually corresponding in number to the pairs of ostia and of aliform muscles. While there may be a chamber of the heart to each segment of the abdomen and to the second and third segments of the thorax, as in cockroaches, the number of chambers is generally much fewer and may even be reduced to a single terminal enlargement. The aorta is the slender anterior prolongation of the dorsal vessel which carries the blood into the head, where it opens behind or beneath the brain. The wall of the heart is muscular and is composed of flattened cells whose outer cytoplasm is differentiated into striated muscle fibrils. These cells are bounded externally and internally by a delicate membrane which may be regarded as a sarcolemma. Apart from the aorta, there are few closed vessels associated with the circulatory system. Among the best known are the abdominal arteries of cockroaches and the antennal arteries. In *Blatta* and the honey-bee the blood is propelled through the antennal arteries by special pulsatile

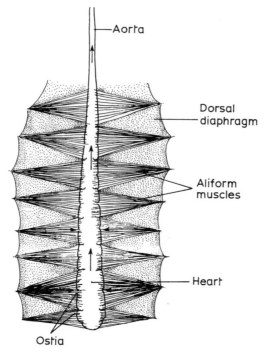

Fig. 40   Dorsal vessel of a Coleopteran, ventral view
Arrows show direction of blood flow.

organs (accessory hearts) situated at their bases. Pulsatile organs are also found in the thorax, where they maintain circulation of the blood in the wing veins.

The blood. The blood or haemolymph is the only extracellular fluid in insects. It is clear, colourless or very pale yellow or green, and consists of the liquid plasma, in which are suspended numerous colourless blood cells, or haemocytes. The plasma, consisting of about 85% water, usually has a pH of 6.4–6.8 and contains amino acids, proteins, fats, sugars (mainly the disaccharide α-trehalose) and inorganic salts (mainly sodium, potassium and chloride ions). It serves as a store of water, transports food materials and hormones, and conveys limited quantities of oxygen and carbon dioxide (p. 75). Its hydrostatic properties enable it to transmit pressure changes, as in the splitting of the old cuticle at moulting or the eversion of the wings of newly emerged adults. The haemocytes (Fig. 41) are very variable in form and many different types have been distinguished, though some of these are probably developmental stages or the result of temporary changes in shape. The circulating blood contains 1000–100 000 cells per mm³, but many more are found adhering to the surfaces of the viscera, where they sometimes form fixed phagocytic organs. There are four main categories of haemocytes:

1. Prohaemocytes, small cells with deeply staining cytoplasm and large nuclei; these are often seen undergoing mitosis, and are regarded as young forms of haemocytes.

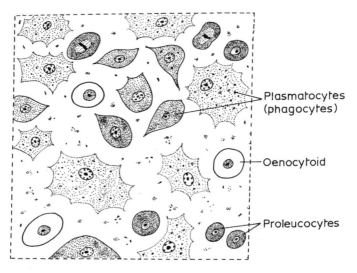

Fig. 41   Insect haemocytes (after Wigglesworth)

2. Phagocytes, which are basiphil and of variable appearance and character; their amoeboid activities enable them to digest tissue debris and invading bacteria, and they greatly increase in numbers during ecdysis and metamorphosis. Three kinds have been distinguished: plasmatocytes, granular cells and spherule cells. The phagocytes have the property of congregating around and enclosing foreign bodies; they also collect at the site of a wound, forming a plug which facilitates healing.

3. Oenocytoids, which are rounded cells with acidophil cytoplasm. They bear a resemblance to small oenocytes, but their function is not known.

4. Cystocytes, which are rounded cells with relatively large nuclei, and are probably involved in the clotting of the blood.

The circulation of the blood. This begins in an anterior stream that is maintained by waves of contraction, passing from behind forward, over the heart. During diastole blood is drawn into the heart, through the

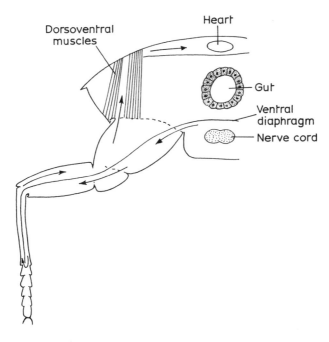

Fig. 42 Transverse section of thorax of *Blatta* (Dictyoptera: Blattidae), showing course of blood circulation

ostia, under a negative pressure. During systole a positive pressure is set up and the blood is driven forward in the heart cavity and eventually leaves the open anterior end of the aorta in the head. Here some of it circulates through the antennae, but ultimately the blood enters the visceral sinus after a proportion has circulated through the legs and wing veins. Undulatory movements of the ventral diaphragm direct a blood flow backward in the perineural sinus. Leaving the latter, through spaces along its sides and posterior end, the blood ascends among the viscera. It then becomes drawn into the pericardial sinus by contractions of the aliform muscles. This alters the contour of the dorsal diaphragm, and passage of the blood into the sinus occurs through perforations in this membrane (Fig. 42). The property of rhythmical contraction of the heart lies in the muscle fibrils of its walls. This automatism is evident in the isolated heart or even in severed portions of it since they continue to beat in the usual rhythmic manner. The pulsation rate is influenced by many external, endocrine and pharmacological factors. Thus, it is increased as the temperature is raised; it may vary in different instars of the same insect. It has long been known that in *Sphinx ligustri* the heart beat of the moth is at the rate of 40–50 per minute when at rest and 110–140 during activity. In the larva the rate is highest (80–90 per minute) in the early instars and lowest in the pupa, when it declines to 10–12 beats per minute; during hibernation it ceases almost entirely.

Insect thermoregulation. Insects are commonly regarded as 'cold-blooded' or poikilothermic animals, in which the body temperature differs little from that of the surroundings. This is true of the less active species, in which little heat is generated by muscular contraction, and also of smaller forms where the relatively large surface area allows heat to be lost rapidly. However, in some relatively large, actively flying insects the intense metabolic activity of the flight muscles raises the internal temperature of the thorax well above that of the environment. Active control of heat loss may then occur through the circulatory and respiratory systems. It has also long been known that when it is cold some insects, such as Sphingid moths, locusts and large beetles, can fly only after the thoracic temperature has risen to a level above that of the ambient air. They bring this about before take-off through a 'warming up' process in which the thoracic muscles contract repeatedly, though the wings undergo little more than small quivering movements. In the hawk-moth *Manduca sexta* the thoracic temperature has to be raised to about 38° C in this way before the insect can fly, but it may then do so even though the ambient temperature is as low as 15° C. The air trapped among the scales that cover the body of Lepidoptera insulates the thorax very effectively, but the abdomen (which is less well insulated) remains much cooler. If the thoracic temperature rises to above about 40° C, however, the heart beat rate increases and heat is transferred from the thorax through the blood to the abdomen, where it is lost by radiation from the surface and by warming the air expelled from the air-sacs and tracheae. Species of *Bombus* (bumble-bees) exhibit a similar form of thermoregulation, as does the honey-bee *Apis mellifera*, though in the latter species heat is lost through the head rather than the abdomen.

THE EXCRETORY ORGANS, FAT-BODY AND OTHER HAEMOCOELIC STRUCTURES

The function of an excretory system is to maintain a relatively constant internal environment for the tissues of the body. Among other things, this involves the removal of the nitrogenous products of protein breakdown and the regulation of the ionic composition of the haemolymph. The chief excretory organs are the Malpighian tubules, whose structure is described on p. 65 and which work in conjunction with the hind gut. Some other tissues are, or were, thought to play a subsidiary role, and are therefore also conveniently discussed here.

Malpighian tubules. These remove excretory materials from the

82

blood in the form of urine, which is secreted into the lumen of the tubule and ultimately discharged into the hind gut, where its composition may be modified by resorption before it passes out with the faeces. The urine may be a clear aqueous liquid or a thick suspension, and its composition differs in different insects. The principal nitrogenous material is uric acid – or perhaps its ammonium, sodium or potassium salts – usually appearing in the form of crystalline spheres. Some species secrete substantial quantities of allantoin, allantoic acid, urea or ammonia. Inorganic salts, in solution or as granules or spheroidal concretions, also occur.

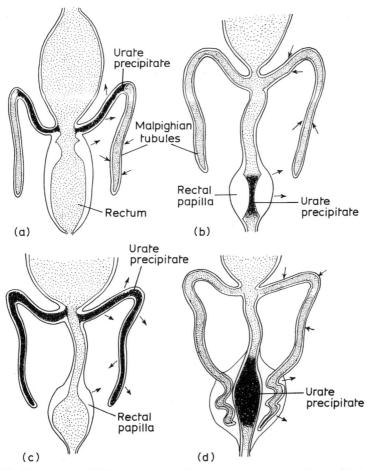

Fig. 43   Diagrams of different types of excretory systems in insects (adapted from Wigglesworth)

(a) *Rhodnius prolixus* (Hemiptera: Reduviidae); (b) Orthoptera, Neuroptera and many Coleoptera; (c) Culicidae and other Diptera; (d) *Tenebrio* (Coleoptera: Tenebrionidae). Arrows indicate presumed flow of water and bases; dark areas show zones of urate precipitation. For explanation see text.

83

Various functional modifications of the Malpighian tubules occur in different insects (Fig. 43); many of these permit the elimination of nitrogenous materials while conserving the limited supply of water available to terrestrial organisms. In *Rhodnius* (Fig. 43a) the distal part of each tubule secretes a solution of sodium or potassium acid urate while the proximal part reabsorbs much of the water and bases, the latter in the form of bicarbonate. Uric acid is thus precipitated as crystalline spheres in this part of the tubule while the water and bases are recirculated continually. Further absorption of water and sodium ions occurs in the rectum. In *Lepisma*, Orthoptera, Neuroptera and many Coleoptera (Fig. 43b) the Malpighian tubules only contain fluid while precipitation of a white crystalline mass of uric acid takes place in the rectum through whose walls water absorption is carried out. In mosquitoes and Muscid flies (Fig. 43c) the Malpighian tubules contain solid uric acid throughout their length, and a method of precipitation occurs different from that found in *Rhodnius*. In many Coleoptera and the larvae of Lepidoptera the distal parts of the Malpighian tubules are closely attached to the walls of the rectum (the so-called cryptonephridial system). This device seems to facilitate water conservation by using the combined absorptive capacity of the rectum and Malpighian tubules. In the mealworm (*Tenebrio*) (Fig. 43d), where such an arrangement occurs, the Malpighian tubules only contain clear fluid and the rectum is mainly occupied by a dry mass of uric acid, apparently precipitated by the almost complete absorption of the available water.

Other excretory products include calcium salts that are sometimes taken into the body in quantities greatly above requirements. These are present in the Malpighian tubules either as amorphous granules or, less frequently, as solid spheres or crystals. The most general compound is calcium carbonate, which is usually stored during larval life and often used in various ways during metamorphosis, disappearing by the time the imago is reached. Many Dipteran larvae contain calcium carbonate either in the Malpighian tubules or in special cells of the fat-body; in phytophagous larvae of the family Agromyzidae the calcium occurs as laminated bodies or 'calcosphaerites' that are seen clearly in those of the celery fly (*Euleia heraclei*) and other species. At metamorphosis the calcium carbonate dissolves in the blood and becomes deposited on the inner wall of the puparium. Many larvae of the Cerambycidae (p. 155) line the pupal burrow with lime and also close it with an operculum composed of similar material. In the Phasmida the chorion of the eggs is hardened by becoming impregnated with calcium salts.

The physiology of excretion is unusual in the more highly adapted aquatic insects. Ammonia may be the principal excretory product, and there are no special mechanisms for conserving water. On the other hand there may be very active reabsorption of inorganic ions in the hind gut.

The fat-body (Fig. 39). This is present in all insects and is derived from the mesoderm of the walls of the embryonic coelomic cavities. It sometimes shows a segmental disposition and occurs as loose strands, sheets and lobes of tissue. Generally there is a visceral layer around the gut and a peripheral layer beneath the integument. Since the fat-body lies in the haemocoel it is immersed in blood, which also circulates through its interstices. The fat-body is therefore well adapted for its main function – the synthesis and storage of reserve materials. These include fat, proteins and glycogen, all of which can be mobilized as required. In the newly hatched insect the cells of the fat-body are rounded, with a homogeneous cytoplasm free from vacuoles or inclusions. During growth these cells increase in size and become vacuolated so that their boundaries are then hard to see; nuclear changes also occur. In a starved insect the reserve food materials mentioned may become used up, but normally they are drawn upon at certain periods only, i.e. during the change from larva to pupa, during hibernation, and to some extent at each ecdysis. In adult insects the fat-body is often more developed in the female, where it provides nutriment for egg development.

The fat-body also performs an excretory function. In Collembola, Hymenopteran larvae, Orthoptera, etc., special excretory cells containing deposits of urates are present among the ordinary cells of the tissue (Fig. 30). The excretory cells serve in the main as storage cells until their products are eliminated at the time of pupation. In Collembola, which lack Malpighian tubes, urate concretions are deposited and increase in size throughout life; much the same is stated to occur in *Lepisma*, the Dermaptera and Orthoptera, where the Malpighian tubes apparently eliminate little uric acid.

Nephrocytes. These are special cells which occur scattered in the haemocoel or concentrated in certain restricted regions. They are commonly found in strands along each side of the heart, where they are known as pericardial cells (Fig. 39) and are often binucleate. In the larvae of Cyclorrhaphan Diptera they are arranged in a garland-like structure between the salivary glands. Their distinctive feature is a capacity for accumulating the dyestuff ammonia carmine when it is injected into the haemocoel. For this reason they were formerly regarded as organs of 'storage excretion'. This is now thought unlikely, though under experimental conditions they can accumulate a wide variety of colloidal particles by pinocytosis, and thus resemble the reticulo–endothelial cells of vertebrates.

Oenocytes. These are usually large cells, often of a wine-yellow colour to which they owe their name. They occur in larvae and adults of all orders and rank among the largest cells of the body, sometimes measuring up to about 180 μm across. Their large nuclei, and dense eosinophil cytoplasm with an external limiting membrane, are characteristic features. They arise from the ectoderm of the embryo as segmental groups of cells situated close behind the invaginations that give rise to the abdominal spiracles (Fig. 39). They may remain associated with the epidermis as in *Blatta*, migrate into the peripheral fat-body (*Locusta* and *Anopheles*) or come to lie in close association with spiracular tracheae (Lepidoptera). Oenocytes show a cycle of morphological changes and secretory activity at the time of moulting, usually increasing greatly in size just before that process; the cytoplasm becomes vacuolated and the cells may become lobed as in *Rhodnius*. It seems probable that they elaborate some of the materials used in the construction of the cuticle; whether they have other functions is not clear.

THE GLANDS OR ORGANS OF SECRETION

Two main types of special secretory organs occur in insects: the exocrine glands, which are provided with ducts and discharge their secretions outside the body or into the lumen of one or other of the viscera; and the endocrine glands, which have no ducts and whose secretions, known as hormones, usually diffuse into the blood, which transports them to all parts of the body.

Exocrine glands. Only a few of the more important types of exocrine glands may be mentioned here. Wax glands are well seen on the abdominal sterna of worker honey-bees, and are also common in such Homoptera as the scale-insects (Coccoidea) and some aphids. They consist of one or more epidermal cells, often discharging through plate-like pores, or aggregations of pores, in the cuticle. Associated with the mouthparts of all insects are one or more paired secretory organs, the most important of which are the labial glands. Their tubular ducts unite and discharge by a common canal near the base of the hypopharynx, and since they normally secrete saliva they are commonly known as the salivary glands. They may be tubular, lobulate or diffuse structures, sometimes provided with a reservoir. In the larvae of Lepidoptera, sawflies and Trichoptera the labial glands secrete silk and saliva is produced by the mandibular glands. Some insects are provided with repugnatorial glands, such as occur on the abdominal terga of many immature Heteroptera, on the metapleura of their adults, and near the anus in many Coleoptera. Their function is probably defensive, and this is also true of the various types of poison glands, e.g. those associated with the setae of some Lepidopteran larvae or with the sting of wasps and bees (p. 34). Attractant glands, producing volatile secretions attractive to the opposite sex, commonly occur in male Lepidoptera –

often on the wings, where they are associated with special scales, the androconia. In some female Lepidoptera the secretions of glands near the end of the abdomen are pheromones (p. 54) which can attract males from considerable distances. A variety of other pheromone-secreting glands occur in different insect groups. For example, the trail-marking pheromones of ants are secreted by the poison glands and by Dufour's glands at the back of the abdomen, while the 'queen substance' of the honey-bee is produced in the mandibular glands of the queen.

Endocrine glands. Various small, paired glands in the anterior part of the body produce hormones which play a very important role in the control of moulting and metamorphosis (pp. 104 and 113), and may also exert other physiological effects. Of these glands, the most important are the following. (a) The neurosecretory cells of the brain (Fig. 19). These are groups of modified nerve-cells, situated in the dorsal part of the protocerebrum, that produce a peptide hormone which activates the thoracic glands (thoracotropic hormone). Another neurosecretory hormone, known as bursicon, which controls the hardening and darkening of the cuticle of newly moulted insects, also seems to be secreted by the brain, though it is discharged from the thoracic or abdominal ganglia. Neurosecretory cells also occur scattered or in small groups among the ganglia of the ventral nerve cord; their function is not well understood, but in *Rhodnius* they produce a diuretic hormone. (b) The corpora cardiaca. These are usually a pair of small bodies lying one on each side of the aorta, immediately behind the brain, to which they are connected by two pairs of nerves (Fig. 19). They include the swollen endings of neurosecretory axons from the pars intercerebralis cells, and serve as so-called neurohaemal organs, responsible for discharging into the haemolymph the neurosecretory materials produced by the brain. In addition, the corpora cardiaca include intrinsic neurosecretory cells, sometimes segregated into a distinct glandular lobe. Extracts of the corpora cardiaca may therefore include brain hormones as well as substances secreted by the intrinsic cells. Such extracts are known in some cases to affect the lipid and carbohydrate levels of the blood and to control water balance; they may also include materials whose effects are pharmacological rather than associated with the normal physiology of the insect. (c) The thoracic glands. These occur in the prothorax, though apparently homologous organs with a similar function are found in the head of some lower Exopterygotes. They produce hormones (ecdysone and its derivatives) which induce the immature insect to moult and they degenerate in the adult (except in the Archaeognatha and Zygentoma, where moulting continues after sexual maturity. (d) The corpora allata. These glands are closely associated with the stomatogastric nervous system (p. 47, Fig. 19), and produce the so-called juvenile hormones, of which three have been identified chemically. These tend to inhibit the appearance of adult characteristics in the developing insect, and while they are being produced in sufficient quantity they ensure that the moults induced by the thoracic gland hormone give rise to the normal sequence of nymphal or larval instars. However, towards the end of juvenile life the corpora allata become much less active and moulting is then accompanied by the more or less abrupt development of adult features, as is strikingly shown in the metamorphosis of holometabolous insects (p. 111). The corpora allata resume activity in the adult, when their secretions may be necessary for the full development of the ovaries and the accessory reproductive glands of both sexes.

THE REPRODUCTIVE SYSTEM AND REPRODUCTION

The reproductive organs, which differ appreciably in the two sexes, consist of (a) a pair of gonads, which are derived from mesoderm; (b) the system of efferent ducts, which is usually partly mesodermal and partly ectodermal; and (c) the various annexes, such as accessory glands and structures for the temporary retention of the spermatozoa. Closely associated with the external openings of the reproductive system are the external genitalia, discussed on p. 31.

The female reproductive system

The female gonads, or ovaries, discharge the eggs into a pair of tubular lateral oviducts, almost always formed from mesoderm. In the mayflies each oviduct opens by a separate gonopore behind the seventh abdominal sternum, and a condition recalling this primitive state of affairs is passed through in the immature stages of most insects. In the adults, however, the lateral oviducts generally run into an unpaired common oviduct which is then continued into a wider passage, or vagina, whose orifice lies behind the eighth or ninth abdominal sternum (Fig. 44a). These unpaired parts of the reproductive system develop from one or two ectodermal invaginations. Further ectodermal in-growths give rise to the spermatheca, or receptaculum seminis, and to a pair of accessory glands; in the adult these organs usually open by short ducts into the common oviduct or vagina.

The ovaries. Each ovary usually consists of several egg tubes, or ovarioles, which are only occasionally bound together by an outer membrane into a more or less compact organ. The ovarioles may open into the lateral oviduct one behind the other, or they may be arranged in a radiating manner and all enter it at about the same place. There are

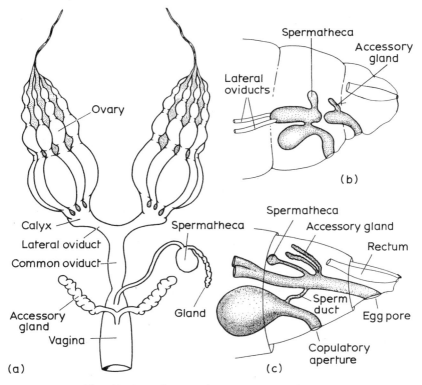

Fig. 44   Female reproductive system of insects
(a) Typical form, diagrammatic; (b) development of efferent ducts in higher Lepidopteran;
(c) adult efferent ducts in higher Lepidopteran.

commonly four to eight ovarioles in each ovary, but some Hymenoptera may have more than 200 and even this number is exceeded in the queens of some termites. Each ovary of some viviparous Diptera, on the other hand, consists of a single ovariole. A typical ovariole (Fig. 45) consists of a terminal filament, a germarium and a vitellarium. The terminal filaments of all the ovarioles of one side are usually united to form a suspensory ligament. The apical germarium contains the primordial germ-cells, or oogonia; these later become differentiated into oocytes and also, when they are present, into nurse cells, or trophocytes. The vitellarium consists of a longitudinal series of developing eggs, the smallest and youngest being those nearest to the germarium. As they grow by the deposition of yolk, the eggs distend the ovariole into a series of follicles, or egg chambers; each egg is enclosed in a layer of follicular epithelium which eventually secretes the chorion, or egg-shell. In the ovarioles of some insects only the lowermost (i.e. oldest) eggs are completely developed and ready to be discharged (Fig. 45); in others

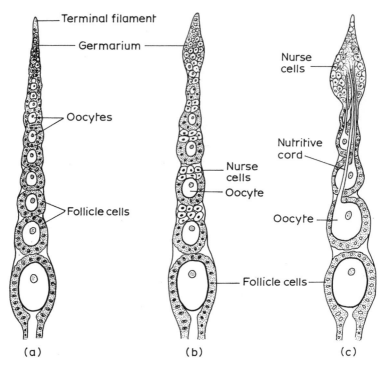

Fig. 45   Three main types of ovarioles, diagrammatic (after Weber)
(a) Panoistic type; (b) polytrophic type; (c) acrotrophic type.

most of the eggs have completed their development by the time
oviposition begins.

There are three types of ovarioles (Fig. 45): (a) The panoistic type has
no nurse cells; the developing egg cell may itself synthesize some
components of the yolk and receives others from the undifferentiated
follicular epithelium, which transfers materials obtained from the blood.
This primitive type of ovariole occurs in the Apterygotes, Odonata,
Orthoptera and other orders. (b) In the polytrophic type each
developing egg is associated with an adjacent group of nurse cells which
are responsible for producing some fractions of the yolk. This type is
found in most Endopterygota. (c) In the acrotrophic type the nurse cells
are confined to the germarium and are connected with the developing
oocytes by progressively lengthening cytoplasmic strands, along which
some of the nutritive materials pass. This kind of ovariole occurs in the
Hemiptera and some Coleoptera. The yolk proteins of insects (vitellins)
are synthesized in precursor form by the fat-body, circulate in the
haemolymph, and accumulate in the developing oocytes by pinocytosis.

Genital ducts and associated structures. Some account of the different kinds of efferent ducts has already been given on p. 88. The vagina commonly ends in a genital cavity whose floor is the subgenital plate formed from the seventh or eighth sternum. The spermatheca is usually a sac-like organ which opens into the common oviduct or vagina by a more or less elongate spermathecal duct. The spermatozoa received in mating are stored here and pass down the duct to fertilize the eggs as the latter move along the common oviduct before being laid. The female accessory glands (colleterial glands) usually open into the vagina and often secrete an adhesive substance for cementing the eggs to each other or to the substrate on which they are laid. In the cockroaches and praying mantids their secretions produce the sclerotized ootheca or egg capsule in which the eggs of these insects are enclosed.

In the higher Lepidoptera (Fig. 44c) there are two reproductive openings. The anterior one, on the eighth sternum, is the copulatory aperture. It leads into a large bursa copulatrix, which is connected by a narrow sperm duct with the common oviduct. The latter is continued into the vagina, along which eggs pass to be discharged through the egg pore on the ninth sternum. The spermatheca joins the common oviduct by a duct in whose wall is a fine fertilization canal. Spermatozoa, enclosed in a proteinaceous sac or spermatophore, are deposited in the bursa copulatrix, from which they eventually make their way to the spermatheca by means of the sperm duct and the spermathecal duct. Later they move down the fertilization canal to fertilize the eggs.

The male reproductive system

The mesodermal parts of the male reproductive system are a pair of gonads, or testes, and two lateral ducts, or vasa deferentia. The latter join a median ectodermal passage, the ductus ejaculatorius, which usually opens to the exterior on the aedeagus, or penis (p. 32). In addition to these essential parts there is frequently a pair of vesiculae seminales, or sperm reservoirs, formed by the enlargement of a part of each vas deferens. Accessory glands of ectodermal origin are also commonly present (Fig. 46).

The testes. Each testis is composed of tubules, or follicles, variable in number, which open by narrow passages, or vasa efferentia, into the vas deferens of their side. The testis is covered outwardly by an epithelial sheath often, though inaccurately, known as the peritoneal layer. Each follicle is lined by epithelium resting on a basement membrane, and it is from the cells of this lining that the primordial germ cells are derived. A succession of zones, in which the germ cells are in different stages of development, are to be distinguished. At the apex of a follicle is the germarium which consists of spermatogonia among numerous somatic

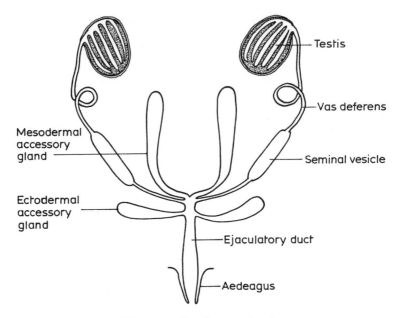

Fig. 46   Diagram of male reproductive system

cells. Lower down each spermatogonium becomes surrounded by somatic cells to form a cyst. By the repeated division of a spermatogonium, from 64 to 256 spermatocytes are produced. In the next zone, the zone of maturation, the spermatocytes undergo reduction division so that their chromosome number is halved; each spermatocyte ultimately produces four spermatids. There follows a zone of transformation in which the spermatids, still enclosed in the cyst wall, are converted into spermatozoa; the latter break out of the cyst by lashing movements of their flagella. At first the spermatozoa adhere by their heads in bundles, but they ultimately become free.

Genital ducts and accessory structures. In mayflies the vasa deferentia remain separate and each enters the penis of its side. From this generalized condition is derived the typical system in which a median ectodermal ingrowth gives rise to the ductus ejaculatorius. Where the vasa deferentia join the anterior extremity of this canal their ends become enlarged ampullae (Fig. 47a) which unite to form a mesodermal vesicle. The accessory glands are of two kinds. In *Blatta* and most Orthoptera numerous glands arise from the vesicle just mentioned and, since they are of mesodermal origin, they are classed as mesadenia (Fig. 47b). In other insects from one to three pairs of accessory glands may occur, and those arising from the ectoderm of the ductus ejaculatorius are termed ectadenia. In many cases the accessory glands produce substances which go to form a kind of capsule, or spermatophore, that encloses the spermatozoa. It is deposited in the bursa copulatrix or vagina of the female during mating, the spermatozoa ultimately becoming free. Spermatophores vary in form and structure, and several may be produced during a single mating. They occur in Orthoptera, Dictyoptera, Lepidoptera and other orders. In a few insects peptide secretions of the male accessory glands affect the female, reducing her readiness to mate again or stimulating her to lay eggs. Vesiculae seminales are found in many insects and are developments of the vasa deferentia. In *Blatta* they take the form of numerous outgrowths of the mesodermal vesicle (Fig. 47), and as the testes degenerate in adult cockroaches spermatozoa are then only found in the seminal vesicles.

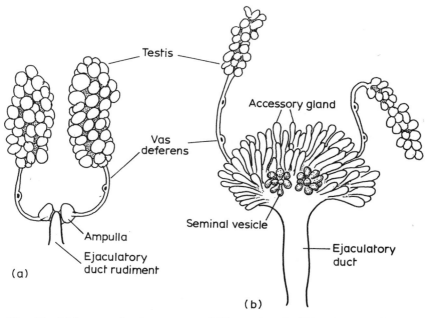

Fig. 47 Male reproductive system of *Blatta orientalis* (Dictyoptera: Blattidae) (a) In sixth-instar nymph; (b) in adult. Both at equal magnification. (Adapted from Qadri.)

Reproduction

In most insects reproduction depends on copulation between adults of opposite sex. The female then lays eggs, from each of which a single immature insect hatches after a more or less prolonged incubation period. Exceptions to these various generalizations, however, are not uncommon and are dealt with below.

93

Sperm transfer. This normally occurs during copulation by methods indicated above, but a few insects show anomalous forms of sperm transfer. In many Apterygotes the males deposit semen externally in small droplets, which are then taken up into the genital tract of the female when she moves over them. The dragonflies are unique in that before mating the male transfers spermatozoa to a secondary copulatory organ near the front of the abdomen, from which the female receives them when the pair flies in tandem (Fig. 65). In bed-bugs (*Cimex*) and a few related Heteroptera, the spermatozoa are transferred by the aedeagus, but pass through the abdominal body wall of the female into the haemocoel, thence migrating to the ovaries, where fertilization takes place.

Parthenogenesis. In this type of reproduction the eggs undergo full development without having been fertilized. It occurs in representatives of most orders and may be obligate – when males are absent or very rare and non-functional – or facultative, when it coexists with normal bisexual reproduction. Four important types of parthenogenesis are known: (a) In most Hymenoptera and some other insects the females lay two kinds of eggs. Those which are unfertilized have only the reduced (haploid) number of chromosomes and give rise exclusively to males, whereas the fertilized eggs, with the full diploid number of chromosomes, produce only females (including the sterile females or workers of the social species). The usual method of sex determination by sex chromosomes is therefore replaced by this more flexible method. (b) In some sawflies, some stick-insects and one species of scale-insect, the female again lays two kinds of eggs. Those which have been fertilized produce about equal numbers of males and females, but in the unfertilized eggs there is a fusion of the egg nucleus with the second polar body. This restores the diploid chromosome number but such eggs develop only into females. (c) A striking type of obligate parthenogenesis occurs in some aphids, stick-insects, weevils and moths. The eggs are formed without meiosis and only female progeny result. Males do not occur in these species, which are able to reproduce rapidly but lack the genetic variability found in bisexual forms. (d) In some aphids and Cynipid gall-wasps there is cyclical parthenogenesis: one or more parthenogenetic generations alternate with a bisexual generation. In these cases parthenogenesis occurs in the summer so that rapid reproduction can occur under favourable conditions, while the advantageous genetic effects of bisexual reproduction are not entirely lost.

Viviparity. In some insects embryonic development is completed within the body of the female parent, which therefore produces living young instead of laying eggs. Such viviparity may mean little more than the retention within the vagina of otherwise normal and fully-yolked eggs until the young insects hatch out and are expelled. In tsetse flies (*Glossina*) and Pupiparan Diptera such as the sheep ked *Melophagus*, however, the larvae remain after hatching in the enlarged vagina of the

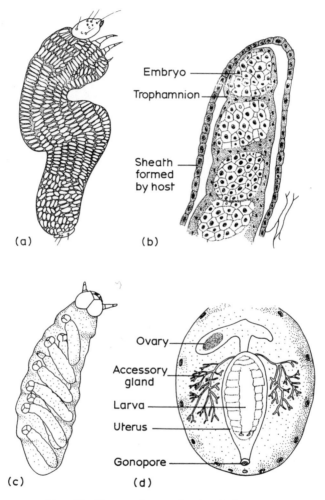

Embryo
Trophamnion
Sheath formed by host
(a)   (b)

Ovary
Accessory gland
Larva
Uterus
Gonopore
(c)   (d)

Fig. 48   Types of reproduction in insects

(a) Remains of larva of *Autographa gamma* (Lepidoptera: Noctuidae) distended with pupae of the polyembryonic parasitoid *Litomastix truncatella* (Hymenoptera: Chalcidoidea: Encyrtidae) (after Silvestri). (b) Portion of a polyembryonic chain derived from a single egg of *Ageniaspis fuscicollis* (Hymenoptera: Encyrtidae) (after Marchal). (c) Paedogenetic larva of *Micromalthus debilis* (Coleoptera: Micromalthidae) with daughter larvae ready to emerge (after Hinton). (d) Viviparity in *Melophagus ovinus* (Diptera: Hippoboscidae); ventral aspect of abdomen seen as a transparent object showing larva developing in uterus.

female, where they feed and grow and are deposited as mature larvae ready to pupate (Fig. 48d). In other cases (e.g. aphids and the ecto-parasitic earwig *Hemimerus*) the eggs have no chorion and are practically devoid of yolk; a special placenta-like structure is therefore developed to nourish each embryo.

Paedogenesis. This term denotes reproduction by a juvenile stage. It occurs in only a few species, one of the best-known examples being the gall midge *Heteropeza* (Cecidomyiidae). Here, as in the other known examples, reproduction involves both parthenogenesis and viviparity. Within the body of the parent larvae, unfertilized eggs give rise to daughter larvae. These then eat their way out of the body of the parent larvae which die during the process. The daughter larvae may repeat this cycle or give rise to normal male and female insects. Paedogenesis also occurs in the complex life-cycle of the beetle *Micromalthus* from N. America and S. Africa (Fig. 48c).

Polyembryony. Polyembryony is the production of two or more – often very many – embryos from a single egg (which may be fertilized or develop parthenogenetically). It occurs in a Strepsipteran (*Halicto-xenos*) and has evolved in several more or less widely separated genera of parasitic Hymenoptera. The essential feature of the process is the separation of the blastomeres of the egg into groups of cells, or morulae, each of which grows into an adult insect. Very early in development the egg develops a surrounding sheath, or trophamnion (Fig. 48b), which absorbs food material from the tissue fluids of the host and passes it on to the growing embryo. This covering accommodates itself to the increasing size of the polyembryonic mass which, in extreme cases, forms a tortuous chain of embryos filling the haemocoel of the host, which finally dies. The simplest cases of polyembryony are in *Platygaster* (a Proctotrupoid) whose species parasitize the Hessian fly *Mayetiola destructor* and its allies. In *P. hiemalis* some of the eggs produce single embryos while the others divide and give rise to two individuals. In various other parasites embryonic fission results in the production of eight or ten to over 100 individuals from a single egg; they are always of the same sex. An extreme phase is reached in the Chalcid parasite, *Litomastix truncatella*, of the common Silver Y moth, *Autographa gamma*, where the division of a single egg produces up to about 1000 individuals (Fig. 48a).

3

Development
and metamorphosis

EMBRYONIC DEVELOPMENT

The egg. A typical insect egg (Fig. 49a) is covered by an outer shell, or chorion, which is variously sculptured or ornamented. The chorion is secreted by the follicular epithelium and may consist of several layers; these include a very thin wax layer, which reduces water loss, and others containing protein but no chitin. Beneath the chorion is the delicate vitelline membrane, which is a product of the egg itself; further inner layers may be deposited after fertilization and during embryonic development. Insect eggs usually contain a large amount of yolk. This is a mixture of protein, lipid, carbohydrate and other materials lying within the meshes of a cytoplasmic reticulum. As in other Arthropods, the egg of insects is centrolecithal, a thin peripheral layer of cytoplasm – the periplasm – surrounding the yolk. One or more specialized pores or canals in the chorion are known as micropyles; through these the spermatozoa enter the egg at fertilization. In some insects the micropyles are also the channels through which oxygen diffuses into the egg; in other cases special respiratory channels, called aeropyles, occur separately and in some insects part or all of the chorion forms a plastron (p. 76), allowing respiration under water. Maturation of the egg usually follows the entry of spermatozoa. The egg nucleus moves towards the periphery and undergoes meiotic division, the polar bodies are segregated and the female pronucleus fuses with one of the spermatozoa, thus restoring the diploid chromosome number.

The blastoderm and germ-band. After fertilization the zygote nucleus divides repeatedly and many of the resulting cleavage nuclei pass outwards to form, with the periplasm, a continuous superficial cell-layer, or blastoderm. Other cleavage nuclei, surrounded by adjacent cytoplasm, remain behind as yolk cells. While the blastoderm is developing, some of the dividing nuclei may pass to the posterior pole of the egg to form the primordial germ cells (Fig. 49b); in other species

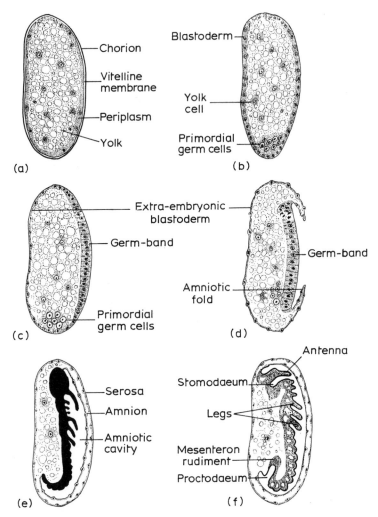

Fig. 49 Successive stages in the embryonic development of an insect
(a) Cleavage and migration of nuclei to periplasm; (b) formation of blastoderm; (c) development of germ-band; (d) development of amniotic folds; (e) embryo enclosed in amniotic cavity; (f) longitudinal section of embryo at (e). In (b)–(f) the chorion and vitelline membrane are omitted.

however, the germ cells are not segregated until later. As development proceeds the blastoderm thickens along the mid-ventral line, so giving rise to the germ-band (Fig. 49c) which is destined to produce all the tissues of the embryo. The rest of the egg consists chiefly of yolk enclosed by the thin extra-embryonic blastoderm.

Developmental physiology. Early embryonic development is controlled by three important centres; these are not visibly differentiated, but their activities can be demonstrated experimentally. An anterior cleavage centre initiates nuclear division and migration. Near the posterior pole of the egg is the activation centre; this apparently produces a chemical substance which diffuses forwards and determines the formation of the germ-band. Only after this has taken place can the activation centre be eliminated experimentally without ill effects. Fig. 50b and c, for example, show the respective effects of ligaturing off the posterior pole of the egg before and after the germ-band has been determined. In the position corresponding with the thorax of the future embryo lies the differentiation centre, from which visible differentiation of the germ-band proceeds, and which only becomes active after the product of the activation centre has reached it. An egg ligatured at an early stage anterior to the position of the differentiation centre may therefore develop into a dwarf embryo behind the ligature (Fig. 50d). Before the work of the differentiation centre is complete the egg is capable of considerable 'regulation', i.e. parts of the egg can, under experimental conditions, develop into structures other than those to which they would normally have given rise. Later, the developing egg becomes 'mosaic' and localized injuries induced by, say, ultraviolet radiation cause corresponding defects in the larva. The time at which the developing egg passes from the regulation to the mosaic condition differs in different species. Thus, in the dragonfly *Platycnemis* regulation is possible up to the late blastoderm stage, and an egg ligatured during the period of regulation may produce two dwarf embryos (Fig. 50e). In *Drosophila* and other Diptera however, the egg has already reached the

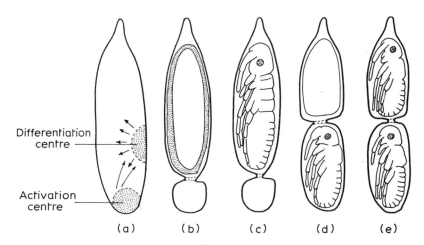

Fig. 50   Regulation of development in *Platycnemis* (Odonata: Platycnemididae)
For explanation see text. (After Seidel.)

mosaic stage by the time it is laid, while in the honey-bee this condition
is achieved at a stage intermediate between those of *Platycnemis* and
Drosophila. A consequence of the early but histologically unrecognizable
differentiation of the embryo is that the blastoderm can be divided into a
number of 'presumptive areas', each normally giving rise to a particular
germ layer or region of the later embryo. Such blastoderm 'fate maps'
show a general similarity within the Pterygotes, Archaeognatha and
Zygentoma, but an appreciably different pattern occurs in the more
distantly related Collembola and Diplura.

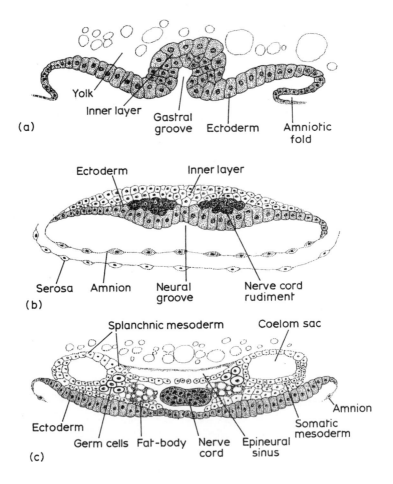

Fig. 51   Transverse sections through germ-band of an insect at successive
stages of development

(a) Formation of gastral groove and inner layer; (b) beginnings of neural groove and
ventral nerve cord; (c) development of coelom sacs and separation of embryo from yolk
to form the epineural sinus.

Embryonic membranes and gastrulation. Sooner or later the germ-band becomes enclosed by amniotic folds that arise from its edges. These folds grow towards one another so as to meet and fuse, thus enclosing the germ-band within a space known as the amniotic cavity (Fig. 49d and e; Fig. 51). Of the covering membranes thus formed, the outer layer, or serosa, is continuous with the extra-embryonic blastoderm, and the inner membrane, or amnion, is continuous with the margins of the germ-band. These two membranes, and the cavity they enclose, function as an insulating cushion which protects the growing embryo from injury.

During growth of the amniotic folds gastrulation takes place as a ventral furrow-like ingrowth on the middle line of the germ-band. It begins at the site of the future stomodaeum and gradually extends to the caudal end of the germ-band, whose cells thus become deployed as a lower, or inner, layer beneath the outer layer, or ectoderm (Fig. 51). In most insects the inner layer gives rise to mesodermal structures and rudiments of the mid gut, but the latter may arise in various ways and this has led to a less strict interpretation of embryonic germ layers than was formerly the case.

Segmentation. Very early in development the two-layered germ-band or embryo, as it may now be called, becomes divided by transverse furrows into a series of segments which ultimately number 20. Segmentation is a gradual process beginning anteriorly and extending backward (Fig. 52). The embryo is at first divisible into a protocephalic or primary head region and a protocormic or primary

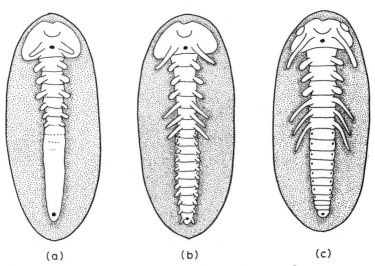

(a)   (b)   (c)

Fig. 52   Ventral side of developing insect embryos
(a) Protopod; (b) polypod; (c) oligopod.

101

trunk region. As development progresses the first three protocormic segments become added to the protocephalic region. The next three body segments are grouped to form the thorax and the remaining 11 segments, together with the terminal non-segmental telson, constitute the abdomen. Each segment except the first typically develops a pair of outgrowths, or embryonic appendages (Fig. 52). The first or pre-antennal segment is formed of the large procephalic lobes. The first pair of appendages or antennae belongs to the second segment, while the very small second pair is transitory and soon disappears. The third, fourth and fifth pairs grow, respectively, into the mandibles, maxillae and labium. The next three pairs of embryonic appendages are usually larger and more conspicuous; they are the forerunners of the thoracic legs. Finally, there follow 11 pairs of abdominal appendages of which the last pair becomes the cerci and the remaining pairs are usually resorbed before hatching. The presence of these evanescent limb rudiments can best be interpreted as indicating descent from a many-legged ancestral stage. The number of recognizable abdominal segments varies in the adults among different groups of insects, since some of the anterior and posterior segments tend to disappear or undergo great reduction.

Mesoderm. The cells of the inner layer become arranged, for the most part, in two longitudinal bands which are shortly afterwards marked off into segments corresponding with those bearing the appendages (Fig. 49). Most of these mesodermal segments acquire, in generalized insects, a pair of cavities, or coelom sacs. The dorsal or splanchnic walls of these sacs give rise to the gonads, visceral muscles and fat-body, while the ventrolateral or somatic walls produce the muscles of the body and the appendages. The body cavity begins as the epineural sinus, which is mainly formed by the separation of the yolk from the embryo in the mid-ventral region (Fig. 51c). This process extends laterally and upward, and results in the epineural sinus and most of the coelom sacs becoming confluent, thus forming the permanent body cavity or haemocoel. The primordial germ cells soon migrate forward and, after separating into two groups, they penetrate into the gonad rudiments, where they become established.

Nervous system. Shortly after gastrulation the central nervous system develops as a pair of longitudinal neural ridges of the ectoderm, separated by a median neural groove (Fig. 51b). The neural ridges become segmentally constricted into neuromeres, or primitive nerve ganglia, while their intersegmental portions give rise to the connectives. It will be noted that the whole of the nervous system and the sense organs are ectodermal in origin, and that their rudiments become

102

separated from the outer ectoderm which forms the body wall (Fig. 51c). The ganglia of the acron and of the first three head segments amalgamate to form the brain, while the succeeding three cephalic neuromeres fuse to become the suboesophageal ganglion. The neuromeres that follow develop into the thoracic and abdominal ganglia.

Alimentary canal. An ingrowth of the ectoderm, just behind the antennae, forms the stomodaeum or embryonic fore intestine and a corresponding posterior ingrowth or proctodaeum gives rise to the hind intestine (Fig. 49f). The mesenteron rudiments usually arise as groups of cells closely associated with the stomodaeal and proctodaeal ingrowths; these cells multiply, grow towards each other and finally enclose the yolk in the form of a complete tube – the mesenteron, or embryonic mid intestine. By the disappearance of the walls separating the mesenteron from the stomodaeum and proctodaeum, respectively, a through passage is established in the alimentary canal. The Malpighian tubules arise as outgrowths of the proctodaeum, close to its union with the mesenteron. Though often regarded as ectodermal in origin, there is some reason to think that they are endodermal or arise from an undifferentiated meristematic zone. The salivary glands arise as paired ectodermal ingrowths at the sides of the labial segment.

Tracheal system. The tracheae develop from paired lateral ingrowths, near the bases of the appendages, on the meso- and metathorax and on the first eight abdominal segments. The mouths of these invaginations become the spiracles and, at their inner ends, anterior and posterior longitudinal extensions meet and fuse to form the main tracheal trunks.

Later phases of development. The embryo always forms on the ventral surface of the egg, but in the lower insects it becomes invaginated into the abundant yolk that is present in these forms. This process occurs through the embryo traversing an arc so that its ventral surface now faces the dorsal side of the egg. After a short time it begins to reverse its position and ultimately regains the ventral side of the egg. These movements of the embryo during development are termed blastokinesis, but the significance of the process is obscure. The germ-band forms the ventral part of the developing insect and, in order to complete the embryonic body, its margins begin to grow upward. The final result is the completion of the embryo on the dorsal side though the details of the process differ among different insects. The upward growth involves not only the ectoderm, or body wall, but also the epineural sinus and the mesoderm, while the developing mid intestine ultimately encloses the yolk. The embryonic membranes later rupture and, becoming contracted, are finally resorbed.

POST-EMBRYONIC DEVELOPMENT

Hatching. When ready to emerge from the egg an insect has to force its way through the chorion in order to reach the outer world. In many cases the chorion is torn open by means of provisional structures known as hatching spines or egg bursters. These are located on the head, or other parts of the body, where they may remain until the insect has undergone its first moult. In other instances, notably among some Phthiraptera and Hemiptera-Heteroptera, a preformed egg cap, or operculum, is pushed open to allow the insect to emerge. The force used in hatching is chiefly due to muscular activity but, as a preliminary, an insect may swallow air or the amniotic fluid, and the resulting increase in bulk and turgidity play their part in the process.

Growth. Insects grow in cycles which alternate with the periods when moulting takes place (see below). The tissues may grow through cell multiplication, through an increase in the size of the individual cells or through both processes occurring together. In Endopterygote insects it is often found that those tissues which grow mainly by cell multiplication pass over from larva to adult with little change, while those which develop by cell hypertrophy break down in the pupal stage and are replaced by new adult tissues. The soft cuticle of some insects stretches considerably during growth, but the more strongly sclerotized parts such as the head capsule grow discontinuously, the enlargement becoming apparent after each moult. Such structures often increase in size by an approximately constant ratio at every moult (Dyar's law). However, if there is an unusually long or short interval between two successive moults then the ratio may be proportionately larger or smaller than normal. The various parts of the body tend to grow at rates which differ from each other and from the growth rate of the whole body. This often results in allometric growth; the size of a part is then a constant power function of the size of the whole body, so that when the two dimensions are plotted against each other on logarithmic scales a straight line is obtained.

Moulting. In order to accommodate the growing tissues, immature insects shed their cuticle at intervals; this process is known as moulting, and the cast skin forms the exuviae. Before it moults the insect stops feeding and may become quiescent for a short time. Meanwhile the epidermal cells enlarge and may divide mitotically, the old cuticle becomes detached from the epidermis (a process known as apolysis) and the latter begins to lay down a new cuticle. The space between old and new cuticles then becomes filled with the moulting fluid, which is

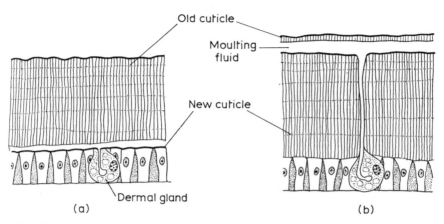

Fig. 53   Early stages of moulting in cuticle in which an exocuticle is absent
(a) New epicuticle formed, digestion of old endocuticle scarcely begun; (b) digestion and
absorption of old endocuticle almost complete. (After Wigglesworth.)

secreted by the epidermis and contains two important enzymes, a
protease and a chitinase (Fig. 53). These dissolve the old endocuticle and
the products of digestion are absorbed through the epidermis; the newly
formed cuticle remains unaffected by the enzymes. What is left of the
old cuticle is now ready to be shed, an act that may be referred to as
ecdysis. The insect contracts its abdominal muscles and increases the
pressure of blood in the head and thorax. It may also distend itself by
swallowing air, or water in aquatic forms, and the resulting forces
rupture the old cuticle along predetermined lines of weakness – the
ecdysial cleavage line of the head and a median dorsal line in the thorax.
When the old skin has split the insect gradually struggles out, often
aided by gravity, since many insects suspend themselves head downwards when moulting. In issuing from the old skin, the insect
withdraws its limbs from their former coverings and the old linings of
the tracheae, fore gut and hind gut are left behind with the exuviae. The
newly moulted (teneral) insect has a soft, flexible, lightly pigmented
cuticle; it swallows air (or water) and so again increases its volume.
Many of the muscles remain contracted for a time, and in this way blood
pressure expands the wings and other appendages to their full size.
Finally, the cuticle hardens and darkens, though it may continue to
increase in thickness for a considerable time.

The intervals between one moult and the next are sometimes known
as stages or stadia, and the form assumed by the insect in any particular
stadium is called an instar. Thus, the insect hatches from the egg as the
first instar; at the end of the first stadium it moults into the second
instar, and so on. For some time before ecdysis the new instar lies within

105

the old but unshed cuticle, and is then known as a pharate instar. The number of instars differs greatly in different groups of insects, but is often approximately constant within a group. In some relatively primitive insects like the Ephemeroptera and Plecoptera there may be more than 20 pre-imaginal instars; in the Cyclorrhaphan Diptera there are four, and in the Lepidoptera from four to ten. In many Apterygotes (Archaeognatha, Zygentoma, Collembola and *Campodea*) the insects continue to moult after reaching sexual maturity, but in the Pterygota the adults never do so. The hormonal control of moulting is discussed on p. 113.

Metamorphosis. The appearance and structure of the newly hatched insect differs more or less extensively from that of the adult. Its development therefore involves changes of form, or metamorphosis, which may include the loss of purely juvenile structures as well as the differentiation of distinctively adult organs. The magnitude of these changes varies from group to group, but two main types of metamorphosis may be distinguished: incomplete metamorphosis – also known as direct, or hemimetabolous, development – and complete metamorphosis (indirect, or holometabolous, development).

Hemimetabolous development occurs in the Apterygotes and almost all Exopterygotes (Fig. 54). The immature stages, sometimes referred to as nymphs, usually resemble the adults in habits and in many structural features, and metamorphosis consists mainly of a relatively gradual differentiation of adult characters. The wings and external genitalia usually make their appearance at an early stage as external rudiments which increase in size and complexity with each successive instar. The simple gonad rudiments of the young nymph gradually differentiate and grow and the efferent ducts of the reproductive system develop progressively. The number of segments in the antennae, tarsi and cerci may increase with successive moults, and the compound eyes grow with the differentiation of additional ommatidia. There are often changes in coloration, in the proportions of various structures, and in the number and distribution of cuticular bristles. The changes occurring at the moult into the adult are sometimes rather more striking than those at earlier ecdyses. This is especially obvious in the Ephemeroptera, Odonata and Plecoptera, where the young stages are aquatic, with gills and other structures which are lost on transformation into the terrestrial adults.

Holometabolous development occurs in virtually all the Endopterygotes. Here there is a series of active, feeding larval instars – which usually resemble each other closely, but may differ enormously from the adult in habits and structure – followed by a single quiescent pupal instar, which does not feed and which finally moults into the adult.

Compared with the hemimetabolous insects, holometabolous ones show a marked suppression of adult features in the larval stages, combined with a strong tendency towards the evolution of specifically larval organs which are lost at the change into the pupa. The complex internal changes which accompany pupation are described on p. 111.

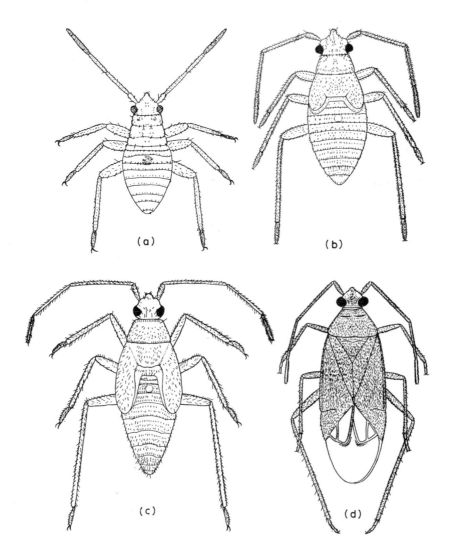

Fig. 54   Incomplete metamorphosis of *Lygocoris pabulinus* (Hemiptera: Miridae) (a) Second instar; (b) fourth instar; (c) fifth instar; (d) adult. (After Petherbridge and Thorpe.)

107

A few Exopterygote insects – the Thysanoptera, Aleyrodidae and male Coccoidea – have a metamorphosis which resembles that of the Endopterygotes. The earlier instars differ appreciably from the adult and the life-cycle includes a period of extensive structural change comparable with that found in the Endopterygote pupa – the Thysanoptera and male Coccoidea have, in fact, two or, in some Thysanoptera, three pupal instars.

The Endopterygote larva. The larvae of holometabolous insects display an enormous range of structural variation and are adapted for life in a very wide variety of environments. In general they may be distinguished from the immature stages of Exopterygote insects by a number of external features. There are no compound eyes, but their place is often taken by one or more pairs of lateral ocelli; dorsal ocelli are absent. External wing pads and genital appendages are absent, though internal rudiments usually occur beneath the cuticle of at least the older larvae. Finally the general integument is commonly less sclerotized and in some cases the head capsule, cephalic appendages and legs are greatly reduced or absent.

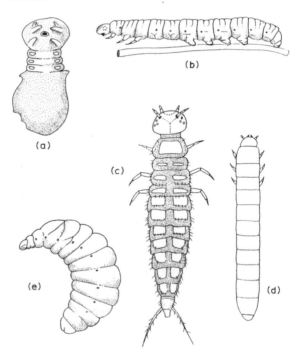

Fig. 55   Types of Endopterygote larvae

(a) Protopod (Proctotrupoidea) (after Kulagin); (b) polypod (Lepidoptera); (c) oligopod (Coleoptera); (d) oligopod (*Tenebrio*); (e) apodous (*Apis mellifera*) (after Nelson).

Endopterygote larvae may conveniently be divided into a number of different types (Fig. 55) though intermediate forms are not uncommon. The highly specialized protopod type (Fig. 55a) occurs in the early instars of a few endoparasitic Hymenoptera and Diptera. It resembles the early embryonic stage of many insects and is little more than a precociously hatched embryo, with its ill-defined segmentation, its limbs rudimentary or absent and its incompletely differentiated internal organs. The polypod type, typified by the Lepidoptera (Fig. 55b) and many sawflies, is a structurally more advanced form provided with a number of abdominal processes which may be used in locomotion, though their serial homology with the thoracic legs is doubtful. The oligopod type (Fig. 55c and d) is the prevailing form in the Coleoptera and Neuroptera. It has a well-developed head, antennae and thoracic legs, but no abdominal processes except sometimes for a pair of cercus-like appendages. According to their general facies, the members of this group may be subdivided into several forms, of which two are worth special mention. Campodeiform larvae (Fig. 55c) are usually active predators with relatively long legs and often a somewhat depressed, sclerotized body with a prognathous head and powerful mouthparts. The more reduced scarabaeiform larvae, found in the cockchafers and some other beetles, are characteristically C-shaped, with shorter legs, less highly developed mouthparts and a more membranous integument (Fig. 84b and d). The last major type is the apodous larva, which lacks all legs or similar processes (Fig. 55e). Such larvae usually live among abundant food and are characteristic of the Diptera, the aculeate and parasitic Hymenoptera and, among Coleoptera, of the weevils. According to the extent to which the head capsule is reduced and retracted into the thorax, apodous larvae may be further subdivided into eucephalous, hemicephalous and acephalous types (p. 165).

Towards the end of the last larval instar, the insect becomes less active, stops feeding and prepares for the moult into the pupa. It may construct a cocoon or pupal cell (see below), and as the pupal organs develop within the larval integument its body often becomes somewhat contracted and depressed. This phase of development is sometimes known as the prepupa but it is more accurately described as the pharate pupa (cf. p. 106).

The Endopterygote pupa. This instar differs from the larval phase in many respects. It is more or less quiescent, it does not feed and it is the site of more or less profound internal changes which transform the larval organization into that of the adult (pp. 111–13). Externally, the pupa is usually rather like the adult in form; it has well-developed external wing pads, thoracic legs and antennae, but the cuticle is often thin and lightly pigmented. It is a vulnerable stage in the life cycle, with few special means of defence, and is therefore often concealed in the soil, in debris or in crevices. It may be enclosed in a silken cocoon, spun by the larvae from the labial glands (many Lepidoptera) or Malpighian tubules (many Neuroptera). In other cases a pupal cell is constructed from particles of soil, chips of wood or other debris, held together by various secretions, and in the Cyclorrhaphan Diptera the persistent cuticle of the last larval instar is transformed into a hard, dark, ovoidal puparium which protects the delicate adecticous exarate pupa inside it (Fig. 56c). Freely exposed pupae, such as occur in the ladybirds (Coccinellidae) and some Lepidoptera, are often protectively coloured and have a rather thick integument. For some time before the pupal cuticle is shed, the fully formed adult lies within it; these older 'pupae' are sometimes able to move actively (e.g. in the Trichoptera), but strictly it is the pharate adult which is responsible for the movements.

Two main types of pupae may be recognized. The decticous pupa, found in the Neuroptera, Mecoptera, Trichoptera and a few primitive Lepidoptera and Hymenoptera, is provided with functional mandibles which are used by the pharate adult to break out of the cocoon or pupal cell before the adult emerges. The adecticous type of pupa, found in the

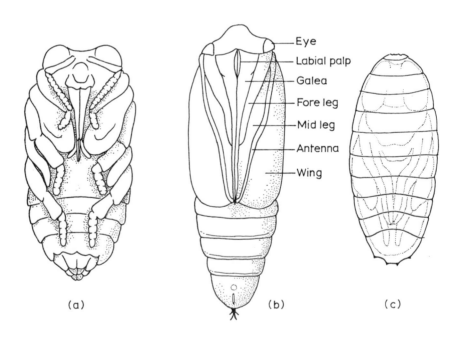

Eye
Labial palp
Galea
Fore leg
Mid leg
Antenna
Wing

(a)   (b)   (c)

Fig. 56   Types of pupae

(a) Exarate pupa of *Apis mellifera* (Hymenoptera: Apidae); (b) obtect pupa of a Noctuid moth; (c) puparium of a Cyclorrhaphan Dipteran (Muscidae) showing the exarate pupa

other Endopterygotes, has no functional mandibles. It may escape from the cell with the aid of various spines or other special processes or, as in the Coleoptera and Hymenoptera, it moults into the adult within the cell. Adecticous pupae may, like all decticous ones, be exarate, with the appendages projecting freely from the body (Fig. 56a) or they may be obtect, as in most Lepidoptera, with wings, legs, antennae and mouthparts firmly soldered down to the body (Fig. 56b).

Internal metamorphosis. In hemimetabolous insects the development of external and internal structures is gradual and direct. The organs of the nymph generally become transformed into those of the imago with little change beyond increase in size, alterations of proportion and limited structural elaboration. In the holometabolous life-cycle, however, the onset of pupation marks the beginning of a variable, though often extensive, destruction of larval organs and tissues (histolysis), accompanied by a rapid equivalent differentiation of adult structures (histogenesis). These processes continue throughout the pupal stage and may not be fully completed until after the adult has emerged.

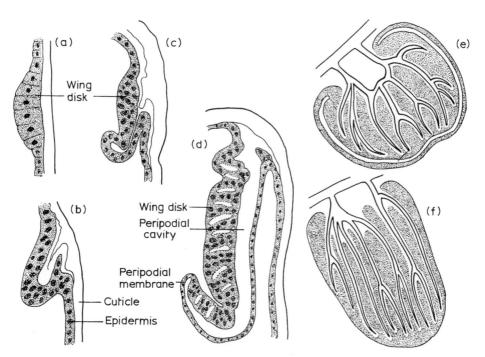

Fig. 57   Imaginal disks of wing of *Ephestia kuehniella* (Lepidoptera: Phycitidae) (a)–(d) Sections through successively older wing disks; (e), (f) surface view of young and old disk, showing tracheal supply.

In the more primitive Endopterygota such as the Neuroptera, and also in the Coleoptera, relatively little histolysis occurs and a considerable proportion of the larval tissues and organs pass over to the adult with only slight modifications. On the other hand, in the Hymenoptera and Diptera the epidermis, alimentary canal, salivary glands and many muscles of the larva are replaced by entirely new adult formations, and in some cases the fat-body, Malpighian tubules and heart also undergo the same fate. Even those structures which are not histolysed may experience considerable histological redifferentiation.

Histolysis begins with the death of the tissues concerned, which may then break up and dissolve without the intervention of phagocytic blood-cells. Often, however, the latter engulf and digest the disintegrating tissue fragments or even attack the recently dead tissues by invading them while they retain much of their structural integrity. The breakdown products of histolysis accumulate in the blood, where they provide materials used in histogenesis. The cells from which the adult tissues develop seem to have retained a latent capacity for imaginal differentiation which has been largely or entirely suppressed during the larval phase. In some cases these cells remain histologically indistinguishable from neighbouring cells for much or all of the larval phase; in others they become recognizable as histoblasts which are sometimes present from the embryo or from some later larval stage as organ rudiments or imaginal disks or buds (Fig. 57). The imaginal disks of the wings, legs, mouthparts, antennae and external genitalia arise as slight folds or thickenings of the epidermis which may come to lie in sac-like invaginations (Fig. 57c). Their growth and differentiation accelerate rapidly as the larval period comes to an end and they are everted at pupation. The imaginal buds of the epidermis, gut, glands, main tracheal trunks, etc., are nests of cells localized in the walls of the larval organs; they proliferate actively in the pupa, supplementing or replacing the larval tissues.

Imaginal disks, especially those of *Drosophila*, have provided very favourable material for investigating the physiological, biochemical and genetic bases of determination, i.e. those developmental processes whereby zones of initially labile cells become progressively more committed to develop into specific adult structures such as the leg, wing, antenna or genitalia. In *Drosophila* imaginal disks differentiate embryonically from groups of cells; cell division in the incipient disk soon stops, but is resumed after hatching, starting in the eye and wing disks during the first larval instar, then at various later times up to the third instar in the other disks. High ecdysone concentrations during the third instar promote the differentiation of the disks. Searches for proteins specific to each type of disk (e.g. leg disks as against wings) suggest that these are few and only doubtfully of importance in the process of determination. However, the different types of disk do seem to display distinct patterns in the spatial distribution of the same proteins at different periods of development, though it remains unclear how these differences are related to the cellular processes characteristic of the morphogenetic patterns in each kind of disk. The disks do, in fact, differ in the site, extent and nature of five such processes: cell growth, cell division, cell death, movement or changes of cell shape, and the secretion of extracellular material such as cuticle. Disturbance of these morphogenetic patterns experimentally or through the action of mutant genes may sometimes be resisted, as it were, so that the developing structure appears to be normally determined; in other cases a disturbance of the pattern is sufficiently profound to lead to the differentiation of an abnormal structure, as in the so-called homeotic mutants where, for example, a haltere disk may give rise to a wing or an antenna disk to a leg-like structure.

Hypermetamorphosis. Insects in which two or more of the successive larval instars differ widely in form are said to undergo hypermeta-morphosis. The process is characteristic of certain parasitic groups, and the alterations in larval form are accompanied by changes in their mode of life. Thus, in the Meloidae or oil beetles the first instar is an active hard-skinned campodeiform larva which is transported to the nest of its host, usually a bee, and there moults first into a soft-bodied, short-legged larva and later into one or more fleshy grub-like instars without legs or with vestigial ones. Hypermetamorphosis also occurs in all Strepsiptera, in the Neuropteran family Mantispidae and in many parasitic Hymenoptera, where the first-stage larvae are very variable in appearance (Fig. 114).

Hormonal control of moulting and metamorphosis. Growth, moulting and the realization of imaginal characters during post-embryonic life are under the control of a balanced system of hormones produced by endocrine glands in the anterior part of the body (p. 87). The processes involved seem to be fundamentally similar in both the Exopterygote and Endopterygote insects. The neurosecretory cells of the brain produce a hormone which activates the thoracic glands or their homologues and causes the latter to secrete a second hormone or a mixture of similar hormones. It is these, which have now been synthesized chemically and are sometimes known as ecdysone and its derivatives, which induce the insect to moult. While the insect is still young, however, a third group of hormones produced by the corpora allata and known as 'juvenile hormones' are also present in sufficient quantity to inhibit the development of imaginal features. The moults induced by the thoracic gland hormone therefore result in a sequence of larval or nymphal instars. Later in larval or nymphal life the production of the juvenile hormone ceases or is reduced in a more or less abrupt fashion, and the previously inhibited adult structures can now develop. Quantitative differences in the changing balance between the hormones of the thoracic glands and the corpora allata thus seem to underlie the difference between the relatively sudden transition to the imago in holometabolous insects and the more gradual change in hemimetabolous ones. Experimental proof of the above explanation has been obtained in many ways. For example, young insects deprived of their corpora allata moult into miniature adult-like forms while the implantation of active corpora allata into late nymphs or larvae leads to the production of supernumerary immature instars.

Diapause. In some insects, under certain conditions, any one of the developmental stages – egg, nymph, larva or pupa – can pass into a more or less prolonged state of arrested development or diapause; even the adult may enter what has been called 'reproductive diapause', during which the reproductive organs remain non-functional. Development cannot then be resumed, even under apparently favourable conditions, until the diapause has been 'broken'. Various environmental changes are now known to be responsible for inducing diapause, though they normally exert their effect some appreciable time before development is arrested. The most important environmental influence seems to be the number of hours of daylight per day; a regime of short day-lengths (8–12 h of light per day) generally induces diapause, but in some insects an opposite relationship holds. In temperate climates diapause commonly occurs in the overwintering developmental stage, and is usually broken through exposure to a period of low temperature. The immediate cause of diapause in the nymph, larva or pupa is probably a temporary lack of the thoracic gland hormone necessary for moulting and growth. In the silkmoth *Bombyx*, however, the eggs may be induced to enter diapause by a hormone which had previously been released into the blood of the female parent from neurosecretory cells in the suboesophageal ganglion. From a biological standpoint, diapause is an adaptation which often permits survival without feeding during adverse environmental conditions, and which tends to synchronize development so that all members of an insect population resume activity together when conditions become favourable.

4

Classification and biology

If two kinds of animals differ constantly from each other in some definite but relatively minor structural character or characters, they are said to be distinct species. The structural differences are presumed or, in some cases, are known to be indicators of a barrier to interbreeding between the two kinds. Species are then grouped into genera, a genus being an assemblage of species showing evidence in common characters of close relationship. Genera in turn are arranged in the higher category of a family, whose components share many important characters. An order consists of all those families that show major features that link them together into a single natural assemblage. To continue ascending this hierarchical scheme, orders collectively form a class, while classes are grouped on the basis of common fundamental characters into a phylum. Certain intermediate taxonomic categories are also adopted, the most widely used being the subfamily or group of genera forming a section of a family; the superfamily, or group of families smaller than an order; and the suborder. It will suffice to give one example showing the systematic position of the ant *Formica rufa* Linnaeus.

SPECIES: *rufa* Linnaeus
  GENUS: *Formica* Linnaeus
    SUBFAMILY: Formicinae
      FAMILY: Formicidae
        SUPERFAMILY: Scolioidea
          SUBORDER: Apocrita
            ORDER: Hymenoptera
              CLASS: Insecta
                PHYLUM: Arthropoda

Species have a biological reality, in that each is a group of populations between which gene-flow occurs, but which is isolated reproductively from other similar groups. In dealing with the higher categories, however, one is concerned only with concepts. An order, a family or a genus represent taxonomists' ideas about how the aggregates termed species may be grouped together so as to show their relationships. An essential step in the classification of any group of animals is to name them so as to allow future reference. The system of nomenclature in universal use is binomial, i.e. each kind of animal bears two names, the first generic and the second specific. This convention dates from the publication of the 10th edition of the *Systema Naturae* of Linnaeus in 1758, when binomial nomenclature was first definitely established for zoology. During the subsequent growth of taxonomy nomenclature has become a matter of some complexity, and in order to regulate the procedure an International Code of Zoological Nomenclature has been followed by taxonomists since 1901.

The Code lays down that scientific names of animals must be Latin or latinized words, or considered and treated as such when not of classical origin. The name of a family is formed by adding the suffix -idae to the stem of the name of the type genus, e.g. *Blatta*, Blattidae. The suffixes -oidea and -inae are added similarly to form superfamily and subfamily names, but no rules are laid down for names in higher categories than that of a superfamily. A generic name is a substantive in the nominative singular. The name of a species must be either an adjective agreeing grammatically with the generic name, e.g. *Musca domestica*, a substantive in apposition with the generic name, e.g. *Stratiomyia chamaeleon*, or a substantive in the genitive, e.g. *Psila rosae*. Geographic names and names of persons when used as specific designations are also expressed in the genitive, e.g. *Phormia terraenovae, Odontotermes horni*. When the name of the author is quoted after a specific name it follows without mark of punctuation, e.g. *Tabanus rusticus* Linnaeus. When a species is transferred to a genus other than that in which it was originally placed the name of the author of the species is then given in parenthesis, thus: *Blatta lapponica* Linnaeus has become *Ectobius lapponicus* (Linnaeus); it will be noted that the specific name conforms grammatically with the new generic name. The valid name of a species or genus is that name under which it was first properly published and no name published prior to the 10th edition of the *Systema Naturae* is valid. A generic or specific name that has been replaced on account of its being invalid is known as a synonym. It may also be noted that the specimens from which the published descriptions of species are drawn up are called types; they are of various kinds and have received special names, but one sort, the holotype is of special significance since it is a unique specimen designated by the author of a new species. The importance of types being carefully preserved is obvious when it is realized that much existing taxonomic work depends on access to them for its ultimate clarification. Descriptions which seemed sufficient often prove inadequate in the light of later, more exact and discriminating standards. The type is then decisive in matters of doubtful identity.

The orders of insects

The most satisfactory arrangement of the orders of insects would be one which reflected their probable evolutionary history and relationships. Though some features of insect phylogeny are established with reasonable certainty, there are others on which there is still substantial disagreement. For this reason it seems best to set out the orders in a simple scheme which does not claim to be a fully phylogenetic classification; some of the problems involved are then discussed further on pp. 182–94.

I. Apterygote insects

ORDER 1. Diplura
ORDER 2. Protura
ORDER 3. Collembola
ORDER 4. Archaeognatha
ORDER 5. Zygentoma

II. Exopterygote insects

ORDER 6. Ephemeroptera
ORDER 7. Odonata
ORDER 8. Plecoptera
ORDER 9. Grylloblattodea
ORDER 10. Orthoptera
ORDER 11. Phasmida
ORDER 12. Dermaptera
ORDER 13. Embioptera
ORDER 14. Dictyoptera
ORDER 15. Isoptera
ORDER 16. Zoraptera
ORDER 17. Psocoptera
ORDER 18. Phthiraptera
ORDER 19. Hemiptera
ORDER 20. Thysanoptera

III. Endopterygote insects

ORDER 21. Neuroptera
ORDER 22. Coleoptera
ORDER 23. Strepsiptera
ORDER 24. Mecoptera
ORDER 25. Siphonaptera
ORDER 26. Diptera
ORDER 27. Lepidoptera
ORDER 28. Trichoptera
ORDER 29. Hymenoptera

I. Apterygote insects. *Primitively wingless forms; antennae, when present, with or without intrinsic flagellar muscles; mandible usually with only one cephalic articulation; abdomen with at least some pregenital appendages present in adult; sperm transfer without copulation; metamorphosis slight, usually with moulting after sexual maturity.* This is not a natural group, though opinions differ on the relationships of the five orders and on the best ways of grouping them. Some authorities regard the first three orders below as forming a monophyletic assemblage, the Entognatha, with the remaining two orders more closely allied to the winged insects.

ORDER 1. **DIPLURA**. (*diplos*, double; *oura*, a tail)

Small, eyeless, mostly unpigmented insects with moniliform antennae provided with intrinsic muscles in flagellar segments. Mouthparts for biting, entognathous. Abdomen 11-segmented, terminating with variably developed cerci or unjointed forceps; no median tail filament; styli and usually eversible vesicles present. No ovipositor; tarsi one-segmented.

About 600 species of Diplura are known. They live in the soil but also frequent decaying vegetable matter of various kinds. The largest forms (Japygidae) measure up to 50 mm long, but an average is 2–5 mm in length. Excepting Japygidae, with their darkened sclerotized forceps,

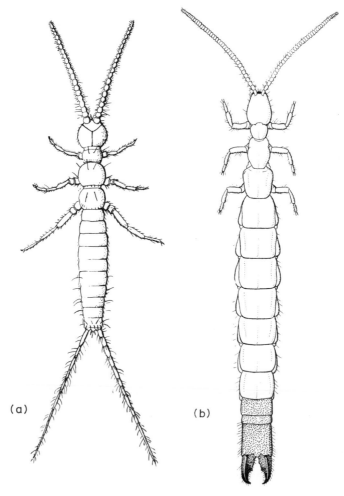

(a)   (b)

Fig. 58   Diplura
(a) *Campodea;* (b) *Japyx.*

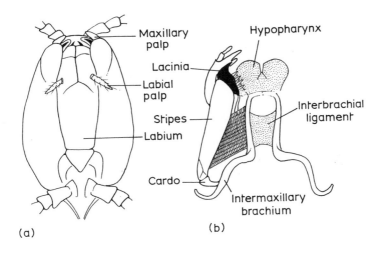

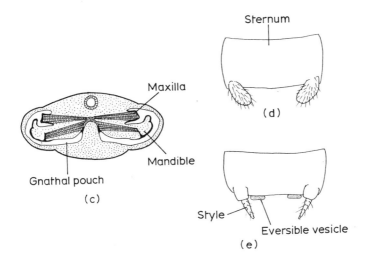

Fig. 59   Diplura

(a) *Heterojapyx*, ventral view of head; (b) *Heterojapyx*, right maxilla, hypopharynx and intermaxillary brachia; (c) *Heterojapyx*, diagrammatic transverse section of head, showing entognathous condition; (d) *Campodea*, first abdominal segment in ventral view; (e) *Campodea*, fourth abdominal segment in ventral view. (a–c after Snodgrass.)

these insects are unpigmented. Though formerly associated with the Archaeognatha and Zygentoma, the Diplura are obviously a separate group, perhaps nearer to the Protura and Collembola. The mouthparts (Fig. 59) are entognathous to the extent that the mandibles and maxillae lie in pockets from which they are protruded when feeding. The legs have unsegmented tarsi and usually bear two claws. Styli are present on abdominal segments 1 to 7 or 2 to 7, and eversible vesicles are usual on segments 2 to 7 (Fig. 59). External genitalia are very little developed or wanting. Malpighian tubes are represented by papillae or are absent; while only three pairs of spiracles are present in Campodeidae, nine to 11 pairs occur in other families. There are three principal families, the Projapygidae being the most primitive: their short, segmented cerci are traversed by the ducts of special glands. The Japygidae all have forcipate cerci and in the Campodeidae (Fig. 58) these structures are long, fragile and many-segmented. Only the last named insects occur in Britain, where they number about a dozen species.

ORDER 2. **PROTURA**. (*protos*, first; *oura*, a tail)

Minute colourless insects without eyes or antennae; mouthparts entognathous for piercing. Abdomen of 11 segments and a definite telson, cerci absent.

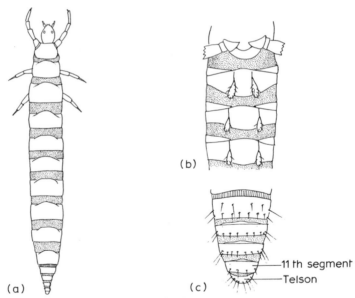

Fig. 60   Protura

(a) *Acerentulus*, dorsal view; (b) *Australentulus*, first three abdominal segments, ventral view; (c) *Acerentulus*, terminal abdominal segments, dorsal view. (All after Wallace and Mackerras.)

These minute creatures (Fig. 60) seldom attain more than 1 mm in length; they are widely distributed and about 12 species have been found in Britain. They are local and need looking for in moist soil, in turf, beneath bark of trees, under stones, etc. On eclosion from the egg Protura have eight abdominal segments and three more are added later, this kind of post-embryonic growth, or anamorphosis, being found in no other insects. Antennal functions are performed by the front legs, which are held forward. Organs apparently homologous with the postantennal organs of Collembola are present, one on each side of the head. The mouthparts show basic resemblances to those of the other entognathous Apterygotes. Rudiments of limbs are borne on the first three abdominal segments and are evidently homologous with the pair on the first segment of *Campodea* (Fig. 60). The legs have one-segmented tarsi and single claws. Tracheae are only slightly developed, as in *Eosentomon*, or are absent as in *Acerentomon*; two pairs of spiracles occur in the tracheate forms. About 200 species of Protura are known. The order is apparently a divergent offshoot from the ancestors of insects; nothing is known of the embryology.

ORDER 3. **COLLEMBOLA**. Springtails. (*kola*, glue; *embolo*, a peg)

Very small insects with entognathous, biting mouthparts; antennae four-segmented; tarsi fused with tibiae. Abdomen of six segments sometimes fused together; 1st segment with a sucker-like ventral tube, 4th usually with a forked springing organ.

Collembola (Fig. 61) rarely exceed 5 mm long and occur from the poles to the equator. They are often immensely abundant as individuals and occur on and below the ground, among herbage, in decaying matter, under bark, in nests of ants and termites, and in other damp situations. An acre (approx. 0.4 ha) of meadow has been found to support nearly 230 000 000 of these insects from the surface to a depth of 9 inches (approx. 23 cm). The eyes are typically eight ocelli on each side, but may be wanting; just behind the antenna there is often a characteristic postantennal organ. The mouthparts resemble those of Diplura and, when feeding, they are partly extruded from pockets within the head; well-developed superlinguae are present. The antennae, like those of Diplura, have intrinsic flagellar muscles – a feature shared by no other insects. The abdomen usually bears three ventral structures derived from paired appendages; those of the first segment are fused to form the ventral tube, which is probably an organ for respiration, for absorbing moisture from surfaces, and for adhesion. A furca, or springing organ, is borne on the fourth segment and, when not in use, is retained beneath the abdomen by a 'catch', or retinaculum, formed by the reduced appendages of the third segment. External genitalia are wanting and the sexes are almost always alike. Except in *Sminthurus* and its allies, tracheae are wanting (see p. 68); there are no Malpighian tubules and excretion is performed partly by the fat-body and partly by the periodic shedding of the cells of the mid gut. The gonads have the germarium lateral in position and ovarioles are not developed. Segmentation of the egg is at first total and there is no amnion or serosa. The

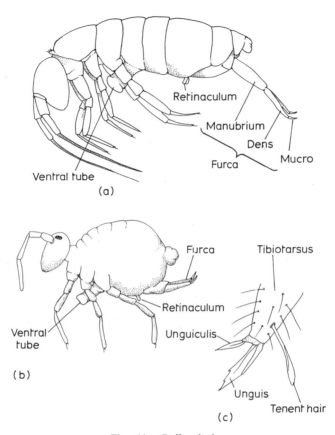

Fig. 61   Collembola

(a) *Tomocerus*, lateral view (after Folsom); (b) *Sminthurus*, lateral view (after Wallace and Mackerras); (c) *Entomobrya*, apex of tibiotarsus (after Handschin).

order is divided into the suborders **Arthropleona** (Fig. 61a), with cylindrical body and without evident fusion of its segments, and **Symphypleona** (Fig 61b), with globular body and with the thoracic and first four abdominal segments closely amalgamated. About 1500 species of Collembola are known: several rank as injurious, the most important being *Sminthurus viridis*, which is a pest of clover and lucerne.

ORDER 4. **ARCHAEOGNATHA** (= Microcoryphia). Bristletails.
(*archaios*, primitive; *gnathos*, jaw)

Apterygote insects with body more or less cylindrical or compressed and bearing scales; mouthparts normal, external in position; mandibles with one articulation to head-capsule; compound eyes large, often touching; dorsal ocelli present; antennae many-segmented but only the basal segment with intrinsic muscles;

coxae of mid and hind legs each bearing a small style; abdomen 11–segmented *with spiracles on 2nd to 8th segments; cerci many-segmented, shorter than the otherwise similar median filament; genital appendages well-developed, but no gonangulum at base of ovipositor.*

The bristletails are small or medium-sized primitive insects found in many terrestrial habitats among leaf-litter and under stones or logs; some species, such as *Petrobius maritimus*, occur above tide-marks on rocky sea-shores. They run and jump actively and feed on algae, lichens, other plant materials and probably also on dead arthropods. The Archaeognatha are most similar in structure to the Zygentoma (silverfish and their allies), and the two groups are sometimes united as the order Thysanura (*sens. lat.*). The mouthparts (Fig. 62) are of the generalized mandibulate type, with the usual structures well-developed, but the mandibles are characteristically pointed at the apex with a basal

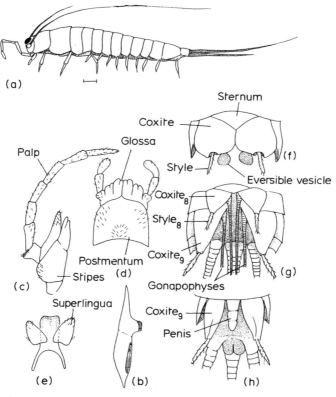

Fig. 62   Archaeognatha

(a) *Machilis*, lateral view; (b)–(e) *Petrobius*, mandible, maxilla, labium and hypopharynx; (f) *Nesomachilis*, ventral view of a pregenital segment; (g) *Machilis*, female abdominal terminalia and ovipositor; (h) *Nesomachilis*, male terminalia. (After Snodgrass.) Scale line = 1 mm.

123

molar area and a single condyle. The abdomen bears well-developed segmental appendages (Fig. 62), consisting of a pair of coxites and styles on the 2nd to 9th sterna, with one or more pairs of segmentally arranged eversible vesicles also present. The male external genitalia consist of a conspicuous median aedeagus flanked by a pair of gonapophyses (parameres), all lying between the coxites and styles of the 9th abdominal segment (Fig. 62). The female has a well-developed ovipositor (Fig. 62) composed of the paired, rod-like gonapophyses of the 8th and 9th abdominal segments, all four structures fitting closely together to form a tube between which the eggs pass when being laid. There are 12–20 Malpighian tubules and nine pairs of spiracles, each giving rise to tracheal branches which do not unite with those from other spiracles. There are about 250 species from all parts of the world. The Machilidae are mainly a northern hemisphere family and the Meinertellidae are mostly from the southern hemisphere.

ORDER 5. **ZYGENTOMA** (= Thysanura *s. str.*). Silverfish. (*zygon*, yoke; *entomos*, cut up)

Body more or less depressed, often with scales; antennae without intrinsic flagellar muscles; compound eyes small and separate or absent; ocelli absent; mandibles with anterior and posterior cephalic articulations, molar and incisor areas confluent; coxae of legs without styles; tarsi with two to four segments and paired claws; abdomen 11-segmented, with or without eversible vesicles; cerci many-segmented, about as long as the similar median process; external genitalia well-developed, ovipositor with gonangulum.

The silverfish and their allies (Fig. 63) consist of about 330 species and are represented in all regions. They are very similar in many respects to the Archaeognatha, with which they have been united in a single order (Thysanura *sens. lat.*), but they probably have a closer evolutionary relationship with the winged insects (Pterygota), resembling them especially in the condition of the mandibles and the structure of the ovipositor. Most species occur outdoors, under bark or rotting logs or in the soil; some live in the nests of ants or termites and a few species are minor domestic pests. Among these the silverfish *Lepisma saccharina* and the firebrat *Thermobia domestica* are widely distributed; *Lepisma* prefers cool, damp places while *Thermobia* is found in warm, dry situations. Members of the order feed on plant and animal matter, including algae, fungi and organic detritus; some domestic species can damage wallpaper.

In most general anatomical features the Zygentoma are very similar to the Archaeognatha. Like them, the antennae are many-segmented and the mouthparts are generalized, mandibulate and exposed externally. However, the mandibles resemble those of the Pterygota in having anterior and posterior articulations with the head-capsule, the maxillary

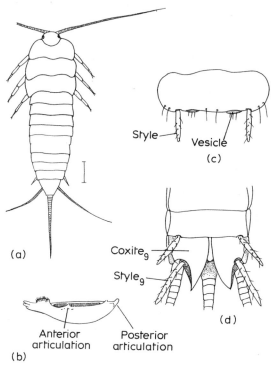

Fig. 63   Zygentoma

(a) *Lepisma saccharina*, dorsal view; (b) *Ctenolepisma*, left mandible (modified after Snodgrass); (c) *Atopatelura*, abdominal segment, ventral view (after Watson); (d) *Ctenolepisma*, male terminalia, ventral view (after Snodgrass). Scale line = 2 mm.

palps are five-segmented and the paraglossae are simple. The thoracic segments are more or less equal in size and may be extended laterally into paranotal lobes that contribute to the flattened appearance of the body. The legs, whose coxae lack styles, have two to four tarsal segments and a pair of pretarsal claws. The 11-segmented abdomen bears eight or fewer pairs of segmental appendages, each in the form of a coxite and style, and eversible vesicles may also be present. The external genitalia are generally similar to those of the Archaeognatha, but the ovipositor includes a gonangulum homologous with that found in the Pterygote insects. Sperm transfer is indirect and not unlike that of the Archaeognatha. Internally the Zygentoma have a simple gut, with four to eight Malpighian tubules and a well-developed tracheal system with longitudinal and transverse trunks, two pairs of thoracic spiracles and eight pairs in the abdomen. Most Zygentoma belong to the cosmopolitan family Lepismatidae, but the Nicoletiidae are also a widely distributed family.

125

II. Exopterygote insects. *Winged or secondarily apterous insects; metamorphosis usually incomplete, the larvae (sometimes called 'nymphs') usually resembling the adults in form and habits, with compound eyes and externally developing wing-pads and genital appendages.* This group of 15 orders of insects shows considerable diversity of structure and habits, though the great majority of its members agree in having an incomplete metamorphosis. It is convenient to think of it as made up of three groups of orders: (a) the Ephemeroptera (mayflies) and Odonata (dragonflies) which retain some archaic features; (b) a group of nine or so Orthopteroid orders, whose interrelationships are far from clear (Plecoptera, Grylloblattodea, Orthoptera, Phasmida, Dermaptera, Embioptera, Dictyoptera, Isoptera and Zoraptera); and (c) a more specialized group of Hemipteroid orders (Psocoptera, Phthiraptera, Hemiptera and Thysanoptera).

ORDER 6. **EPHEMEROPTERA**. Mayflies. (*ephemeros*, living a day; *pteron*, a wing)

Soft-bodied insects with large eyes, minute antennae and atrophied mouthparts. Wings membranous, longitudinally plicated, held vertically in repose, hind pair small or even atrophied. Cerci slender, many-jointed, usually accompanied by a median caudal filament. Nymphs aquatic, with plate-like or filamentous tracheal gills.

The Ephemeroptera (Fig. 64) are known as mayflies, many of which live only a few hours as imagines though this feature is compensated by the lengthy nymphal life which may last three years. The venation is very primitive with all the main veins and their branches present; unlike most recent insects the media consists of both MA and MP while the characteristic plication of the wings enables both convex and concave veins to be identified readily. Between the forked branches of the main veins, intercalary veins are present as in the Odonata. The hind wings are largest in Siphlonuridae; in other families they are much reduced or even atrophied as in *Cloeon* and *Caenis*. The legs of the adults are useless for walking and only enable them to cling to objects while resting. The first winged stage is the unique subimago which resembles the imago except for a translucent cuticle which covers the whole insect, giving it a dullish appearance. It undergoes an ecdysis, giving rise to the imago, which is recognizable by its clear shining appearance and full coloration. Mayflies take no food as imagines; the alimentary canal remains in a thin-walled condition and is used for taking in air, the mid intestine acting as an aerostatic organ. The nymphs are essentially phytophagous and like the imagines have long cerci and usually a median caudal filament. They inhabit lakes, ponds and streams and present notable adaptive modifications. Burrowing forms (e.g. *Ephemera* and *Hexagenia*)

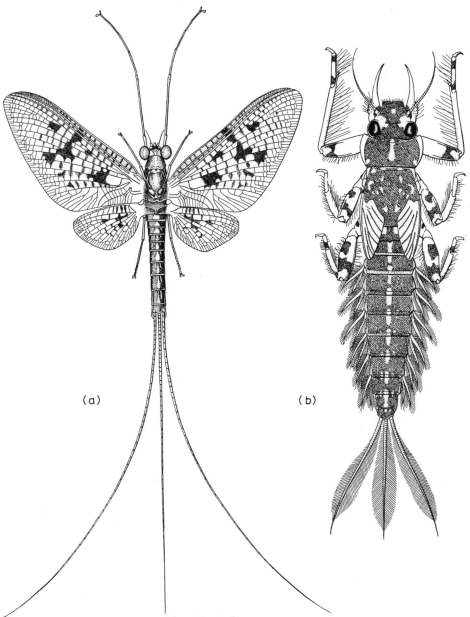

(a)   (b)

Fig. 64   Ephemeroptera
(a) *Ephemera*, male; (b) nymph of *Polymitarcys*.

have cylindrical bodies and fossorial fore legs. Species inhabiting swift streams have flattened bodies and hooked spines or other adaptations for clinging to rocks (*Ecdyonurus, Iron, Epeorus* and others). Inhabitants of

127

sandy streams have the gills covered by opercula formed by the upper lamellae of the second pair; the branchial chamber thus formed is guarded by hair-fringes against the entry of particles suspended in the water (*Caenis* and *Tricorythus*). Forty-six species of mayflies occur in Great Britain and over 400 kinds in N. America, while about 2000 species are known in the whole world.

ORDER 7. **ODONATA**. Dragonflies and damselflies. (*odous*, gen. *odontos*, a tooth)

Large insects with very elongate bodies, large eyes, and minute antennae. Mouthparts specialized and strongly toothed; cerci small, one-segmented. Two pairs of membranous, glassy wings each with a pterostigma and numerous cross veins, held erect or outspread at rest. Nymphs aquatic; labium modified into a retractible prehensile organ.

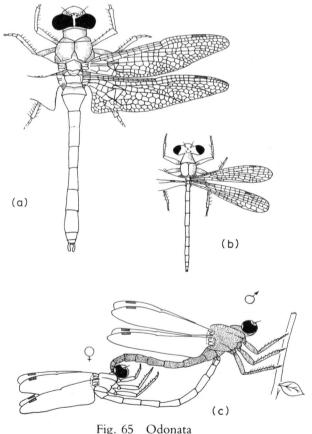

(a)

(b)

♂

♀

(c)

Fig. 65   Odonata
(a) An Anisopteran; (b) a Zygopteran; (c) mating posture of Odonata.

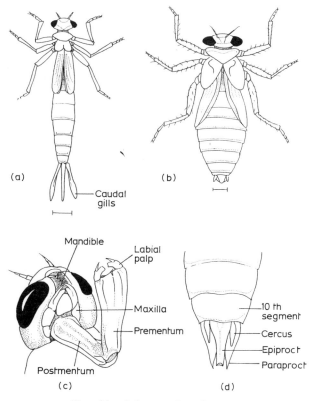

Fig. 66   Odonata, larval stages

(a) Zygopteran larva (*Ischnura*); (b) Anisopteran larva (*Synthemis*); (c) lateroventral view of Anisopteran larval mouthparts, showing modified labium; (d) terminal abdominal segments of *Anax* larva (Anisosptera). ((a) and (b) after O'Farrell, (c) after Weber, (d) after Snodgrass.) Scale lines = 2 mm.

All Odonata are predators and devour insects of various kinds which they seize while in flight with the legs, which bear a spiny armature for the purpose on the femora and tibiae. The prothorax is very small, but the meso- and metathorax have conspicuously enlarged pleura that slant steeply backward. This results in the terga and wings being pushed posteriorly, while the sterna become situated far forward (Fig. 65c). The legs, in consequence, lie close behind the mouth and are thus enabled readily to seize the prey; they are unfitted for locomotion and the tarsi are three-segmented. The venation shows no close affinity with that of other insects, and the wings, like those of mayflies, are incapable of being folded with the hind margin over the back. Each wing (Fig. 65a bears a pterostigma and vein Sc ends in a conspicuous nodus, or incision, near the middle of the costal margin. The division of the wing area into numerous quadrate cells by a multitude of cross-veins is also a

129

characteristic feature of considerable taxonomic importance. The abdomen is composed of ten segments with vestiges of an eleventh segment. The male genital armature is unique in being a secondary structure located on the ventral side of the second segment. The gonopore, however, lies on the ninth segment and semen is transferred to the penis before mating. During pairing the clasping organs at the apex of the abdomen of the male are used to seize the female by the head or prothorax; the female then curves her abdomen forwards so as to bring the genital opening into contact with the penis. The whole process occurs while the insects are in flight. There are usually marked colour differences between the sexes and the female often has a short three-valved ovipositor. Oviposition may be endophytic (i.e. the eggs are inserted into slits cut by the ovipositor in aquatic plants), or exophytic, when the eggs are dropped freely in the water or superficially attached to vegetation. The nymphs are aquatic and prey upon small Crustacea, insects, and other invertebrates. They are somewhat sluggish and more or less protectively coloured. Their most characteristic feature is the modification of the labium into a prehensile organ or 'mask' (Fig. 66c). This is hinged between the pre- and postmentum and can be stowed away between the legs; when a victim is seized the mask is suddenly extended with great rapidity and the prey impaled on the spine-like labial palps. Dragonflies are divided into two main suborders (Fig. 65): (1) the **Zygoptera**, which have very slender bodies, and two pairs of wings which are alike with narrow bases and are held vertically above the abdomen when at rest; and (2) the **Anisoptera**, which have stouter bodies, with the hind wings broader basally than the fore wings and the two pairs held horizontally in repose. The nymphs of the Zygoptera (Fig. 66a) are slender in form and the body ends in three elongate caudal gills. In the Anisoptera (Fig. 66b) the nymphs are more robust and caudal gills are absent, but there is an elaborate system of tracheal gills that project in longitudinal rows into the cavity of the hind gut. About 5000 species of dragonflies are known; of these, over 360 species occur in N. America and 40 species breed in Great Britain.

ORDER 8. **PLECOPTERA**. Stoneflies. (*plekein*, to fold; *pteron*, a wing)

Soft-bodied insects usually with long thread-like antennae and cerci; tarsi three-segmented. Wings membranous, hind pair with an enlarged, plicated anal lobe. Mouthparts for biting, ligula four-lobed. Nymphs aquatic with filamentous tufted gills.

This small order includes some 1700 species, of which 34 occur in Great Britain. They are Orthopteroid insects but are not closely related to any other living order. Tegmina are undeveloped and there is no

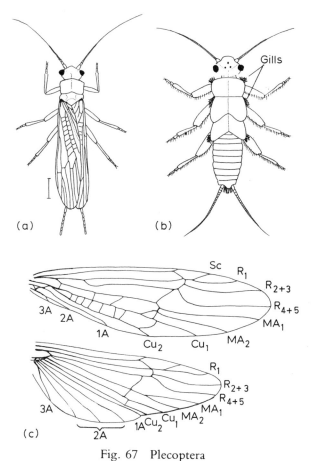

Fig. 67   Plecoptera

(a) *Isoperla* adult; (b) Perlid nymph; (c) wing venation of *Nemoura*. ((a) and (b) adapted from Frison.) Scale line = 2 mm.

ovipositor. Stoneflies are weak fliers seldom found far from the streams inhabited by their nymphs. They are carnivorous or herbivorous and breathe by filamentous gills which are usually disposed in tufts near the bases of the legs or cerci (Fig. 67), though in the family Eustheniidae of Australia and New Zealand, pairs of lateral gills are situated on the abdominal segments. Nymphal life is often long and in *Perla* and related genera it may last nearly 4 years; during that time more than 30 instars may be passed through.

ORDER 9. **GRYLLOBLATTODEA** (genus *Grylloblatta*)

Apterous, eyes reduced or absent, no ocelli. Antennae moderately long, many-segmented, filiform. Mouthparts for biting. Legs approximately similar to one

131

another, tarsi five-segmented. Cerci long, eight-segmented; female with a long ovipositor; male genitalia asymmetrical.

This small order includes eight species in three genera found principally in the Rocky Mountains, where *Grylloblatta campodeiformis* (Fig. 68) was discovered by Walker in 1914, but also in Japan and Russia. While showing some specializations, such as the reduced eyes and no wings, they appear to be the living remnants of a stock from which both the Orthoptera and Dictyoptera were derived and are therefore of great phylogenetic interest. *Grylloblatta* is omnivorous, nocturnal and takes about five years to complete its development.

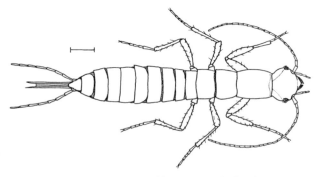

Fig. 68   *Grylloblatta campodeiformis*
(After Key.) Scale line = 2 mm.

ORDER 10. **ORTHOPTERA**. Locusts, grasshoppers, crickets, etc.
(*orthos*, straight; *pteron*, wing)

Fore wings modified into tegmina; mouthparts for biting; hind legs usually modified for jumping; tarsi almost always three- or four-segmented; female with well-developed ovipositor; cerci almost always unsegmented, usually short; specialized stridulatory and auditory apparatus often developed.

These insects are sometimes called Saltatoria because they are all more or less capable of jumping actively, using the powerful tibial levator muscles that are accommodated in the enlarged hind femora. They number about 20 000 species, mainly from tropical and subtropical regions, and fall into five superfamilies (Fig. 69). Of these the Gryllacridoidea, Tettigonioidea, Grylloidea and Acridoidea contain most of the species, while the Tridactyloidea is a small, somewhat aberrant group. The **Gryllacridoidea** have long antennae, four tarsal segments and a long ovipositor, but they are unusual in rarely having a stridulatory apparatus or tympanal organs. Many are wingless and they occur in a variety of habitats; some are arboreal, others soil-dwelling or cavernicolous, and they are mostly nocturnal insects, many being

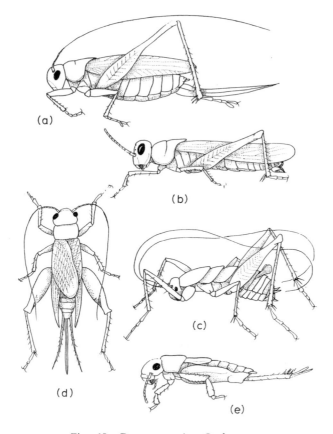

Fig. 69   Representative Orthoptera

(a) *Decticus verrucivorus* female (Tettigonioidea) (after Chopard); (b) *Oedipoda caerulescens* (Acridoidea) (after Chopard); (c) *Troglophilus* female (Gryllacridoidea) (after Seliskan); (d) *Acheta domesticus* female (Grylloidea); (e) *Tridactylus mutus* (Tridactyloidea) (after Tindale).

predatory or feeding on dead insects. They include the wetas and king-crickets of Australasia, the cave-crickets and the camel-crickets, and are not well represented in Europe, though *Tachycines asynamorus* now occurs there in greenhouses after being introduced from E. Asia. The **Tettigonioidea** (long-horned grasshoppers, katydids and bush-crickets) have long antennae, four-segmented tarsi, a complete, well-developed ovipositor, a stridulatory apparatus on the fore wings of males, and tympanal (auditory) organs in the fore tibiae. They are usually found among herbage, often on bushes and trees, and are predominantly green or brown in colour. Many are quite large insects: *Tettigonia viridissima* is a striking species and the parthenogenetic, predacious *Saga pedo* from Mediterranean coastal areas is one of

133

Europe's largest insects. Bush-crickets are generally active at dusk or at night, but some species sing in the daytime. They are mostly phytophagous and the eggs are laid singly in the soil or embedded in plant tissue, often in neat rows. The **Grylloidea** (crickets) have long antennae, three-segmented tarsi, stridulatory organs on the fore wings of the male, tympanal organs on the fore tibiae, and a long, needle-like ovipositor with reduced inner valves. Crickets are omnivorous, living in holes, burrows, under logs, among leaf-litter, in ants' nests or in trees, according to species. They include the domestic House Cricket *Acheta domesticus* (now often abundant on rubbish dumps) while an allied family, the Gryllotalpidae (mole-crickets), are remarkable for their subterranean habits and the highly specialized fossorial fore legs. The **Acridoidea** (short-horned grasshoppers and locusts) are a large group of phytophagous Orthoptera with short antennae, three-segmented tarsi and a short, stout ovipositor used for depositing the eggs in the soil (Fig. 143). The majority stridulate by rubbing a row of pegs on the inside of the hind femur against a ridge on the fore wing, but other stridulatory mechanisms are known and some species are silent. Tympanal organs may be present near the front of the abdomen. This superfamily includes the familiar grasshoppers of meadows and grasslands, as well as the highly destructive locusts whose biology is discussed on pp. 292–3. Allied to them are the grouse-locusts or groundhoppers (Tetrigidae) which resemble small grasshoppers but have a pronotum that extends backwards to cover most of the abdomen. The last superfamily, the **Tridactyloidea**, includes the pygmy mole-crickets, found burrowing in sandy ground near water, and the more highly subterranean Cylindrachetidae, which show a remarkable convergent resemblance to the mole-crickets (Gryllotalpidae).

ORDER 11. **PHASMIDA**. Stick-insects, leaf-insects. (*phasma,* an apparition)

Large, often apterous insects, frequently of elongate, cylindrical form, more rarely depressed and leaf-like. Mouthparts for biting. Prothorax short, legs similar to one another, tarsi nearly always five-segmented. Cerci short, unsegmented; ovipositor complete but concealed. (Fig. 70).

This order includes about 2500 predominantly tropical plant-feeding species. Most are sluggish and resemble in form and colour some part of the plant on which they feed. Males are often rare and the eggs, which are laid singly and usually fall to the ground, often develop parthenogenetically. None of them possesses a specialized stridulatory or auditory apparatus. There are two families. The Phylliidae are usually rather thick-set species, but also include leaf-like genera such as *Phyllium*. The Phasmatidae are usually more elongate and do not include

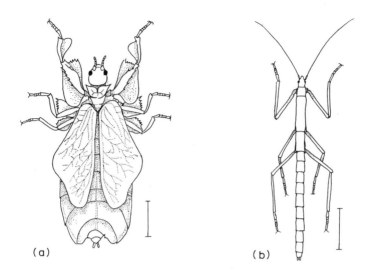

Fig. 70   Phasmida
(a) *Phyllium frondosum* (after Redtenbacher); (b) *Carausius morosus*. Scale lines = 2 cm.

leaf-mimics; *Carausius morosus* is widely used as a laboratory insect, feeding on privet.

ORDER 12. **DERMAPTERA**. Earwigs. (*derma*, skin; *pteron*, a wing)

Fore wings represented by small tegmina; hind wings large, membranous and complexly folded. Mouthparts for biting, ligula two-lobed; tarsi three-segmented; abdomen usually terminated by forceps. (Fig. 71).

This order numbers about 1200 species divided into three suborders. Of these the largest by far is the Forficulina, exemplified by *Forficula auricularia*, the common earwig of Europe which has become established in North America and New Zealand. It is omnivorous in habit and the female shows parental care for the eggs and young nymphs. The forceps are modified cerci and, in some forms, are present as many-jointed appendages during the immature stages. *Hemimerus* and *Arixenia* are aberrant genera, each usually placed in a suborder of its own. The former is a wingless ectoparasite of the rat *Cricetomys*; the latter, also wingless, lives in caves with bats; both are viviparous.

ORDER 13. **EMBIOPTERA**. Web-spinners. (genus, *Embia; pteron*, a wing)

Elongate soft-bodied insects living in silken web-like tunnels. Two pairs of equal-sized, long, smoky wings usually with signs of venational degeneration.

135

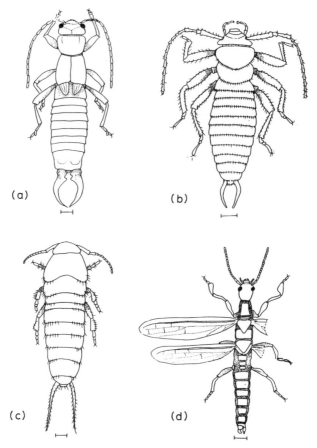

Fig. 71   Dermaptera and Embioptera
(a) *Forficula auricularia*, male (Forficulidae); (b) *Arixenia esau* (Arixeniidae) (after Jordan);
(c) *Hemimerus talpoides* (Hemimeridae); (d) *Notoligotoma nitens* (Embioptera; Oligo-
tomidae) (after Ross). Scale lines: (a) (c) and (d) = 1 cm, (b) = 2 mm.

*Mouthparts for biting, ligula four-lobed; tarsi three-segmented, 1st segment of
anterior pair greatly swollen; cerci two-segmented. Females apterous. (Fig. 71).*
    The members of this small order live in silken tunnels beneath stones
or loose bark of trees. They are gregarious and several individuals, along
with nymphs and eggs, inhabit one tunnel system. The silk is produced
by numerous glands lodged in the inflated first segment of the anterior
tarsi, the ducteole from each gland discharging ventrally at the apex of a
bristle. These glands are present in individuals of both sexes and of all
ages. Except in the primitive genus *Clothoda*, the tenth abdominal
segment and the cerci are modified asymmetrically in the male for
pairing. About 300 species are known and they occur throughout the
warmer regions of the world. One or two species only are found in

southern Europe and fewer than 20 inhabit the warmer parts of the USA. The Embioptera are rather an isolated order and a form not unlike *Clothoda* is known from the Lower Permian.

ORDER 14. **DICTYOPTERA**. Cockroaches, Mantids. (*dictyon*, a network; *pteron*, a wing)

Antennae nearly always filiform with many segments. Mouthparts for biting. Legs similar to each other or fore legs raptorial, tarsi with five segments. Fore wings more or less thickened into tegmina with marginal costal vein. Cerci many-segmented, ovipositor reduced and concealed, male genitalia asymmetrical; eggs contained in an ootheca. (Fig. 72).

Although often formerly put in one order with the Orthoptera, they are in many ways distinct, as indicated above. The cockroaches, forming the suborder Blattaria, include about 4000 species, predominantly tropical in distribution and typically nocturnal and omnivorous or vegetarian. The eggs are enclosed in an ootheca which is carried about by the female for a longer or shorter period. *Blatta, Periplaneta* and *Blattella* are three widely distributed domestic genera.

The suborder Mantodea includes about 2000 species which are exclusively carnivorous and are found in all the warmer parts of the world. They capture other insects by means of their front legs, which have rows of spines on the apposable femur and tibia (Fig. 5c). *Mantis religiosa*, the Praying Mantis of southern and central Europe, has been introduced into N. America.

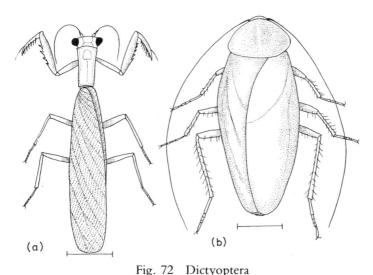

(a)   (b)

Fig. 72   Dictyoptera

(a) *Orthodera ministralis* (Mantodea) (after Key); (b) *Periplaneta americana* (Blattaria). Scale lines = 1 cm.

ORDER 15. **ISOPTERA**. Termites. (*isos,* equal; *pteron,* a wing)

Social insects living in large communities; soft-bodies and generally pale coloured. Mouthparts for biting, ligula four-lobed; cerci very short. Either with two pairs of elongated similar wings, which are soon shed, or without wings. Apterous forms with rudimentary eyes or none and mainly of two types, viz. soldiers with large heads and jaws or a pointed rostrum and workers with normal heads and jaws.

The members of this order are structurally very similar to the Blattaria. All termites are social and polymorphic and live as highly organized colonies in nests, or termitaria. The primitive species merely tunnel into wood, but others form special nests, often of great size, and composed of earth and wood mixed with faecal matter and saliva. Four chief castes, composed of individuals of both sexes, may occur in a species. These castes consist of functional reproductive forms of two kinds and sterile forms of two principal kinds. The usual reproductive caste is the fully-winged primary reproductive, or alate, form (Fig. 73). At suitable times individuals of this caste swarm from the nest, shed their wings and, after mating, found new colonies headed by the king and queen. Brachypterous and apterous forms may also occur and are, functionally, a supplementary reproductive caste replacing the primary reproductives should these die. In the more specialized termites only a single fertilized female is present in a colony. This individual, which may be derived from either of the two castes just named, undergoes remarkable post-metamorphic growth in some species where it may be as long as 10 cm. In the sterile castes the gonads are greatly reduced and non-functional in both sexes. Their members are divisible into workers and soldiers (Fig. 74). The workers are the most numerous individuals

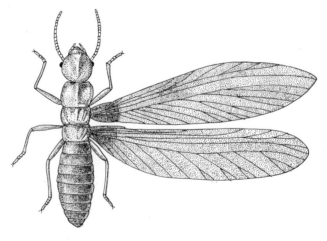

Fig. 73 *Kalotermes,* macropterous (alate) form (after Banks and Snyder)

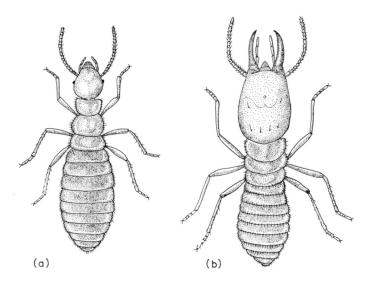

(a)   (b)

Fig. 74   *Prorhinotermes simplex*
(a) Worker; (b) soldier. (After Banks and Snyder.)

in a colony; they build the nest and keep it provisioned. Owing to their gnawing propensities they have earned for the termites their notoriety as destroyers of timber, woodwork and other materials. The soldiers act as defenders of the nest and usually have large sclerotized heads and jaws. In the specialized genus *Nasutitermes*, however, they are replaced by nasute forms with pyriform heads drawn out into a rostrum, and very small jaws. A frontal gland discharging a defensive secretion through a frontal pore is commonly present. This type of chemical warfare is specially developed in the nasute forms, which emit a pungent, sticky secretion through the rostrum. The lower termites feed on wood and harbour a rich Protozoan fauna in the hind intestine as discussed on p. 217. The higher termites feed on fungi, humus and organic matter from the soil and some species cultivate fungus gardens (p. 216). About 1900 species of Isoptera are known. The few European forms are found in southern parts of that continent; about 55 species occur in N. America, but most termites live in the tropics.

ORDER 16. **ZORAPTERA** (*zoros*, pure; *apteros*, wingless)

Minute winged or apterous insects. Mouthparts for biting. Thorax with the segments of nearly equal size, tarsi with two segments. Short segmented cerci present, ovipositor absent.

The first species of this group were recognized by Silvestri in 1913 and there are now 22 species, all placed in the genus *Zorotypus* and found in all the warmer regions of the world. They live gregariously under bark or in humus. They were formerly classified as Psocids but the structure of the head and thorax suggest Orthopteroid affinities.

ORDER 17. **PSOCOPTERA**. Booklice, psocids. (genus *Psocus; pteron,* a wing)

Very small soft-bodied winged or apterous insects with modified biting mouthparts. Venation reduced and seldom with cross-veins; fore wings with pterostigma; tarsi two- or three-segmented; cerci absent. (Fig. 75).

The small insects of this order are worldwide in distribution and nearly 2000 species are known. They have long multiarticulate filiform antennae, and an enlarged postclypeus; the maxillae are single-lobed, each ensheathing an elongate rod or 'pick' (representing the lacinia), and

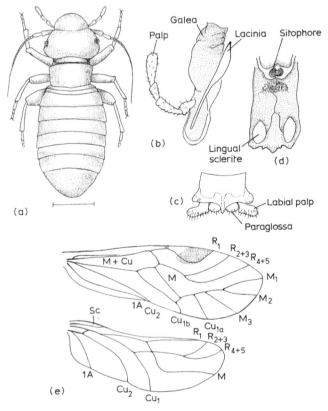

Fig. 75   Psocoptera

(a) *Liposcelis* (after Smithers); (b)–(d) maxilla, labium and hypopharynx of *Stenopscocus stigmaticus* (after Badonnel); (e) wing venation of *Amphigerontia*. Scale line = 0.2 mm.

there are no cerci. These insects are known as booklice, since several kinds often occur among books and papers in little-used rooms; others are found among stores of cereal products, straw or chaff, but more usual habitats are among vegetation or on the bark of trees, among lichens or on old palings. They are more or less gregarious and lay their eggs in groups covered with silken threads. The rod-like 'pick' is possibly used for rasping off fragments of bark or other plant tissues. Despite their delicate structure, fossil Psocoptera are known from as early as the Permian and they probably represent a generalized Hemipteroid stock.

ORDER 18. **PHTHIRAPTERA**. Biting and sucking lice. (*phtheir*, louse; *aptera*, without wings)

Small wingless insects ectoparasitic on birds or mammals; antennae short, three- to five-segmented; eyes vestigial or absent; mouthparts for biting or highly modified for piercing and sucking blood; tarsi one- or two-segmented, with one or two pretarsal claws; abdomen with eight to ten recognizable segments; cerci absent; external genitalia reduced. (Fig. 76).

These insects are highly adapted for an ectoparasitic life on warm-blooded vertebrates, living in all stages among the fur or feathers of the host and feeding on keratinous epidermal products or, in the more specialized sucking lice, on the blood of their host. The more generalized members of the order, sometimes grouped together to form

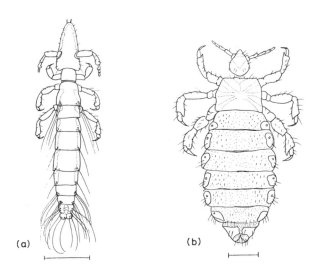

(a)   (b)

Fig. 76   Phthiraptera
(a) Pigeon louse, *Columbicola columbae*; (b) human body louse, *Pediculus humanus*. (After Séguy.) Scale lines = 0.5 mm.

the Mallophaga, have reduced biting mouthparts and are predominantly found on birds, though some, such as the family Trichodectidae, are ectoparasites of mammals. A second major group of Phthiraptera includes only two species of the aberrant blood-sucking genus *Haematomyzus*, found on elephants and warthogs. A third group consists of the specialized Siphunculata (= Anoplura); these are sucking lice, whose very highly modified, styliform mouthparts, concealed in a ventrally placed pouch (Fig. 154), enable them to pierce the skin of their mammalian hosts and feed on blood. *Pediculus humanus* is the human Head and Body Louse and species of *Linognathus* infest cattle and other ungulates. For further information on the Phthiraptera and their medical importance, see pp. 227 and 314.

ORDER 19. **HEMIPTERA**. Plant-bugs, cicadas, leafhoppers, aphids, scale-insects. (*hemi*, half; *pteron*, a wing)

Wings very variably developed with reduced or greatly reduced venation; fore pair often more or less corneous; apterous forms frequent. Mouthparts for piercing and sucking with mandibles and maxillae stylet-like and lying in the projecting grooved labium; palps never evident. A quiescent pupa-like instar sometimes present.

This order includes more than 56 000 species and is the largest and most diverse among the Exopterygote insects. Its members are best recognized by the mouthparts, which are very constant in their essential structure. The wings present no common venational or other features and are often reduced or absent. The mouthparts are adapted for piercing and sucking up plant or animal juices. The labium or rostrum projects downward from the head and forms an anteriorly grooved channel within which lie two pairs of needle-like stylets. At the base of the labium the groove is absent and the stylets are roofed over in this region by the labrum. The mandibles form the outer (or anterior) pair of stylets and the maxillae are lodged between them. The maxillary stylets interlock so as to enclose an anterior or food canal and a posterior or salivary canal (Fig. 77). Just before the maxillae diverge in the head the food canal opens into the cibarium. The common salivary duct opens into a salivary pump which discharges the salivary secretion at the apex of the hypopharynx into the salivary canal. The mandibles are the chief piercing organs and the maxillae are afterwards inserted into the puncture. Ordinarily, the stylets are forced into the tissues by their protractor muscles, being guided by the labrum and the grooved labium. As they gradually penetrate, bringing the head nearer to the leaf surface, the labium becomes shortened by being bent or looped. In the scale-insects and white-flies the stylets may exceed the length of the whole insect and, when retracted, are coiled within an internal pouch, or

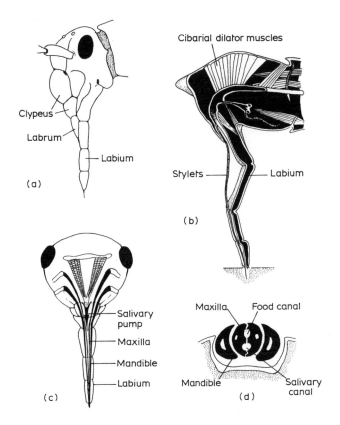

Fig. 77   Mouthparts of Hemiptera

(a),(c) Lateral and frontal view of Hemipteran head and mouthparts (schematic, after Weber); (b) longitudinal section of head and mouthparts of *Graphosoma* (Pentatomidae) (after Weber); (d) schematic transverse section through stylet bundle, showing food and salivary channels.

crumena. The four stylets are interlocked to function as a single structure; they are inserted into the plant partly by the action of the protractor muscles and partly by means of a muscular clamp, near the apex of the labium, which alternately grips and releases the stylets after the manner of forceps. Plant-feeding Hemiptera suck sap into the gut by the action of a muscular cibarial pump; it then enters the pharynx and passes into the mid intestine. By virtue of their universal sucking propensities many Hemiptera cause a vast amount of direct or indirect injury to cultivated plants. Certain aphids and leafhoppers also convey highly destructive virus diseases from plant to plant during feeding. Especially noteworthy are diseases of potatoes, tobacco, maize and sugar-cane that are transmitted in this manner, some discussed in greater detail on pp. 294–7.

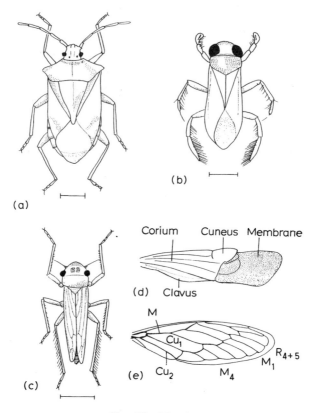

Fig. 78   Hemiptera

(a) *Pentatoma rufipes* (Heteroptera: Pentatomidae); (b) *Corixa punctata* (Heteroptera: Corixidae); (c) *Cicadella viridis* (Homoptera: Cicadellidae); (d) fore wing of *Leptoterna dolobrata* (Heteroptera: Miridae); (e) fore wing of a Cicada (Homoptera: Cicadidae) (after Berlese). Scale lines = 3 mm.

Hemiptera are divided into two main groups that are often regarded as separate orders, the Heteroptera and Homoptera. The **Heteroptera** or plant bugs have the fore wings usually modified into hemelytra (Fig. 78d) which, while at rest, overlap flat on the abdomen; also, the base of the labium is separated from the anterior coxae by a sclerotized area of the head wall. Most members of this suborder are plant feeders and among them are a number of injurious species including the Chinch-bug (*Blissus leucopterus*) of the USA, the Cotton Stainers (*Dysdercus*) of the tropics and the Apple Capsid (*Plesiocoris rugicollis*) of Europe. A propensity for animal food is found in some others, such as the predacious family Reduviidae and most aquatic bugs, which imbibe the body fluids of insects and other small animals. Bed-bugs (*Cimex*) and the Reduviid *Triatoma* consist of blood-suckers of man (Fig. 155). A number of

144

Heteroptera are aquatic in habit and include the Water Boatmen (Corixidae) (Fig 78b), Water Scorpions (Nepidae) (Fig. 114b), and the Giant Water-bugs (Belostomatidae).

The **Homoptera** are all terrestrial, phytophagous species and have the fore wings either leathery or membranous but of uniform consistency, folded roof-like along the sides of the body. The labium arises far back on the head or even between the fore coxae. Many Homoptera show three characteristic features in their economy: the abundant discharge of a sugary waste product or 'honey dew' from the anus, especially notable in aphids; the prevalent excretion of wax either in a powdery form or as threads; and the presence in the abdomen of a peculiar organ – the mycetome – which harbours micro-organisms supposedly symbiotic in function (cf. p. 218). Among the different families of Homoptera the Cicadas (Cicadidae) are well-known for the shrill sounds emitted by the males, and the Lantern-flies (Fulgoridae) are large tropical insects usually of brilliant coloration. The Froghoppers (Cercopidae) are small insects whose nymphs live within a frothy exudation which is believed to prevent desiccation and afford protection from enemies. The abdominal spiracles of Cercopids open into a ventral cavity formed by the downgrowth of the tergites and pleurites which meet beneath the sterna. This cavity is closed anteriorly, but air enters posteriorly through a kind of valve. The froth results from the fluid, exuded from the anus, forming a film over this valve and becoming blown into bubbles by air expelled through the latter. The Cicadellidae are leafhoppers and the Delphacidae are the planthoppers. Both families are entirely phytophagous, embedding their eggs in the tissues of their host-plant; they include some species injurious to cultivated plants (see p. 295).

A major section of the Homoptera – the so-called Sternorrhyncha – includes four distinctive groups, the Psylloidea (jumping plant-lice), the Aphidoidea (aphids), the Coccoidea (scale insects) and the Aleyrodoidea (whiteflies). The **Psylloidea** are represented by only one family, the Psyllidae, whose members are small, actively jumping insects resembling miniature cicadas, with less active, flattened larvae. The **Aphidoidea** (Fig. 79) are a large group, including many destructive species (p. 294). They all pass through a more or less complex life-cycle on one or more plant hosts and are commonly termed 'green-fly', 'black-fly' or plant-lice. The Aphididae comprise the greater number of the species; they bear a pair of short dorsal tubes or cornicles on the abdomen, through which an alarm pheromone can be exuded. In this family the parthenogenetic generations are viviparous. Winter is usually spent in the egg, which is commonly laid on a woody plant termed the primary host. In the spring an apterous agamic female (fundatrix) hatches out which produces very similar offspring (fundatrigeniae), but

145

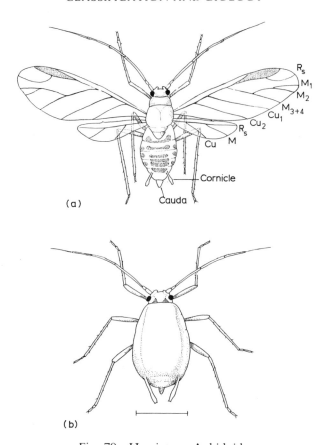

Fig. 79   Hemiptera: Aphidoidea

(a) *Myzus persicae*, alate form; (b) *Myzus persicae*, apterous form. (after Edwards and Heath.) Scale line = 1 mm.

soon winged agamic females (migrantes) develop and these fly to some herbaceous plant or secondary host. All through the summer new generations of winged or wingless agamic females (alienicolae) are produced on the secondary host, the winged forms relieving over-crowding by flying to other plants. In early autumn winged alienicolae known as sexuparae fly back to the primary host and produce males and females (sexuales). After mating, eggs are laid and the cycle is thus com-pleted (Fig. 145). Members of the family Phylloxeridae undergo a more complex life-cycle and differ from the Aphididae in that the cornicles are absent and reproduction is never viviparous. The Adelgidae affect Coniferae (Fig. 105e and f). Their sexual generation always occurs on spruce (*Picea*) and the agamic forms on *Larix, Pinus, Abies,* etc. The **Coccoidea** (Fig. 80) include several families of scale-insects and mealy-bugs. They rank among the most highly modified of all insects and are

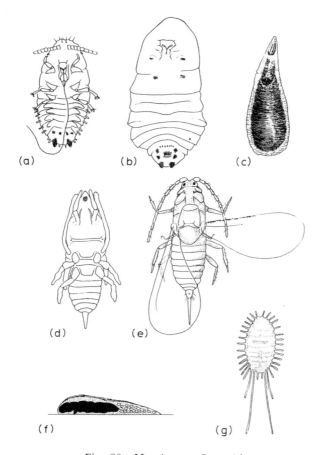

Fig. 80   Hemiptera: Coccoidea

(a)–(e) *Mytilaspis fulva* (Diaspididae): (a) first instar; (b) adult female removed from scale; (c) scale of female, dorsal view; (d) male pupa; (e) adult male. (f) *Lepidosaphes*, schematic longitudinal section of female with eggs beneath scale (after Weber). (g) *Pseudococcus adonidum*, waxy covering of female, dorsal view.

notable for their extreme sexual dimorphism. In the mealy-bugs the insect is covered with a fine waxy exudation, while in the true scale-insects the 'scale' is a covering formed by the persistent exuviae of the previous instars glued together with a dermal secretion. Many coccids are well-known injurious insects, and some of the more important are referred to on p. 297. On the other hand, *Dactylopius coccus* yields cochineal, and *Laccifer lacca* of India produces a resinous exudation or lac providing commercial shellac. In the early instars the two sexes of coccids are very similar and the young insects are active, with well-developed antennae, legs and mouthparts (Fig. 80a). Those producing females pass through one or two instars fewer than the males. In the more primitive types, or mealy-bugs, including *Monophlebus, Pseudo-coccus,* etc., the females continue active, but in most forms they become sedentary after the first or second instar and the appendages undergo various degrees of reduction (Fig. 80b). Culmination is reached in *Physokermes* and other genera where the antennae and legs have totally atrophied. In the males the third or fourth instar is a prepupa and the succeeding instar is a pupa; during these phases the original appendages disappear and the imaginal organs that replace them are external growths. In the male imago only the fore wings are present, the hind pair being represented by slender halteres that are linked to the wing-bases by hooklets (Fig. 80e); mouthparts are absent. Finally, the **Aleyrodoidea** include a single family, the Aleyrodidae or whiteflies, whose members are minute, midge-like insects with wings covered by a powdery wax that gives them a white appearance. The mature larvae are flattened, sedentary forms, often decorated with wax filaments, which form a kind of pupa-like phase during which transformation to the adult occurs. *Aleyrodes proletella* is a pest of brassicas and *Trialeurodes vaporariorum* is the Greenhouse Whitefly that damages tomatoes and cucumbers under glass.

ORDER 20. **THYSANOPTERA**. Thrips. (*thusanos,* a fringe; *pteron,* a wing)

Minute slender insects with short six- to ten-segmented antennae and very narrow wings with long hair fringes. Mouthparts stylet-like, for rasping. Tarsi very short, ending in a vesicle; cerci absent; one or more pupal stages present. (Fig. 81).

Thysanoptera frequent many kinds of plants besides being found in decaying wood, fungi and the soil. About 5000 species are known and they occur all over the world. While rarely exceeding 4 mm long, these insects are very abundant as individuals (cf. p. 250). Most species are sap-feeders, and some are enemies of cereals and other cultivated crops such as peas and fruit trees; their attacks on the flowers often lead to sterility or to the fall of the fruit. The head bears a ventral rostrum that is formed by the labrum above, the labium below and laterally by the stipital plates of the maxillae. It thus encloses the mandible, the two maxillary stylets and the hypopharynx. The mandible, which is a stout stylet, is the left one, its counterpart being vestigial. Each maxilla consists of a palp-bearing plate, together with a slender pointed stylet articulating with it. During feeding the rostrum is closely applied to a leaf; the tissues are lacerated and broken up by the three stylets named, and then sucked up through the rostrum by the pumping action of the cibarial sucking pump. During development four instars commonly occur, the third and fourth instars being the prepupa and pupa

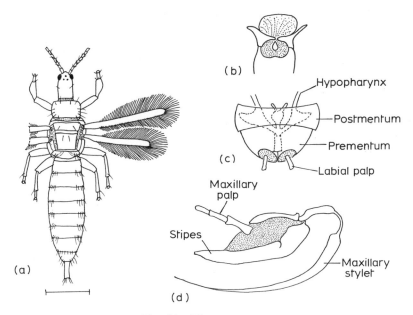

Fig. 81   Thysanoptera

(a) *Liothrips oleae* (after Melis); (b) pretarsus of *Trichothrips* (after Uzel); (c),(d) labium and maxilla of *Limothrips cerealium* (after Jones). Scale line = 0.5 mm.

respectively. Both these instars are resting stages in which no food is taken, and they commonly occur in the soil. External buds of the wings and appendages are evident, and these instars are comparable with the pupal stage of the higher insects. While Thysanoptera form an isolated order, they are clearly members of the Hemipteroid group, probably closest to the Hemiptera.

III. Endopterygote insects. *Winged or secondarily apterous insects; metamorphosis complete (holometabolous); larvae usually differing greatly from adult in form and habits, with simple ocelliform eyes and internally developing wings and external genitalia; a pupal instar almost always present.*

ORDER 21. **NEUROPTERA**. Alder-flies, lacewings, etc. (*neuron*, a nerve; *pteron*, a wing)

Small to large soft-bodied holometabolous insects with two pairs of membranous wings without anal lobes; venation generally with many accessory branches and numerous costal veinlets; Rs often pectinately branched. Mouthparts for biting, antennae well-developed, cerci absent. Larvae campodeiform with biting or suctorial mouthparts; predacious and aquatic or terrestrial; pupa decticous, exarate.

149

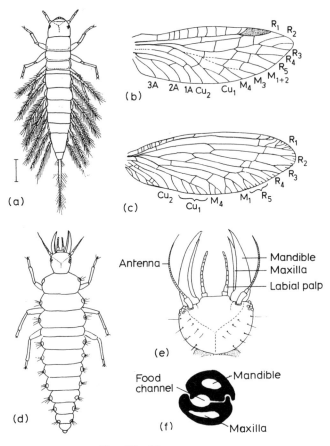

Fig. 82   Neuroptera

(a) Larva of *Sialis*; (b) wing venation of *Sialis* (after Needham); (c) fore wing of *Sisyra* (Plannipennia: Sisyridae) (after Comstock); (d) larva of *Chrysopa* (Plannipennia: Chrysopidae); (e) head and mouthparts of *Chrysopa* larva (after Withycombe); (f) transverse section through interlocking mandible and maxilla of *Chrysopa* larva, showing food channel. Scale lines = 2.5 mm.

This rather heterogeneous order (Fig. 82) may be divided into the suborders Megaloptera and Planipennia. The **Megaloptera** have the more primitive venation with fewer accessory veins and the pectination of Rs is usually undeveloped; their larvae have biting mouthparts. The alder-flies (*Sialis*) and their allies have aquatic larvae with seven or eight pairs of hair-fringed abdominal appendages. *Corydalis*, which occurs in North and South America, attains a wing expanse of 15 cm with gigantic mandibles in the male. The Snake-flies (*Raphidia* and similar genera) have a long neck-like prothorax and an elongate ovipositor; their larvae live under bark, especially of conifers.

The **Planipennia** include the majority of Neuroptera. The venation usually shows a pectinate Rs and a great development of secondary branching, especially as bifurcations along the wing margins. The larvae occur on vegetation, in the earth, or are aquatic. All have exserted, piercing mouthparts of similar basic design. The mandibles and maxillae (Fig. 82e) form long, pointed jaws and are closely co-ordinated to enclose a groove-like suction canal through which the body fluids of the prey are imbibed; six out of the eight Malpighian tubes become silk glands and the larvae spin their cocoons through an anal spinneret. As in the Megaloptera, the pupae are primitive and decticous and the pharate adult is capable of walking or climbing before emergence. Of the main families the Hemerobiidae (brown lacewings) and Chrysopidae (green lacewings) are notably beneficial since their larvae destroy large numbers of aphids and other small insects. The Sisyridae and Osmylidae have aquatic larvae, those of the former living in association with freshwater sponges, whose tissues they pierce with their mouthparts. The Nemopteridae have very long filiform hind wings and larvae with very long necks, sometimes exceeding the whole of the rest of their bodies. The Myrmeleontidae are large insects with subfiliform antennae; their larvae, or ant-lions, commonly make conical pitfall traps in the soil for capturing their prey (Fig. 113a and b). The Ascalaphidae are closely related, but the antennae are longer and clubbed; their larvae lurk under stones, on leaves or on trees. The Mantispidae are predators and resemble the Mantids in the formation of their raptorial legs; the life-cycle involves hypermetamorphosis and the larvae become external parasites of spiders' eggs or of wasps. The Coniopterygidae seldom exceed 8 mm in wing expanse and have greatly simplified venation, but their larvae are Planipennian in structure. They occur on trees and shrubs, the larvae preying upon minute insects and other Arthropods; the adults are covered with a powdery exudation from epidermal glands and resemble whiteflies. About 4000 species of Neuroptera are known, and of these 60 occur in Great Britain.

ORDER 22. **COLEOPTERA**. Beetles. (*koleos*, a sheath; *pteron*, a wing)

Minute to large holometabolous insects whose fore wings are modified into elytra that meet in a line down the back; hind wings membranous, folded beneath the elytra or absent; prothorax large; mouthparts for biting. Larvae of diverse types but never typical polypod; pupae adecticous, usually exarate.

The Coleoptera, with over 370 000 described species, ranks as the largest order in the animal kingdom. Their habits are very varied but many are ground insects that live either in the soil, or in decaying matter

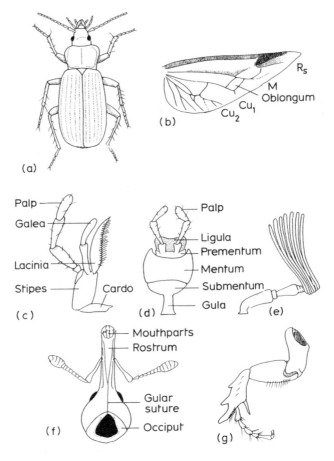

Fig. 83   Coleoptera

(a) Carabid beetle (schematic); (b) hind wing of Carabid; (c), (d) maxilla and labium of Carabid; (e) lamellate antenna of a Scarabaeid; (f) ventral view of head of *Pissodes* (Curculionidae) (based on Hopkins); (g) fore leg of a Scarabaeid (*Colpochila*) (after Britton).

associated with it. Several families are aquatic and great numbers of species are phytophagous both as larvae and adults. In addition, various species live in timber and dry, stored products. Beetles are relatively uniform in external structure. The head (Fig. 83) is characterized by the common presence of a gula (p. 15) and the legs are well adapted for running or often also for burrowing. The hind wings are the effective organs of flight and when the insect is in the air the elytra play no active part in propulsion and are held upwards at an angle with the body. The wings are often long and may be intricately folded beneath the elytra; sometimes they are much reduced or wanting and, in such cases, the elytra are often fused together. In the Staphylinidae and related families the elytra are much shortened, while in the oil beetles (*Meloe*) they are vestigial. The wing venation is often degenerate and difficult to homologize with that of other insects; there is a predominance of longitudinal veins and, except in Adephaga, cross-veins are either absent or very few.

Coleopteran larvae (Fig. 84) afford excellent examples of adaptation to particular modes of life. Thus, in the Adephaga and the Staphylinidae the larva is usually campodeiform with the antennae, legs and sense organs well developed, thereby fitting it for an active predatory life. Elongate simple or jointed processes resembling cerci and known as urogomphi are borne on the ninth abdominal segment; the tenth segment usually functions as a pseudopod. Less active larvae, which have no need to search far for food, are characteristic of a large number

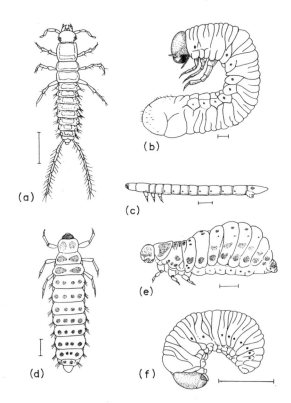

Fig. 84   Coleoptera: larval forms

(a) *Loricera* (Carabidae) (Based on Schiödte); (b) *Melolontha* (Scarabaeidae) (after Eidmann); (c) *Agriotes* (Elateridae); (d) Coccinellidae (after Eidmann); (e) Colorado Potato Beetle *Leptinotarsa decemlineata* (Chrysomelidae) (after Diehl); (f) *Tomicus piniperda* (Scolytidae) (after Eidmann). Scale lines = 2 mm.

of families. They are a modified campodeiform type with the appendages and sense organs reduced. Examples are larvae of the Coccinellidae (ladybirds), Elateridae (wireworms) and Chrysomelidae (leaf-beetles). The scarabaeoid type of larvae is subterranean in habit and occurs in cockchafers, dorbeetles and their allies. Crescentic in form, it has a large sclerotized head, well-developed legs, a soft, inflated abdomen and conspicuous cribriform spiracles. Among wood-boring larvae (e.g. Cerambycidae) the body is usually fleshy and unpigmented with stout jaws and a small sclerotized head partly withdrawn into the broadly transverse thorax. Legs are greatly reduced and sometimes atrophied. An extreme type of larval modification is found in weevils (Curculionidae) which live among immediately available food. Usually crescentic in form and entirely apodous, these larvae are mostly eyeless, with the antennae reduced to small papillae and there are no urogomphi.

Coleoptera are divided into four suborders, the Adephaga, the Polyphaga, and two small groups, the Archostemata and the Myxophaga. The **Adephaga** usually have filiform antennae and the hind coxal cavities are so large that they completely divide the first apparent abdominal sternum; the hind wing usually has a short rectangular cell, the oblongum. The larvae (Fig. 84a) are campodeiform with distinct tarsi and usually paired claws. Included in this suborder is the single superfamily Caraboidea, whose members are mainly predators both as adults and larvae. Most of the terrestrial forms belong to the large family Carabidae (ground beetles), including the Cicindelinae (tiger beetles). Many aquatic Caraboids are included in the Dytiscidae (diving beetles) while the Gyrinidae (whirligig beetles) are much modified for skimming on the surface of water. The **Archostemata** include the archaic Cupedidae, with wood-boring larvae, and the **Myxophaga** consist of the minute, aquatic Sphaeriidae and allied families. The **Polyphaga**, however, are an enormous group, including the greater part of the order. The antennae are varied in character: often clubbed, lamellate, or geniculate. The hind coxal cavities do not completely divide the first apparent abdominal sternite and the hind wings lack an oblongum and have few cross-veins. The larvae are of very varied types but all have a combined tibiotarsus with a single claw. The Hydrophiloidea, with one main family, are mostly aquatic; the maxillary palps are lengthened and partly replace in function the antennae which handle bubbles of air for respiration. The Staphylinoidea includes the Staphylinidae (rove beetles) and the Silphidae (carrion beetles) which have the elytra more or less shortened and the abdomen exposed. The superfamily Scarabaeoidea is an easily recognized group since its members have fossorial fore legs (Fig. 83g) and a lamellate antennal club of plate-like components (Fig. 83e); their larvae are scarabaeiform (Fig. 84b). Included here are the

Lucanidae or stag beetles and the Scarabaeidae or chafers and dung beetles. The Buprestoidea includes one family of metallic, often green or blue, insects; their larvae are legless borers living beneath the bark of trees and notable for their greatly widened prothorax. In the somewhat similar Elateroidea, the largest family is the Elateridae which include many of the tropical 'fire-flies' and the more numerous click beetles whose larvae or 'wire-worms' (Fig. 84c) are destructive root-feeders of crops. The Dermestoidea includes the family Dermestidae (larder beetles) with densely hairy larvae which often damage wool and other dry animal materials. The very large group, the Cucujoidea, includes a clavicorn series of families, many of which have a marked antennal club. Typical of these are the Coccinellidae (ladybirds) that are mostly beneficial since their larvae (Fig. 84d) and adults prey largely upon aphids. The heteromerous series of families includes a great variety of forms whose main common feature is that the hind tarsi have four segments while the others have five. Some of the most important families are the Tenebrionidae, which includes the mealworms (*Tenebrio*) and flour beetles (*Tribolium*), and the Meloidae. To the last-named family belong the blister beetles, whose blood usually contains a blistering agent termed cantharidin. A commercial product was formerly prepared from the dried elytra of the 'Spanish Fly', *Lytta vesicatoria*. *Meloe* and its allies undergo hypermetamorphosis (p. 113) and their larvae are parasitic in the nests of solitary bees or the egg-masses of grasshoppers; the adults are known as oil beetles. The extensive superfamily Chrysomeloidea is characterized by the third tarsal segment being bilobed or dorsally grooved and receiving the minute fourth segment at its base. The largest family is the Chryso-melidae (leaf beetles) with nearly 30 000 species. Some, such as the Asparagus Beetle (*Crioceris asparagi*), the Flea Beetles (*Phyllotreta*, etc.) and the Colorado Potato Beetle (*Leptinotarsa decemlineata*), are destructive to crops (see pp. 297–301). The Cerambycidae or 'longicorns' comprise most of the other Chrysomeloids; they are forest insects whose larvae tunnel into the wood of trees. In the superfamily Curculionoidea or weevils the head is usually produced into a well-marked rostrum (Fig. 83f) and the tarsi are apparently four-segmented. Their most important family is the Curculionidae with about 35 000 known species. The rostrum enables the female to bore holes in the medium in which the eggs are deposited. Included here are many injurious kinds such as the Grain Weevils (*Sitophilus*), the Cotton Boll Weevil (*Anthonomus grandis*), the Pine Weevil (*Hylobius abietis*) and others (cf. pp. 305–12). The closely related Scolytidae or bark beetles have a very short broad rostrum and include many species which rank as major forest pests (pp. 306–7).

ORDER 23. **STREPSIPTERA**. Stylops. (*strepsis*, a twisting; *pteron*, a wing)

Minute, sexually dimorphic, holometabolous insects. Males with branched antennae and degenerate biting mouthparts; fore wings modified into small club-like processes; hind wings very large, plicately folded. Females almost always degenerate parasites within the bodies of other insects. Larvae endoparasitic after first instar. (Fig. 85).

In their larval stages Strepsiptera are endoparasites mainly of certain aculeate Hymenoptera and Hemiptera-Homoptera. The first instar larvae are active creatures termed triungulins; on meeting a host they bore into it and undergo hypermetamorphosis (p. 113). The females almost always remain permanently endoparasitic, with the fused head and thorax protruding between adjacent abdominal segments of the hosts. In only a very few cases are the females active and free-living. The males are short-lived and they fly on to the host to mate with the females. Parasitized hosts are said to be 'stylopized', the term being derived from the generic name *Stylops*. Bees of the genus *Andrena* are often affected and the parasitization tends to cause the hosts concerned to acquire altered sexual and other characters. The affinities of the Strepsiptera are obscure. Similarities in the structure of the male and the larva suggests a relationship with the Coleoptera and the group has even been regarded as merely a superfamily of beetles. The resemblance in habits to the Meloidae and their allies is probably due to convergence.

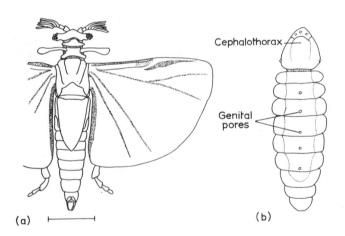

Fig. 85   Strepsiptera

(a) *Halictophagus* male (after Riek); (b) *Stylops* female, ventral view after extraction from host (after Nassonov). Scale line = 1 mm.

ORDER 24. **MECOPTERA**. Scorpion-flies. (*mekos*, length; *pteron*, a wing)

Soft-bodied holometabolous insects with two pairs of elongate similar wings; venation primitive, costal veinlets few; head prolonged into a beak; mouthparts for biting; short cerci present. Larvae oligopod or polypod; pupae decticous, exarate, in earthen cells. (Fig. 86).

A small order of about 400 species but with a world-wide range and a fossil history extending back to the Permian. Its members are usually recognizable by the beak-like head, maculated wings and the prominent external genitalia of the male. They are separable from Neuroptera by the small number of costal veinlets, the dichotomously branched Rs and by the undivided Cu_1. The habit of the males carrying the end of the abdomen upturned has given the name of scorpion-flies to species of *Panorpa* and their allies. The imagines prefer shaded places and both they and the larvae are mainly carnivorous. The larvae live in leaf-litter or superficial soil layers; those of *Panorpa* bear three pairs of thoracic legs and eights pairs of abdominal prolegs, while in *Boreus* only thoracic legs are present. There are only four British species which belong to *Panorpa* and *Boreus*. The last named, an isolated genus, has vestigial wings and its larva is exceptional in feeding upon mosses. Six genera and about 50 species occur in North America. Numerous fossilized wings from Permian rocks are referred to the Mecoptera, and the order is claimed to be closely related to forms that are ancestral to most of the Endopterygota.

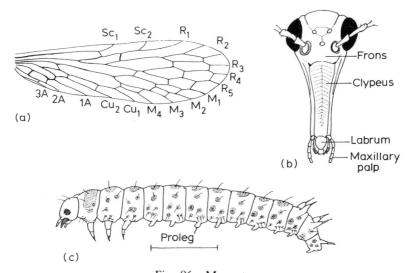

Fig. 86   Mecoptera

(a) Fore wing of *Panorpa* (after Comstock); (b) head of *Panorpa*, anterior view (after Eidmann); (c) larva of *Panorpa* (based on Miyake). Scale line = 5 mm.

157

ORDER 25. **SIPHONAPTERA**. Fleas. (*siphon*, a tube; *apteros*, wingless)

Very small, apterous, laterally compressed holometabolous insects whose adults are ectoparasites of warm-blooded animals; mouthparts for piercing and sucking. Larvae vermiform, free-living; pupae adecticous, exarate in silken cocoons.

The Siphonaptera are readily separated from other apterous parasitic insects as they are flattened laterally, and not dorsoventrally. Ocelli are present or absent and the antennae are short, three-segmented organs reposing in grooves. The mouthparts (Fig. 88) are for piercing and have some features resembling those of the lower blood-sucking Diptera. The stylet–like laciniae are finely denticulate and are the actual piercing organs. They are closely apposed to the long, slender epipharynx to form the food channel. Ventrally the edge of each lacinia is grooved and the apposition of the two grooves forms a salivary canal which receives a small process of the hypopharynx bearing the end of the salivary duct.

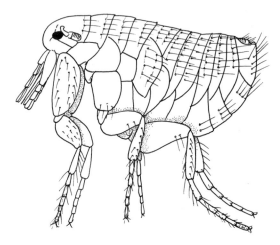

Fig. 87   Siphonaptera: *Xenopsylla cheopis*
After Waterston. Reproduced by permission of the Trustees of the British Museum (Natural History).

The stipites are short, triangular blades and the palps are four-segmented. The labium is a small basal plate bearing elongated palps composed of a variable number of segments; their concave inner surfaces enable them to ensheath the laciniae. Fleas are covered with a tough cuticle and the legs, with five-segmented tarsi and two claws, are adapted for clinging and leaping. The maximum vertical jump of the human flea (*Pulex irritans*) is stated to be about 19 cm. All fleas are blood-sucking ectoparasites of birds or mammals and rarely exceed 4 mm in length. Usually each species has its particular host or range of

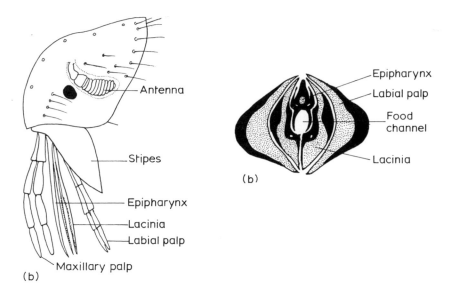

Fig. 88 Siphonaptera
(a) Head of a flea, showing mouthparts; (b) transverse section of mouthparts in feeding position (after Wenk).

hosts, but many can live at least temporarily on some unusual host. Thus the rat-flea, *Xenopsylla cheopis* (Fig. 87), frequently migrates to man and is the most potent vector in the transmission of bubonic plague which affects both rodents and man (see p. 325). The eggs of fleas are normally found in the haunts or sleeping places of the hosts. The larvae are whitish and vermiform, with a well-developed head bearing biting mouthparts and 13 trunk segments; they feed on particles of organic matter found in the hosts' lair or, in the case of the human flea, upon such matter among the dust and dirt of floors. The pupae are exarate and are enclosed in silken cocoons. About 1400 species of fleas are known.

The order is an isolated one, but it shows some affinity with Diptera. This is borne out in (a) the nature of the mouthparts; (b) the number of Malpighian tubes being four, as in most Diptera; and (c) the larvae resembling those of Nematocera. However, the structure of the spermatozoa suggests a close evolutionary relationship with the Mecoptera.

ORDER 26. **DIPTERA**. Flies. (*dis*, two; *pteron*, a wing)

Moderately sized to very small holometabolous insects with a single pair of membranous wings, the hind pair modified into halteres; mouthparts for sucking or for piercing also and usually forming a proboscis. Larvae apodous, vermiform, terrestrial, aquatic or parasitic; pupae adecticous, weakly obtect or exarate and in a puparium; usually no cocoon.

Most flies are diurnal and many visit flowers for nectar, while many others feed on decaying organic matter and various fluid substances. There is also a number of flies that are predators on smaller insects or have acquired blood-sucking habits. The single pair of wings is borne on the mesothorax and the metathoracic wings are modified into halteres, or balancers (p. 29). The mouthparts differ greatly in various families but in most cases the elongate labium forms the chief part of the proboscis (Figs 89–91, 117 and 158).

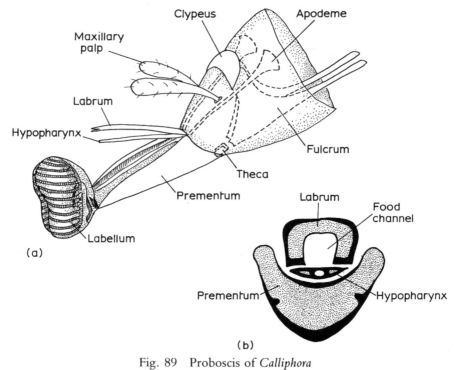

Fig. 89   Proboscis of *Calliphora*
(a) Lateral view, muscles omitted; (b) transverse sections of prementum and associated structures.

A prevalent type of mouthparts is seen in the bluebottles (*Calliphora*). Here the proboscis (Fig. 89) consists of a broad, basal rostrum, shaped like an inverted cone, and a distal haustellum bearing a pair of modified labial palps, the labella. The rostrum is formed by the clypeal region combined with the basal parts of the maxillae and labium. Situated within the rostrum is a stirrup-shaped cuticular framework, or fulcrum. On the anterior surface of the rostrum the fulcrum appears as an inverted **V**-shaped sclerite (Fig. 89), which is probably a derivative of

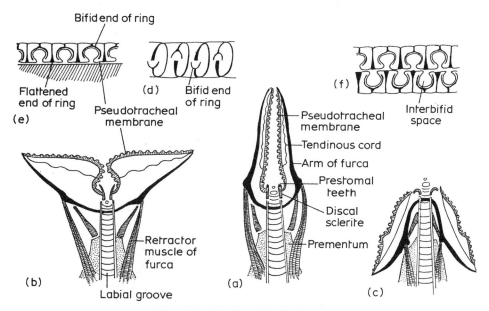

Fig. 90   Labella of *Calliphora*

(a) Resting position; (b) filtering position; (c) direct feeding position; (d) inner view of part of a pseudotrachea, showing four rings; (e) lateral view of part of pseudotracheal membrane applied to feeding surface; (f) outer view of part of a pseudotrachea.

the original clypeus. The foot piece of the stirrup strengthens the posterior wall of the cibarium and lateral extensions unite it with the clypeus. The clypeus and adjacent parts provide origins for the dilator muscles of the cibarium and the flexor muscle of the labrum. In front of the fulcrum are the maxillary palps, and on each side is a darkly sclerotized rod-like maxillary apodeme which articulates with the labrum. The cibarium is closely attached to the posterior wall of the fulcrum and just in front of the latter it becomes enclosed in a small U-shaped theca which keeps its cavity distended. The haustellum probably represents the prementum and distal parts of the mentum. Its anterior surface is inflected to form a median labial groove, or gutter. Posteriorly the haustellum is strengthened by a large concave plate, the prementum. The labial groove is sclerotized and each side is supported by a rod-like paraphysis. The groove is largely roofed in anteriorly by the labrum, whose inner lining is a channel forming a half tube that is closed by the hypopharynx. In front of the labrum the labial groove is closed by folds of the integument and is continued to the prestomum. This is an aperture that is bounded and kept open by the arms of the discal sclerite. Attached to the latter are the prestomal teeth. Proximally the discal sclerite is connected to the paraphyses of the labial groove. The main skeletal support of the labella are the two arms of the furca,

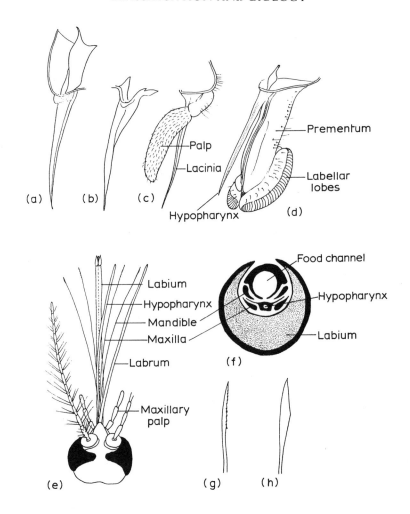

Fig. 91   Mouthparts of blood-sucking Diptera

(a)–(d) *Tabanus atratus* (after Snodgrass); (e)–(h) mosquito, *Culex*. (a) Labrum; (b) mandible; (c) maxilla; (d) labium; (e) dorsal view of extended mouthparts; (f) schematic transverse section of labium and associated structures (after Eidmann); (g) apex of maxillary stylet; (h) apex of mandibular stylet.

whose base articulates with paired processes of the prementum. The membrane covering the distal surface of the labella contains a series of food channels, or pseudotracheae. These channels are kept open by a framework of incomplete cuticular rings which give them the appearance of tracheae. Each ring is bifurcated at one end and flattened at the other, the flattened and bifurcated extremities alternating (Fig. 90e and f). The pseudotracheae open on the external surface of the labella through the cleft at the forked extremities of the cuticular rings. The pseudotracheae all converge to the prestomum and there are three sets of these channels to each labellum, i.e. those that run into an anterior collecting canal, those that run into a posterior collecting canal and a group between the two whose components open directly between the prestomal teeth and which serve as conducting channels. When the proboscis is protruded the rostrum is extended through the expansion of the lateral air-sacs at its base and probably also of some cephalic air-sacs. The haustellum is brought into use by the contraction of its extensor muscles, and finally the labella are extended and rendered turgid by blood pressure. The rectraction of the proboscis is mainly effected by the contraction of its numerous muscles. In the resting position the labella are flaccid and the two labella are in apposition (Fig. 90a). When the fly is feeding on fluids the labella assume a filtering position (b) and are pulled apart by the retractor muscles of the furca. The simultaneous injection of blood into the cavity of the labella converts the pseudo-tracheal surface into a pad which accommodates itself to unevenness of any surface to which it is applied. By means of the pumping action of the cibarial muscles, suction is set up and liquid food is filtered in through the pseudotracheae to the prestomum. From here it passes along the channel formed by labrum and hypopharynx and so into the alimentary canal. In the direct feeding position (c) the lateral arms of the furca and the labella are pulled upward against the sides of the haustellum, completely exposing the prestomum. In a slightly less reflected condition the prestomal teeth project vertically downward, but the prestomum is not exposed. This scraping position enables the insect to rasp particles of sugar and other substances. Whereas in position (b) only fluids and particles of a diameter not exceeding 0.006 mm can enter the pseudotracheae, in position (c) much larger particles can be taken in directly along with fluids.

The mouthparts of *Calliphora* and other higher Diptera are highly specialized, and to determine the homologies of their components it is necessary to examine those of the lower Diptera. Mandibles are only present in blood-sucking Nematocera and Brachycera and are usually confined to the female. The maxillae in some representatives of these suborders exhibit almost all the usual parts and comparisons indicate that the apodemes of *Calliphora* are probably derivatives of the stipes. The labella are regarded as modified labial palps and in this connection it may be noted that in some species they are two-segmented. In mosquitoes (*Anopheles*, *Culex* and allied genera) the mouthparts in the female are very slender organs lodged in the labial groove (Fig. 91). The mandibles and the laciniae of the maxillae are modified into long, piercing stylets; the maxillae, being the stronger organs, are used for piercing. During feeding the labium becomes looped backward allowing the maxillae to perforate the skin of the host. The labrum and the other stylets form a bundle which probes until it enters a blood capillary of the host, the hypopharynx injecting saliva which apparently acts as an anticoagulin on the blood. In the males both mandibles and maxillae are much reduced in *Anopheles* and are even more so in *Culex*; they are not used for piercing, the apex of the labrum being merely dipped below the

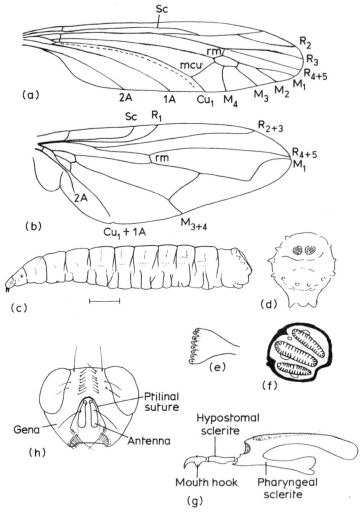

Fig. 92   Diptera

(a) Wing venation of *Tipula* (Nematocera: Tipulidae); (b) wing venation of *Calliphora* (Cyclorrapha: Calliphoridae); (c) larva of *Calliphora*, lateral view; scale line = 2 mm; (d) larva of *Calliphora*, posterior view; (e) anterior spiracle of *Calliphora* larva; (f) posterior spiracle of *Calliphora* larva; (g) cephalopharyngeal skeleton and mouth-hooks of *Calliphora* larva; (h) anterior view of head-capsule of adult Calliphorid (after Smart).

surface of sugary liquid food so that the nutriment can be imbibed through the tubular labrum. Some of the Cyclorrhapha have also acquired blood-sucking habits which occur in both sexes, notably in the Biting Housefly (*Stomoxys*), the tsetse flies (*Glossina*), the Forest-fly (*Hippobosca*), and others. The haustellum (Fig. 158b and d) in such cases is a rigid, horny, piercing organ devoid of pseudotracheae and there are no mandibular or maxillary stylets. The puncture is made by the strong prestomal teeth and the blood is drawn in through the prestomum into the food canal formed by the apposed labrum and hypopharynx. For further information on blood-sucking flies see pp. 230–2.

The horse-flies (Tabanidae) combine the filter feeding method of the blow-fly with the piercing method of mosquitoes. Pseudotracheae are present on the labella and the mandibles and laciniae of the females are broad stylets used for piercing in order to yield a pool of blood (Fig. 91a).

The ptilinum, or frontal sac, is a cephalic organ found in the most highly specialized flies. Its presence is indicated externally by the U-shaped ptilinal suture embracing the insertions of the antennae (Fig. 92h). The suture is an extremely narrow slit along the margins of which the integument is invaginated as a sac or ptilinum which can be everted through the suture before the emergence of the fly. With the aid of the ptilinum the insect ruptures the puparium and pushes through any substrate material. The ptilinum is everted by blood pressure and muscular action and, having served its purpose, it is withdrawn into the head cavity, where it remains.

The thorax of Diptera is characterized by the great size of the mesothorax bearing the wings and the correlated reduction of the segments in front and behind. The most primitive venation occurs in crane-flies and some other Nematocera, the veins being predominantly longitudinal with only a few cross-veins (Fig. 92a) of which rm is a notable landmark. The narrow wing-bases have led to a great reduction of the anal veins and Cu_2 is absent or vestigial. Specialization by reduction of venation is common and is most pronounced in the Cyclorrhapha (Fig. 92b). A true ovipositor is rarely developed, but in *Musca*, and many other flies, the end segments of the abdomen form a telescopic tube, or oviscapt, serving the same purpose.

Dipteran larvae never have thoracic legs and are typically amphi-pneustic or metapneustic; propneustic or apneustic forms occur more rarely. Three thoracic and nine abdominal segments are present, and in Nematocera the head is fully developed (eucephalous). The mouthparts are less modified than in other groups of Diptera and the paired components work horizontally. In the Brachycera the head is incomplete posteriorly and partly embedded in the prothorax (hemicephalous); the mouthparts are highly modified and work in the vertical plane. Among

165

Cyclorrhapha (Fig. 92) the larvae are acephalous and this condition results from remnants of the head being invaginated into the thorax. During this process the mouth becomes carried far inward and communication with the exterior is by means of a secondary passage, or atrium. The apparent head rudiment is in reality a circular papilla-like fold of the neck. Normal mouthparts are atrophied and their place is taken by adaptively modified structures that form the cephalopharyngeal skeleton (Fig. 92g). Of these the paired mouth hooks are alone freely movable and work in the vertical plane; they articulate with a hypostomal sclerite whose two components are joined by a crossbar. This sclerite articulates in turn with the pharyngeal sclerite that is composed of two vertical lamellae united below to form a trough for the support of the pharynx. The pharyngeal sclerite is the homologue of the fulcrum of the imago. The mode of life of Cyclorrhaphan larvae is correlated with the structure of the mouthparts. In carnivorous forms the mouthparts are sharply hooked, whereas in phytophagous forms they are toothed. The pharyngeal floor is ridged in saprophagous forms, less so or smooth in phytophagous forms and wholly without ridges in carnivores.

Dipteran larvae pass through three or four instars and the pupae are adecticous and exarate or weakly obtect. In the Cyclorrhapha the cuticle of the third instar is not shed, but hardens to form a dark-coloured shell, or puparium, enclosing the pupa (Fig. 56c). The puparium ruptures along special lines of weakness through pressure exerted from within. In the higher Cyclorrhapha the inflated ptilinum forces open the puparium and so liberates the imago.

About 64 000 species of flies are known, and of these more than 5200 kinds inhabit the British Isles. The order is of very great economic importance either as larvae or as adults. The pathogenic organisms of some of the most serious tropical diseases such as malaria, sleeping sickness, elephantiasis and yellow fever are transmitted to man through the agency of blood-sucking flies. The housefly and its allies act as mechanical carriers of pathogenic micro-organisms, and in this way contaminate human foods. Various Dipteran larvae induce diseased conditions in the bodies of man and domestic animals, and such infections are included under the term myiasis. Larvae of other species are injurious to the agriculturist and their activities result in great financial losses. Details of all of these injurious Diptera will be found on pp. 313–25. The depredations of members of this order are offset to some extent by those species of carnivorous or parasitoidal habits that destroy large numbers of noxious insects.

Diptera may be divided into three suborders, the Nematocera, Brachycera and Cyclorrhapha. The **Nematocera** have many-jointed antennae, usually longer than the head and thorax, and the maxillary palps have four or five segments. The larvae are usually eucephalous with horizontally biting mandibles. The slender, long-legged craneflies or Tipulidae are familiar insects. The larvae are metapneustic and those of some species of *Tipula*, known as 'leather-jackets', are injurious to the roots of pasture grasses and crops. The Chironomidae or non-biting midges have mostly aquatic larvae that are apneustic. In some species the larvae are known as blood-worms owing to the presence of haemoglobin in the blood plasma. The Culicidae or mosquitoes are slender insects with long piercing mouthparts and the wing margins, together with the veins, are clothed with scales. All the immature stages are aquatic (p. 318), the larvae being metapneustic. With few exceptions, female mosquitoes are able to pierce the skin of vertebrates and feed upon the blood; they also feed on various plant juices and some species may never taste blood at all. The larval habits are varied: some inhabit shady pools, others are found in streams, dykes, tree holes, salt marshes or small containers. Some 32 species of mosquitoes occur in Britain, and of these the commonest is *Culex pipiens*. For further details of their role in disease transmission see p. 316. Among other families of Nematocera are the Simuliidae (blackflies or buffalo gnats), the Mycetophilidae or fungus gnats, and the Cecidomyiidae or gall midges. Included in the **Brachycera** are 14 families of stout-bodied flies with short antennae, generally three-segmented and often with the last segment prolonged into a style. The maxillary palps are one- or two-segmented and the larvae are hemicephalous with vertically biting mandibles. Mention may be made of the Tabanidae or horse-flies, the females of which are blood-sucking in habit, and the Asilidae or robber-flies, which are predators on other insects (Fig. 112a).

The **Cyclorrhapha** consist of all the higher Diptera. Their antennae are three-segmented with a dorsal bristle-like arista (Fig. 92h) and the maxillary palps are one-segmented. The larvae are acephalous and commonly amphipneustic; their mandibles are replaced by mouth hooks movable only in the vertical plane and the pupae are enclosed in a puparium. Among this great assemblage of forms the Syrphidae or hover-flies are without a ptilinum and their larvae include many predators of aphids. Most families possess a ptilinum, but only a few can receive separate mention here. The Tephritidae or fruit-flies include destructive larvae that mine the pulp of cultivated and other fruits. The Drosophilidae or pomace-flies have saprophagous larvae and the Oestridae, which include the warble-flies and bot-flies, have larvae that are endoparasites of mammals. The Muscidae include the Common Housefly (*Musca domestica*) and its allies, together with blood-sucking forms such as the stable-flies (*Stomoxys*); allied are the tsetse-flies (*Glossina*). The Tachinidae are very bristly flies whose larvae are endoparasites of other insects. The Calliphoridae are either similar

167

parasites or, like *Calliphora, Lucilia*, and their allies, have saprophagous larvae. The Hippoboscidae are viviparous and live, as adults, as blood-sucking ectoparasites on birds and mammals; the wingless Sheep Ked (*Melophagus ovinus*) and the Forest-fly (*Hippobosca equina*) are well-known examples (Fig. 116c).

ORDER 27. **LEPIDOPTERA**. Butterflies and moths. (*lepis*, gen. *lepidos*, a scale; *pteron*, a wing)

Small to very large holometabolous insects clothed with scales. Mouthparts with galeae usually modified into a spirally coiled suctorial proboscis; mandibles rarely present. Larvae phytophagous, polypod; pupae usually adecticous, obtect or partially free, usually in cocoons.

An immense order with over 140 000 species which have the wings, and usually the body and appendages, more or less covered with pigmented scales (pp. 11 and 82); over the wing surfaces the scales give rise to characteristic colour patterns. The structural similarity of these insects has led to great uniformity of behaviour. The imagines live on nectar, over-ripe fruit, honeydew and similar sugary liquids, while their larvae with few exceptions feed entirely upon phanerogamic plants – leaves, roots, seeds, wood. In *Micropterix* and its allies, which are pollen feeders, functional and complete mandibles and maxillae (Fig. 93c) are present. In *Eriocrania* mandibles are reduced, the maxillae have lost the laciniae, while the galea of either side is grooved and functions with its fellow as a rather weakly developed suctorial proboscis; in the pupa, however, there are functional mandibles. In the rest of the Lepidoptera mandibles are vestigial or wanting and the proboscis (Fig. 93e) may attain a length greater than that of the insect. Each galea is a tube whose cavity is continuous with that of the head; its flexibility is caused by a series of strongly sclerotized rings separated by thinner cuticular membrane. The two components of the proboscis interlock and thus enclose a median food canal (Fig. 93f). The actual intake of food is effected by the action of a cibariopharyngeal pump.

Extension of the proboscis is partly due to the contraction of three pairs of extensor muscles which exert pressure on the blood by reducing the cranial cavity. This results in blood being forced through a valve in the cavity of the stipes and so into the interior of each half of the proboscis, thus extending the organ as a whole. But extension also involves changes in the distribution of pressure within the galeae and depends on variations in the rigidity of their walls. A reduced labrum, bearing lateral lobes or pilifers, overlies the base of the proboscis. Except in some primitive families maxillary palps are much reduced or absent. The labium is represented by a simple plate bearing three-segmented palps that project conspicuously on each side. Many moths

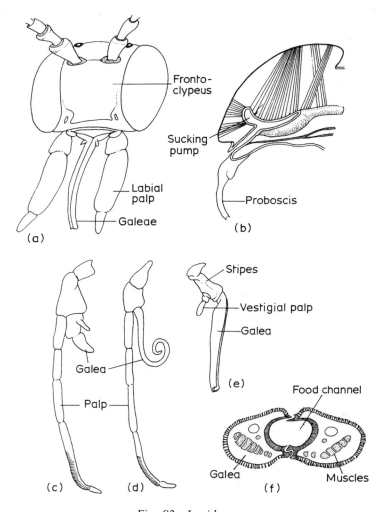

Fig. 93 Lepidoptera

(a) Anterior view of head and mouthparts of *Synanthedon exitiosa*; (b) schematic longitudinal section of head of a Lepidopteran; (c) maxilla of *Micropterix*; (d) maxilla of *Mnemonica*; (e) maxilla of a higher Lepidopteran; (f) transverse section of proboscis of *Danaus*. ((a) , (b) and (f) after Snodgrass; (c)–(e) after Eidmann.)

take no food and their mouthparts consequently display varying degrees of atrophy. The prothorax bears a pair of erectile lobes or patagia well seen in many Noctuidae; tegulae (p. 22) are well developed and characteristic. The venation (Fig. 94) of the most primitive families is of a generalized type with few cross-veins. Specialization involves the ultimate disappearance of Cu_2 from both pairs of wings, the reduction of Rs to a single branch in the hind wing and the formation of a large

169

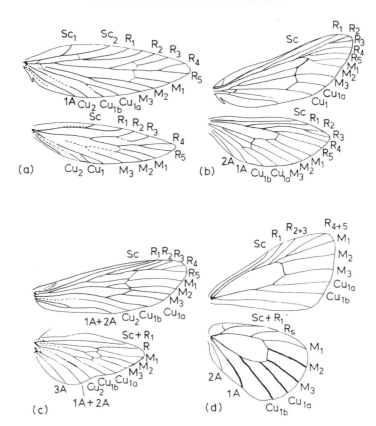

Fig. 94   Lepidoptera: wing venation

(a) *Sabatinca* (Micropterigidae); (b) *Hepialus* (Hepialidae); (c) *Xyleutes* (Cossidae); (d) *Pieris* (Pieridae). (a) and (b) are homoneuran, (c) and (d) are heteroneuran. Note formation of discal cell in (d) through loss of basal section of media. ((a), (c) and (d) after Common.)

discal cell in each wing through the loss of the basal part of the media. The prevalent wing-coupling apparatus shows sexual dimorphism. In the male the frenulum (p. 22) is single and a hook-like retinaculum is usually present beneath the base of Sc; in the female the frenulum is commonly formed of several bristles and the retinaculum is on Cu_1, though a cubital retinaculum may also be present in the male. In the Hepialidae (Fig. 94b) and some other primitive moths a process, or jugum, arises from the base of the fore wing; in flight, the jugum lies on top of the base of the hind wing. In butterflies and certain moths that have lost the frenulum, amplexiform coupling is found: the enlarged humeral lobe of the hind wing is maintained against the stiffened base of the fore wing, thus ensuring synchronous action of the two wings. It may be added that wings are vestigial or absent in the females of certain moths, notably the Psychidae and a few Geometridae. On either side of the metathorax, or the base of the abdomen, in many moths there is a complex tympanum (p. 51); its presence or absence is constant for large groups of families and it can perceive the ultrasonic frequencies emitted by bats.

The larvae or caterpillars have a well-developed head, three thoracic and ten abdominal segments (Fig. 55b). Spiracles are present on the prothorax and first eight abdominal segments. The mouthparts are mandibulate but reduced; the antennae are small three-segmented organs, and behind them is a group of about six ocelli on either side. Each thoracic segment bears a pair of single-clawed legs and a pair of abdominal prolegs is present on segments 3–6 and 10. These organs are fleshy projections whose grasping surface is armed with hooks or crochets that are arranged in circles in the lower families but restricted to an arc or band in the more specialized groups; they help to grip the surface on which the larva is walking or climbing.

In the Geometridae abdominal prolegs are present only on segments 6 and 10, their caterpillars being known as 'loopers' from their method of crawling. Most caterpillars are protected either by their cryptic form and colour, or by the display of warning patterns, or the adoption of concealed habits. The labial glands (p. 86) are modified into silk glands whose secretion is emitted through a median spinneret associated with the labium and hypopharynx. Silk glands may be several times longer than the body in species that form dense cocoons; in all cases the salivary function is taken over by mandibular glands.

The pupa of a few primitive Lepidoptera is decticous, but no higher forms have pupal mandibles, though the pupa in the Exoporia, Monotrysia and lower Ditrysia has the appendages free and most of the abdominal segments movable; aided by a spiny armature, such a pupa usually issues partially from the cocoon to allow the emergence of the imago. In the higher forms the pupa is obtect (p. 111) with only three free abdominal segments and it remains attached to the cocoon by means of a terminal hooked device, or cremaster. Many butterflies have naked and protectively coloured pupae with the cocoon reduced to a pad of silk to which the cremaster is attached.

Economically the order is of great importance because of the damage incurred by the feeding activities of the caterpillars. Only a few examples will be quoted here; others are given on p. 301. Species of *Pieris* or the 'White' butterflies are major pests of cruciferous and other crops. The Gypsy Moth (*Lymantria dispar*) and the Black Arches or Nun Moth (*L. monacha*) are great defoliators of forest trees; the European Corn Borer (*Ostrinia nubilalis*) is destructive to maize in North America; the Codling Moth (*Cydia pomonella*) is a widespread enemy of the apple; and the Mediterranean Flour Moth (*Ephestia kuehniella*) is an almost universally distributed pest in flour mills and grain stores. Two other

171

pests of very wide range are the Pink Bollworm (*Platyedra gossypiella*) of cotton and the Angoumois Grain Moth (*Sitotroga cerealella*) which infests wheat, maize, and other cereals. Mention also needs to be made of the Clothes Moths (*Tinea pellionella, Tineola bisselliella* and *Trichophaga tapetzella*) which attack woollen clothing, rugs, furs, and carpets. To offset this, the silk moths *Bombyx mori* and certain Saturniidae are beneficial in that they provide commercial silks.

Lepidoptera are closely related to the Trichoptera, the two orders probably being derived from a common ancestor. The complete M_4 in the fore wing of archaic Trichoptera and the absence of broad scales, of biting mouthparts and of a cloaca in the female will distinguish them from primitive Lepidoptera such as the Micropterigidae. In larval structure and habits the two orders are widely divergent, the Trichoptera being essentially aquatic and the Lepidoptera terrestrial. Recent morphological studies of the more primitive Lepidoptera by Kristensen and his collaborators have shown that a relatively few families have diverged along distinctive evolutionary paths while the great majority of Lepidoptera form a single specialized homogeneous group. Many of the characters used to define major taxa in the resulting phylogenetic classification are difficult to observe, but four suborders may be recognized. The **Zeugloptera** include only the pollen-feeding Micropterigidae, primitive in most venational features and with biting mouthparts, but having a female reproductive system in which the bursa copulatrix enters the vagina which then joins the hind gut to form a cloaca that opens on the ninth abdominal segment. The larvae, which are unusual in having eight pairs of non-musculated prolegs devoid of crochets, feed on bryophytes or at the base of grass tussocks. The suborder **Aglossata** includes a single family, the Agathiphagidae, with two species of *Agathiphaga* from the S.W. Pacific. These are nocturnal moths with mandibulate mouthparts and apodous larvae which feed on the seeds of the kauri pine (*Agathis*). A third suborder, the **Heterobathmiina**, similarly contains only a single family with about ten S. American species of the genus *Heterobathmia*; the adults are probably pollen-feeders on southern beeches (*Nothofagus*), whose leaves are mined by the larvae. All of the remaining Lepidoptera fall into the suborder **Glossata**, without functional adult mandibles and typically with the galeae forming a proboscis of some sort. Within this suborder four groups can be distinguished. The **Dacnonypha** includes as its main component the Holarctic family Eriocraniidae; these are small diurnal moths with a simple proboscis that lacks intrinsic muscles, and apodous leaf-mining larvae associated mainly with birches. The **Neopseustina** consists of one family with a relict distribution in Asia and S. America. The **Exoporia** includes several families, of which the best known is the relatively large Hepialidae (Ghost Moths and Swift Moths). These, like all higher Lepidoptera, have acquired intrinsic proboscis muscles and an adecticous pupa. However, the Hepialids have retained similar venation in the fore and hind wings (the homoneuran condition found in all primitive Lepidoptera) and the female reproductive tract has separate copulatory and egg-laying apertures, though it is without an internal duct joining the bursa to the vagina. The **Heteroneura** include all of the remaining Lepidoptera, which are distinguished by the simplification of the radial sector vein in the hind wing. A few lower Heteroneuran families such as the Incurvariidae and the Nepticulidae have a characteristic Monotrysian condition of the female reproductive tract, with the bursa copulatrix opening into the vagina, which then joins the hind gut to form a cloaca. The remaining Heteroneura, which make up about 98% of the species in the order, show a distinctive Ditrysian pattern of female reproductive ducts, in which the bursa copulatrix and vagina open separately from each other and from the rectum and there is an internal sperm duct connecting the bursa with the vagina. A frenulum occurs in most species, but several groups have lost this structure and acquired the amplexiform type of wing-coupling. The Cossidae or Goat Moths have an archaic venation. The Pyralidae include among their genera *Acentria* and *Nymphula*, whose larvae are exceptional in being aquatic. The Pterophoridae or Plume Moths have deeply fissured wings and the Tineidae are an extensive family of varied larval habits and include the clothes moths. The Saturniidae are notable for their dense silken cocoons, those of some species being of commercial value; *Attacus* includes the oriental Atlas Moths which attain a wing expanse of 25 cm. The Bombycidae include *Bombyx mori*, a native of China, whose larva is the well-known 'silk worm'. Butterflies form the superfamilies Papilionoidea and Hesperioidea, distinguished by the clubbed antennae and the absence of a frenulum. Other notable groups are the Geometridae, whose larvae are 'loopers', the Hawk Moths or Sphingidae and the great family of Owlet Moths or Noctuidae.

ORDER 28. **TRICHOPTERA**. Caddis-flies. (*thrix*, gen. *trichos*, a hair; *pteron*, a wing)

Moth-like holometabolous insects with two pairs of densely hair-covered wings showing predominantly generalized venation with few cross-veins. Mouthparts reduced; mandibles not functional. Larvae aquatic, generally in portable cases; thoracic legs and paired hook-like caudal appendages present. Pupae aquatic, with strong mandibles.

Trichoptera (Fig. 95) are weakly flying and mostly nocturnal insects, usually found in the vicinity of water. They are obscurely coloured, generally of some shades of brown or grey, and the wings are closed roof-like over the back when at rest. They are closely allied to the

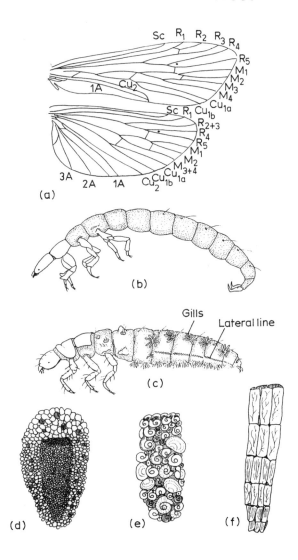

Fig. 95   Trichoptera

(a) Wing venation of *Stenopsychodes* (Rhyacophilidae); (b) Rhyacophilid larva (campodei-form); (c) Limnephilid larva (eruciform); (d)–(f) larval cases of *Molanna* (Molannidae), *Limnephilus* (Limnephilidae) and *Phryganea* (Phryganeidae). ((b) and (c) after Riek.)

Lepidoptera (p. 193), the venation of the family Rhyacophilidae resembling that of *Micropterix* and allied moths. Caddis-flies take only liquid food, which is licked up by the broad haustellum formed by enlargement and modification of the hypopharynx. The maxillae are represented by the galea, stipes and palp. The eggs are laid in masses in

174

or near water and are commonly protected by mucilage. The larvae all have the head well sclerotized with very small antennae and the first pair of legs shortest and stoutest; their abdomen is formed of nine segments, the last bearing a pair of jointed appendages ending in hooks. Caddis larvae present two main types (Fig. 95): in the 'eruciform' type the head is inclined at an angle with the body and there are dorsal, lateral and ventral tufts of abdominal tracheal gills. Such larvae make portable cases of extraneous material bound together and lined with silk produced by the modified labial glands. These cases may be constructed of leaf- or stem-fragments, sand grains, empty mollusc shells or small pebbles and are very constant in character for different genera (Fig. 95d–f). Dorsal and lateral papillae on the first abdominal segment maintain the larva in position within its case and allow an even flow of water between the case and the body of the larva. When walking, the head and the sclerotized first, or first and second, thoracic segments are protruded from the case, which is gripped by the caudal hooks and dragged along at the same time. Larvae of the second (campodeiform) type are usually more active, with elongated body and the head prognathous. They seldom make cases and in many instances live in silken retreats. There are no papillae on the first abdominal segment and gills are usually wanting. The anal appendages are often well developed and are used to grip the silken tunnels or to hold on to rocks when they leave their retreats. Trichopteran pupae breathe cutaneously or by means of gills, as in the larva. They are protected either by the original but adapted larval cases, or by special shelters constructed for the purpose. Strong mandibles are present which enable them to cut their way out for the emergence of the imago. In many species the pharate adults are able to swim in order to reach the surface of the water. For this purpose they use the long middle legs of the pupa, which are fringed with swimming hairs. Less than 3000 species of Trichoptera have been described and, of these, over 180 species inhabit Great Britain.

ORDER 29. **HYMENOPTERA**. Sawflies, ants, bees, wasps and their allies. (*hymen*, a membrane; *pteron*, a wing)

Minute to moderate-sized holometabolous insects with membranous wings, the hind pair smaller and connected with fore pair by hooklets; venation specialized by reduction. Mouthparts for biting and licking. Abdomen with 1st segment more or less closely fused with thorax; a sawing or piercing ovipositor present. Larvae usually polypod or apodous; pupae almost always adecticous, generally in cocoons.

One of the most constant distinctive features of Hymenoptera is the fusion of the first abdominal segment, or propodeum (Fig. 97b) with the metathorax, which occurs in the prepupa and is found in all except the

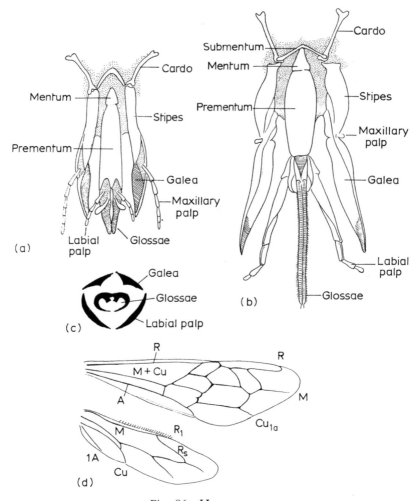

Fig. 96   Hymenoptera

(a) Mouthparts, excluding mandibles, of *Andrena carlini* (after Snodgrass); (b) mouthparts, excluding mandibles, of *Apis mellifera* (after Snodgrass); (c) transverse section through proboscis of *Apis mellifera*; (d) wing venation of *Apis mellifera*.

Symphyta. The propodeum, it will be noted, bears the first pair of abdominal spiracles. The mouthparts show their most generalized condition among sawflies. Mandibles are always present, while the maxillae and labium have all the usual components, though the glossae are fused to form a broad tongue. Only small differences occur in the mouthparts of most adult Hymenoptera. However, in bees (Fig. 96) there is a progressive lengthening, in different genera, of the glossa and associated parts to form, in the more specialized types, a proboscis adapted to extract deeply seated nectar from flowers. In the honey-bee the mandibles are smooth-edged and used for manipulating wax rather than for feeding. The maxillae are greatly elongated with rod-like cardines and the galeae are large thin blades much longer than the stipites; a pair of small membranous lobes probably represents the laciniae and the palps are reduced to papillae (Fig. 96). In the labium there is a long prementum articulating with a small mentum whose apex fits into the angle of a V-shaped suspensory sclerite or submentum (lorum) that articulates with the distal ends of the cardines. The glossa is greatly elongated and ends in a spoon-like lobe, or flabellum; at the base of the glossa there are scale-like paraglossae. The labial palps have the two basal segments flat and blade-like, leaving the distal segments unmodified. When the bee feeds on any easily accessible liquid the

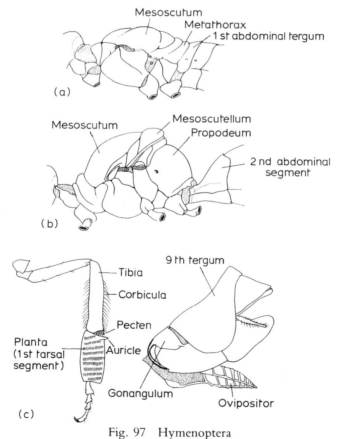

Fig. 97   Hymenoptera

(a) Lateral view of thorax of a Tenthredinid sawfly (Symphyta) (after Weber); (b) lateral view of thorax of *Apis mellifera* (after Snodgrass); (c) hind leg of *Apis mellifera*, showing structures used in pollen collection, viewed from inner side; (d) ovipositor of Gooseberry Sawfly, *Pteronidea ribesii* (after Snodgrass).

maxillary galeae and the labial palps form an improvised tube along with the glossa (Fig. 96c). The flabellum is immersed in the food, and by a rapid backward and forward motion of the glossa the liquid is drawn up the tube; it is then sucked up into the digestive canal by the action of the cibarial pump. Where the food is more inaccessible the glossa may be projected far beyond the ends of the maxillae. The ventral or posterior surface of the glossa bears a deep channel which reaches to the flabellum; the saliva traverses this channel and becomes mixed with the food during ingestion.

The venation of the Hymenoptera (Fig. 96d) deviates widely from the primitive type and during development the veins are demarcated before the tracheae develop. This fact, along with the frequent anastomosis of the veins to form numerous cells, makes the homologies of the veins hard to ascertain. The most generalized condition occurs in the Symphyta and various stages in reduction prevail in other groups of the order. Bees and wasps show intermediate degrees of reduction while extreme conditions occur in the Parasitica where the veins may be restricted to the costal margin or be totally atrophied. Wing-coupling through costal hooklets of the hind wing engaging the reflected hind margin of the fore wing prevails throughout the order (Fig. 96b).

An ovipositor is always present though it is not used to lay eggs in the Aculeata. Its lateral valves are represented by a pair of sensory 'palps', the inner valves are fused to form a stylet and the anterior valves form a pair of lancets which have tongue and groove articulations with the stylet. In the Symphyta the ovipositor functions as a saw, both the lancets and the stylet being prominently toothed and enabling the eggs to be embedded in plant tissues (Fig. 97d). Among the Apocrita, the ovipositor is a piercing organ in many of the Parasitica, while in the Aculeata it has been transformed into a sting (Fig. 12). In most Hymenoptera the eggs pass down the ovipositor channel and may become greatly compressed and stretched to allow of their free transit; in the stinging forms however, the eggs are discharged from the genital pore at the base of the ovipositor and the latter injects venom secreted by modified accessory glands.

A Hymenopteran larva (Fig. 98) has a well-developed head, three thoracic and nine or ten abdominal segments. In the sawflies there are three pairs of thoracic legs and abdominal prolegs are present either on all of the segments (*Xyela*) or, more usually, on segments 2 to 8 and 10. In other Hymenoptera the larvae are apodous (Fig. 55e) but evanescent appendages may appear in the early instars of some Parasitica (Fig. 114b). There are usually nine or ten pairs of spiracles, except in endo-parasitic larvae where the number is variable. A somewhat weak cocoon commonly encloses the pupa, but is wanting in the Chalcidoidea. Hymenoptera rank among the largest and most highly evolved orders of

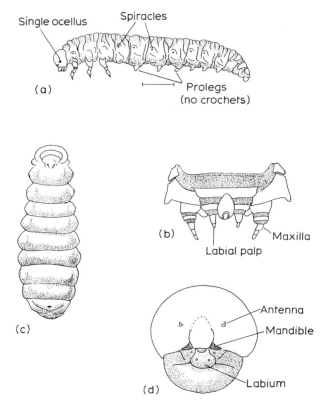

Fig. 98   Hymenoptera
(a) Larva of Plum Sawfly, *Hoplocampa flava* (Tenthredinidae), lateral view (after Miles);
(b) labium and maxilla of *Cimbex americana* larva (Symphyta: Cimbicidae) (after
Snodgrass); (c) larva of *Crabro cephalotes* (Aculeata: Crabronidae) (after Marchal);
(d) anterior view of head of larva of *Sphecophaga* (Parasitica: Ichneumonoidea) (after
Snodgrass). Scale line = 2 mm.

insects and are of special interest from the wide range of biological
features they display. In the complexity of their behaviour they stand in
the forefront of all invertebrates, and they have been the subject of
studies by some of the most famous naturalists. At least 100 000 species
are known, and although the vast majority of these are solitary in habit
like other insects, individuals of some groups live together in great
societies, as is the case with ants and certain bees and wasps (pp. 241–7).
Hymenoptera are also remarkable for the highly evolved state that
parasitism has reached among their larvae; tens of thousands of species
betray this habit and present special respiratory and other adaptations in
accord with their modes of life. Associated with parasitism is the
phenomenon of polyembryony (p. 96) which attains unique develop-

179

ments. Parthenogenesis is also more frequent among Hymenoptera than in any other order of insects; besides being an important factor in social life, it may also be associated with alternation of generations (p. 206).

From the economic standpoint the Hymenoptera confer many benefits upon man. Bees are important pollinators of fruit trees and other plants, while the honey-bee is well known to yield honey and wax. The important part played by the parasitoidal Hymenoptera in controlling the population density of many injurious insects is a recognized feature in pest management. Among noxious members of the order the majority are defoliating larvae of sawflies and the boring larvae of wood-wasps or Siricidae. Of lesser importance are the phytophagous larvae of certain Chalcids.

Hymenoptera are divided into two suborders, Symphyta and Apocrita. In the **Symphyta** the abdomen is broad with no basal constriction or petiole behind the propodeum which is only partially amalgamated with the thorax (Fig. 97a). The larvae are phytophagous and possess thoracic legs and usually abdominal prolegs (Fig. 98a). Most of the species are included in the superfamily Tenthredinoidea, which consists of six families. The Cephidae or stem sawflies are a small group whose larvae tunnel within the stems of graminaceous and other plants, while those of the Siricidae or wood wasps bore into the wood of trees. The Tenthredinid sawflies, whose ovipositor acts as a saw in cutting shallow notches or deep incisions in plant tissues for placing their eggs, mostly have leaf-feeding larvae. Their larvae are caterpillars which differ from those of Lepidoptera in the single ocellus on each side of the head, in the segmental positions of the abdominal prolegs and in the absence of crochets on them. The only other Symphyta are *Orussus* and its allies which form the small superfamily Orussoidea. Their specialized venation, slender retracted ovipositor and the unusual insertion of the antennae – below the clypeus and eyes – separate them from other Hymenoptera. Their larvae are legless ectoparasites of the larvae of wood-boring beetles or Siricids.

The **Apocrita**, which comprise the majority of Hymenoptera, have the abdomen stalked or constricted between the propodeum and the true second segment. They are divided into two main groups, the Aculeata and the Parasitica, which, however, intergrade both as regards structure and in their biology. In the **Aculeata**, or stinging forms, the eighth sternite is retracted, so that the ovipositor appears to issue from the apex of the abdomen. They include a number of large superfamilies of which the Scolioidea are the least specialized. They make no real nest and have more or less parasitoidal habits. The ants or Formicidae are all social insects whose female loses her wings after mating and in most species is aided by numerous wingless workers; the petiole behind the propodeum is raised into one or two nodes. The more primitive ants rear their larvae on insect prey, but other ants store seeds, cultivate fungi or obtain honey-dew from aphids. The true wasps or Vespoidea include many solitary nest-making species nearly all of which store paralysed caterpillars for their offspring; one family, the Vespidae, however, has social habits. The Sphecoidea or digger-wasps feed their larvae on paralysed insects of various orders or on spiders. The bees, or Apoidea, are closely related to them but many of their body-hairs are branched and the hind basitarsus is usually broad (Fig. 97c). Many bees make nests very like those of some solitary wasps but they store a mixture of pollen and nectar for their larvae. A few groups, of which the honey-bees (Apini) and the bumble-bees (Bombini) are the best known, are social.

In the **Parasitica** the trochanters are generally followed by a trochantellus and, in most cases, the ovipositor is exposed almost to its base, the eighth sternite not being retracted. They include an enormous number of species, small or minute in size, whose larvae are ecto- or endoparasites of other insects. The Ichneumonoidea include the largest forms and the venation is well-developed with a pterostigma; to a large extent the ichneumon flies and their allies parasitize caterpillars of Lepidoptera. The remaining Parasitica are mostly small or minute insects with greatly reduced venation, generally with few or no closed cells. The Cynipoidea are best known from their gall-producing members, more than 80% of which are confined to species of *Quercus* (pp. 203–6). A considerable number of other Cynipoidea are endo-parasites of Diptera. The Chalcidoidea include more species than any other superfamily of Hymenoptera (Fig. 108d). They are parasites and hyperparasites except for a small proportion that form galls or develop within seeds; the most notable of these is *Blastophaga*, associated with the pollination of the fig (p. 212). The Proctotrupoidea include many minute egg parasites and resemble the Aculeata in the concealed ovipositor.

For further information on various aspects of Hymenopteran biology, see the sections on social organization (p. 241), parasitoidal insects (p. 222) and flower pollination (p. 207).

5

Evolutionary relationships
of insects

In approaching the study of the evolutionary relationships among insects and their close allies (or, for that matter, among any group of organisms), it is necessary to indicate some of the principles on which phylogenetic inferences should be based. In the past these have differed more or less radically from one group of biologists to another and it is unlikely that general agreement will be reached in the near future. However, there is growing acceptance of the view, first clearly enunciated and developed by Hennig during the 1950s, that monophyletic groups (i.e. those consisting of all the descendants of a common ancestor) are best recognized by the fact that their members share a number of specialized characteristics (synapomorphies). Shared primitive features on the other hand (symplesiomorphies) are not convincing proof of a common origin, since such characteristics may simply have been retained from more remote ancestral forms. It follows that attempts to infer phylogeny without distinguishing between primitive (plesiomorphic) and specialized (apomorphic) features are unsatisfactory in principle. How far synapomorphic characters can be identified and how they may be distinguished from the resemblances due to convergent evolution is, however, not always easy to decide in practice, with the result that even those who accept Hennig's general principle may differ considerably from one another in the schemes of evolutionary relationship that they devise. Moreover, it seems likely that phylogenetically important features of this kind often concern obscure or relatively inaccessible structures which have not been well studied by taxonomists in the past and whose distribution among the taxa in question is therefore inadequately known. Despite these difficulties, and others which arise when one wishes to express a purely phylogenetic scheme in the form of a classification, cladistic arguments, relying on convincing sets of synapomorphic characters, seem destined to play an increasingly important part in defining evolutionary relationships. In the case of the insects this role is likely to be especially important, since the fossil record, though of great interest, is far too imperfect to allow direct recognition of ancestor–descendant connections. In what follows some attempt is made, bearing in mind the difficulties indicated, to reconstruct the relationship of the insects with other Arthropod groups and the connections of the major groups of insects (i.e. the orders) with one another.

INSECTS AND OTHER ARTHROPODS

The Arthropods form the largest group in the animal kingdom and can be recognized by the following characters. The bilaterally symmetrical body is segmented and covered by a chitinous exoskeleton. A variable number of the segments carry paired, jointed appendages that exhibit functional modifications in different regions of the body. The heart is dorsal and is provided with paired ostia, a pericardium is present, and the body-cavity is a haemocoel. The central nervous system consists of a supra-oesophageal centre or brain connected with a ganglionated ventral nerve-cord. The muscles are composed almost entirely of striated fibres and there is a general absence of ciliated epithelium. The earliest well-known group of arthropods, the fossil Trilobita, were aquatic, but among living forms it is only the Crustacea that have retained this mode of life to a predominant extent. No other group of invertebrate animals has so large a proportion of its members terrestrial in habit as do the Arthropods.

Arthropods are divisible into six main groups as follows:

1. Worm-like terrestrial forms bearing a pair of pre-antennae; the body unsegmented externally and with numerous pairs of unjointed legs. Onychophora.

2. Bearing antennae, primarily terrestrial in habit and breathing by tracheae. Myriapoda, Insecta.

3. Bearing antennae, usually aquatic in habit and breathing either cutaneously or by means of branchiae. Trilobita, Crustacea.

4. Without antennae, usually terrestrial in habit and breathing by lung-books and tracheae. Chelicerata.

Some of the main features of these groups are set out below.

The **Trilobita** were marine animals whose remains are abundant in Palaeozoic rocks of Cambrian and Silurian date. The body is highly specialized and divided longitudinally into median and lateral or pleural regions. The appendages, on the other hand, are very primitive and the most anterior consist of a single pair of antennae almost certainly homologous with the Crustacean first antennae. The remaining appendages are biramous and only slightly differentiated among themselves. The first four pairs belong to the head and are forwardly directed. They have large gnathobases that evidently crushed the food, since no jaws are developed.

The **Crustacea** include lobsters, shrimps, crabs, barnacles, and their allies, and are predominantly marine animals; a smaller number inhabit fresh water, while a few kinds of crabs and the woodlice have invaded the land. They are characterized by the possession of two pairs of antennae followed by a pair of mandibles and at least five pairs of legs. In the higher forms the body segments are fixed in number and are grouped into two regions – the cephalothorax and abdomen. The appendages are for the most part specialized to perform a number of functions and are often of the biramous and gnathobasic type. The excretory organs are modified coelomoducts and are usually represented by green glands or shell glands. The genital apertures are located anteriorly, i.e. on the ninth post-oral segment in some cases, up to the fourteenth in others.

The **Chelicerata** include scorpions, king crabs, spiders, mites, ticks, sea-spiders and others and have the body divided into cephalothorax and abdomen. There are no antennae, these organs being replaced by prehensile chelicerae. True jaws are wanting but a varying number of the anterior limbs have developed gnathobases for breaking up the food. Four pairs of legs are present.

The **Onychophora** are in many ways intermediate between the Annelida or worms and more typical Arthropods. They are represented today by rather more than 70 species included in the genus *Peripatus* and its allies. Like many declining groups, they have a discontinuous geographical distribution and are found in warm countries in many parts of the world. Their relationship with arthropods is based on the presence of (a) paired limbs, each ending in two claws; (b) respiration taking place by means of tracheae; (c) the haemocoelic body cavity; (d) a heart with paired ostia; and (e) the general character of the reproductive system. Annelidan characters include (a) segmentally repeated coelomoducts; (b) the structure of the eyes; (c) the rudimentary cephalization, only three head segments being present; and (d) the unstriated muscular body wall. Onychophora inhabit permanently damp localities and occur more especially beneath the bark of trees and underneath stones. The antennae, unlike those of other arthropods, appear to be pre-antennae and arise from the first head segment while the second segment bears the jaws. The tracheal system has a non-segmental arrangement since the absence of hard sclerites has allowed an irregular distribution. The tracheae are very fine tubes, 2–3 μm in diameter, which arise in dense bundles from numerous flask-like pits in the integument.

The higher arthropods evolved a thicker and more rigid cuticle than the Onychophora and consequently individual sclerites became developed so as to allow flexibility. The appendages for the same reason

184

have acquired a jointed structure and are more complex than the unsegmented lobe-like (lobopodial) appendages of the Onychophora.

The **Myriapoda** have a five- or six-segmented head bearing a single pair of antennae. The trunk is composed of numerous leg-bearing segments and is without differentiation into thorax and abdomen. The tracheal system is provided with segmentally repeated spiracles and the excretory organs are Malpighian tubules. These animals almost always hatch from the egg with a smaller number of trunk segments and limbs than are present when they are sexually mature. The addition of new segments takes place by subdivision of the penultimate segment. It is still uncertain whether the Myriapods form a natural, monophyletic taxon, but they can be divided into four groups. The Chilopoda (centipedes) and Diplopoda (millipedes) are the largest, the Symphyla and Pauropoda having a smaller number of species.

The Chilopoda have long, many-segmented antennae and the mouthparts comprise three pairs of appendages not unlike those found in insects. The first pair of legs is modified into jaw-like poison claws and the gonopore is on the penultimate segment of the body.

The Diplopoda have short seven-segmented antennae and their mouthparts are more specialized than those of Chilopoda. The body segments are mostly grouped in pairs under each apparent tergum and the gonopore is on the third segment.

The Symphyla are small colourless Myriapoda with long, many-segmented antennae and mouthparts resembling those of Insecta. The trunk consists of 14 segments, each bearing a pair of appendages and usually a pair of styli and protrusible vesicles. The gonopore is on the fourth trunk segment.

The Pauropoda are small, blind, soft-bodied forms, living in the soil or in other concealed habitats. They have large, branched antennae, mandibles, and one pair of maxillae. The last head segment bears no appendages and the 11 trunk segments are arranged like those of the Diplopods, with nine or ten pairs of legs and an anterior gonopore.

The **Insecta** (Hexapoda) show characters that ally them more closely with the Myriapoda than with any other arthropods. The division of the body into head, thorax and abdomen, the presence of only three pairs of legs and usually of two pairs of wings readily distinguish adult insects from other arthropods.

The relationships between the major Arthropodan groups listed above have been much disputed. There is some evidence, emphasized especially by Manton, Tiegs and Anderson, that Arthropod character-istics have arisen independently in several evolutionary lineages. One of these, constituting the so-called Uniramia, includes the insects, their closest relatives the Myriapods, and the Onychophora, of which the last-mentioned group represents the least modified survivors of the supposedly ancestral Uniramian stock. On this view, the Trilobites, Chelicerata and Crustacea seem to be only rather distantly related to one another and to the Uniramia, and their origins are obscure. An older interpretation of Arthropod relationships, but one which is still defended by modern authorities such as Siewing, Hennig, Lauterbach and Weygoldt, holds that the Arthropoda is a natural, monophyletic assemblage, among which the major evolutionary lines are related as is depicted in Fig. 99.

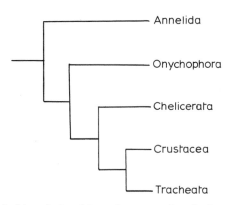

Fig. 99   Probable relationships of some major Arthropodan groups

There is little convincing palaeontological evidence enabling a decision to be made between these alternative interpretations. Already in the Lower Cambrian Burgess Shale deposits of N. America there is an abundant and diverse Arthropod fauna composed of trilobites and some 30 genera of non-trilobitic Arthropods which cannot be placed satisfactorily in any higher taxa and which shed no light on the possibly polyphyletic nature of the group. Probably the most interesting of the Burgess Shale fossils is *Aysheaia pedunculata* which, although marine and differing in some respects from *Peripatus* and its Recent allies, seems to be close to the ancestors of the Onychophora and confirms the archaic character of this group.

THE ANCESTRY OF INSECTS

Both the alternative views of Arthropod phylogeny outlined above concur in associating the insects with the Myriapods rather than the Trilobita, Chelicerata or Crustacea, but they do not agree in the further details of the phylogeny which they offer. For Manton and others who accept the likelihood of widespread convergent evolution, the different groups of Myriapods and most, if not all, of the major groups of Apterygote insects evolved separately from primitive Onychophora-

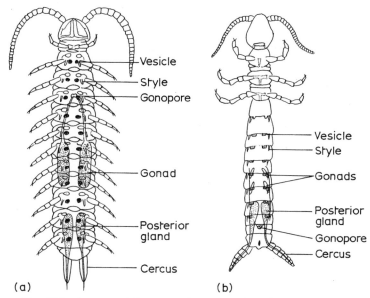

Fig. 100   Structural features of (a) Symphyla and (b) Diplura

like Uniramia with a soft cuticle, unsegmented lobopodial appendages, and little specialization of head-segments. The alternative hypothesis regards the Myriapods and insects as together making up a mono-phyletic group, the Tracheata, whose synapomorphies include the loss of the second pair of antennae and mandibular palps (found in Crustacea) and the acquisition of tracheae and Malpighian tubules. Neither phylogenetic hypothesis seems to be very firmly based, though the monophyletic character of the Tracheata is better supported by cladistic arguments. Even so, the precise nature of the cladistic relationships among the various groups of Myriapods and between them and the insects remain unsettled. The insects (in the sense of all groups of hexapod arthropods) are now increasingly regarded as a monophyletic entity because of an impressive array of synapomorphic characters. Although some of these have been modified in the course of insect evolution, the ground-plan of the insects entails: a three-segmented thorax; three pairs of walking legs; head incorporating three gnathal segments (mandibular, maxillary and labial); abdomen of 11 segments plus a terminal non-segmented telson; legs composed of six basic segments (coxa, trochanter, femur, tibia, tarsus and pretarsus); and probably also a characteristic arrangement of $9 + 9 + 2$ microtubules in the sperm flagellum. It is not improbable that the insects' closest allies among the Myriapoda are to be found in the Symphyla, though the arguments for this depend heavily on symplesiomorphic resemblances between the Symphyla and the Diplura and therefore need to be re-

187

evaluated (Fig. 100). Again, palaeontology has contributed little to the solution of this problem. Myriapod fossils are few and uninformative, while the earliest known insect, *Rhyniella praecursor* from the Rhynie chert of Scotland (Lower Devonian), is a Collembolan and sheds little light on the origin of the class.

APTERYGOTE RELATIONSHIPS

Comparative structural data suggest that the primary evolutionary division among the insects is into a group of Entognathan orders (the Diplura, Protura and Collembola) on the one hand, and all remaining insects on the other. The argument for the monophyly of the Entognatha depends largely on the characteristic way in which the mouthparts are partly or entirely sunk into a gnathal pouch, formed through overgrowth of cephalic folds and from which the tips of the mandibles and maxillae can be protruded for feeding. Manton, it is true, has shown that the Diplura and Collembola have rather different forms of entognathy, but this does not prove that the condition was acquired independently, and the Entognatha also show two other synapomorphies: the compound eyes and the Malpighian tubules, assumed to have been present in primitive insects, are reduced or absent. Within the Entognatha the Diplura show more primitive features than do the Protura and Collembola. These last two orders probably form a monophyletic group since they share several specialized features such as the absence of cerci and abdominal spiracles; the more deeply sunk mouthparts; a groove, the linea ventralis, on the underside of the head; and the reduction or loss of one of the pretarsal claws.

The sister-group of the Entognatha consists of all the remaining insects and can be referred to as the Ectognatha. There is little doubt that it is a monophyletic complex, as it shows a large number of synapomorphies: the second antennal segment (pedicel) contains Johnston's organ; the flagellar segments of the antennae have lost their intrinsic musculature; posterior tentorial arms have been acquired; the tarsi are divided into non-musculated subsegments (tarsomeres); the first abdominal segment has lost its paired appendages; an appendicular ovipositor is derived from the eighth and ninth abdominal segments; and the developing embryo is enclosed in an amniotic cavity. The dominant group of Ectognathan insects is, of course, the Pterygota (winged insects and their secondarily apterous descendants), whose monophyletic character is established by the common possession in their ground-plan of wings and associated thoracic modifications. However, the Ectognatha also includes the primitively wingless insects formerly regarded as a single order and called the Thysanura. There is now little doubt that these form two monophyletic taxa, the orders

Archaeognatha (bristletails) and Zygentoma (silverfish). They appear to share only one specialized feature, the terminal junction of the genital ducts to form a median canal, which must be considered to have evolved convergently since the Zygentoma share far more apomorphic features with the Pterygota, giving a characteristic 'dicondylian' ground-plan. Among these synapomorphies are the distinctive second articulation between a condyle on the clypeal region of the head and an anterior ginglymus on the mandible; the loss of median ligamentous connections between the adductor muscles of the mandibles and the maxillae, with the consequent transfer of the origins of these muscles to the tentorium; the suppression of the hypopharyngeal fulturae; the subdivision of the tarsus into five subsegments; the fully developed gonangula at the base of the ovipositor; and the transverse and longitudinal commissures of the tracheal system. Presumably the various groups of primitively wingless insects underwent some kind of radiation in the Palaeozoic, but there are few signs of this in the fossil record. A Collembolan from the Lower Permian of S. Africa adds nothing to our knowledge of Entognathan relationships, but Machilid-like forms from the Carboniferous and Lower Permian, such as *Dasyleptus brogniarti*, are of some interest since they lack cerci but retain a long, segmented median process. They have been made the sole representatives of a fossil order, the Monura, but too little is known of them to incorporate them with any assurance in the phylogenetic scheme suggested above.

PHYLOGENY OF THE PTERYGOTA

Fossil remains of winged insects are first known from the lower part of the Upper Carboniferous (including those from such well-known localities as Commentry, Westphalia, the Kuznetsk Basin and Mazon Creek, Illinois). It is reasonable to suppose that the Pterygota arose some time before this, perhaps as early as the Devonian. Unfortunately, nothing certain is known of the origin of insect wings and flight; several more or less incompatible hypotheses have been proposed to explain how wings arose, the paranotal theory being perhaps the most likely (p. 25). The Permian period was a time of considerable radiation among the winged insects, as illustrated by many species described from important localities of this age at Elmo (Kansas), Belmont (New South Wales) and the Arkhangelsk region of the Urals. By the end of the Palaeozoic the extant orders Ephemeroptera, Odonata, Orthoptera, Dictyoptera, Plecoptera, Psocoptera and Hemiptera had all come into being, as well as the holometabolous Coleoptera, Mecoptera, Trichoptera and perhaps Neuroptera. In addition to these a considerable number of purely fossil orders have been recognized from the Palaeozoic, though any attempt at incorporating them into a general scheme of

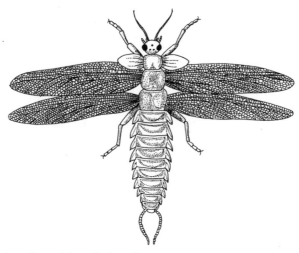

Fig. 101   *Stenodictya lobata* (Palaeodictyoptera) (reconstruction by Handlirsch)

Pterygote phylogeny is severely handicapped by the fact that the fossils usually consist of wing impressions only, with relatively little information available on the structure of other parts of the body. The generally recognized fossil orders of insects are the Palaeodictyoptera (Fig. 101), Megasecoptera, Diaphanopterodea, Protodonata, Protorthoptera, Miomoptera, Protelytroptera, Caloneurodea and Glosselytrodea; in addition to these there are a few further groups of disputed or less well-defined status. Three of the extinct orders, the Palaeodictyoptera, Megasecoptera and Diaphanopterodea, were especially prominent in Carboniferous and Lower Permian times and seem all to have been provided with piercing mouthparts, long cerci and well-developed ovipositors. The Palaeodictyoptera and Megasecoptera were apparently unable to flex their wings over the abdomen at rest, and in this they resemble the modern Ephemeroptera and Odonata, whereas the Diaphanopterodea had evolved a wing-flexing mechanism, apparently independently of that found in most Recent Pterygota. The Protodonata are probably related to the Odonata and there are three orders of uncertain but probably Orthopteroid affinities, the Protorthoptera, Miomoptera and Protelytroptera, the last having a distinctly beetle-like facies, though it is probably an offshoot of the cockroaches. The relationships of the two remaining extinct taxa, the Caloneurodea and Glosselytrodea, are far less clear: they have each been regarded as Endopterygotes by some authorities and as Orthopteroids by others. The Mesozoic insect fauna is best known from the Triassic and least well known from Cretaceous strata. It has a more modern appearance and includes early representatives of three large holometabolous orders. The

Hymenoptera are first represented by Triassic sawflies of the family Xyelidae and the earliest undoubted Diptera by forms like *Architipula* from the Upper Triassic (Rhaetic). Among the Lepidoptera the earliest fossils are Micropterigid-like forms from the Jurassic, followed by several other groups of lower Lepidoptera in the Cretaceous. Tertiary fossils are abundant in Oligocene amber, mainly from the Baltic area; they are mostly referable to present day families and genera and throw little light on major phylogenetic developments within the Insecta.

In the absence of compelling palaeontological evidence on the phylogeny of Pterygote insects it is desirable to consider the cladistic inferences of evolutionary relationships. This can only be done effectively by examining data for the Recent orders, though even there one is often limited by the inadequate morphological information available for some groups. Much discussion has turned around the relationships between the Ephemeroptera, Odonata and the remaining Pterygotes. Three logically possible phylogenetic relationships can be envisaged, and all have been supported by one authority or another. The older view, uniting the Ephemeroptera and Odonata as the Palaeoptera, in contrast with the remaining Neoptera, rested on the absence of a wing-flexing mechanism in the Palaeoptera, which therefore hold their wings outstretched vertically or horizontally at rest rather than folding them back over the abdomen. However, the absence of wing-flexing is likely to be a plesiomorphic feature, as are also the other few characters uniting the Ephemeroptera and Odonata. They do not therefore provide good evidence that the Palaeoptera constitute a monophyletic group. Instead it is perhaps more likely that one should regard the Ephemeroptera as the sister-group of all other extant Pterygota. These (i.e. the Odonata + Neoptera) display what are probably a convincing set of synapomorphic characteristics: the loss of imaginal moulting (as retained by the Ephemeropteran subimago); tracheation of wing-pads from their own and the following segment; basal fusion of the veins R_1 and Rs; unpaired gonopores; and the loss of some primitive cephalic and thoracic muscles.

The identification of major monophyletic groups within the Neoptera also presents some difficulties. Traditionally it has been the custom to recognize three supraordinal groups which, using Martynov's nomenclature, may be called the Polyneoptera, Paraneoptera and Oligoneoptera. The first of these is the complex of 'Orthopteroid' orders, represented today by the Plecoptera, Grylloblattodea, Orthoptera, Phasmida, Dermaptera, Embioptera, Dictyoptera, Isoptera and perhaps also the somewhat specialized Zoraptera. The features which they (or at least their more generalized representatives) have in common are the well-developed mandibulate mouthparts, the enlarged anal lobe of the hind wing, retention of the appendages of the eleventh abdominal segment as cerci, the presence of many Malpighian tubules, and a ventral nerve cord with several separate segmental ganglia. Unfortunately, all of these characteristics (except, perhaps, the enlarged hind wing) are likely to be plesiomorphic Neopteran features, so there is no convincing proof that the Polyneopteran orders form a natural, monophyletic group. Moreover, within this complex it has proved impossible to define convincing supraordinal groupings, apart perhaps from that consisting of the Dictyoptera + Isoptera. The position is even more unsatisfactory when attempts are made to incorporate extinct orders like the Protorthoptera, Miomoptera, Protelytroptera and perhaps others into a phylogeny of the Polyneoptera.

The Paraneoptera or Hemipteroid orders (Psocoptera, Phthiraptera, Hemiptera and Thysanoptera), on the other hand, are very likely to be a monophyletic group as they share a number of specialized features: the reduced venation and absence of an enlarged anal lobe in the hind wing; reduction of tarsal subsegments to three or fewer; the rod–like lacinia; the absence of cerci; the fusion of the gonangulum with the ninth abdominal tergum; four or fewer Malpighian tubules; fusion of the abdominal ganglia; and a biflagellate spermatozoon. Together they appear to form a sister-group of the Zoraptera and they seem to fall into two supraordinal, monophyletic groups. One of these, consisting of the Psocoptera and the Phthiraptera, has many synapomorphic features and may be further subdivided cladistically. The other, consisting of the Hemiptera and Thysanoptera, is less convincingly monophyletic, though it is difficult to know where else the Thysanoptera could be placed.

The third major phyletic branch of the Neopteran insects is composed of the insect orders with a complete metamorphosis, variously known as the Oligoneoptera. Endopterygota or Holometabola. The characteristic metamorphosis, with larval stages followed by a single quiescent pupal instar, is their outstanding synapomorphy, supported by the specialized larval eyes and the internal development of wings and external genitalia. There is no serious doubt of their monophyletic character, though there is no clear indication of their sister-group and virtually nothing is known of their origin apart from the fact that it must have occurred early in insect evolution. Permian deposits already contain fossils that may be referred to the Neuroptera, Coleoptera, Mecoptera and Trichoptera, while the doubtfully Endopterygote orders Caloneurodea and Glosselytrodea are found in both the Carboniferous and Permian. Whatever form this early Endopterygote radiation took, it has left only limited evidence of undoubtedly monophyletic supraordinal groups. The Neuroptera (Sialoidea, Raphidioidea and Plannipennia, sometimes treated as separate orders) agree in having a ground-plan with a specialized form of ovipositor with fused dorsal valves and an intrinsic musculature. The Trichoptera and Lepidoptera have long been regarded as close relatives, though it is only recently that the full extent of their synapomorphies has been revealed. They are now known to share over 20 specialized features in their ground-plan, some of which are as follows: fusion of the prementum and hypopharynx; pronotum with paired setose wart-like structures; fusion of the secondary furcal arms of the pterothorax with the posterior margin of the corresponding epimeron; pretarsus with a strong socketed bristle, the pseudempodium; wings with an extensive covering of setae (modified into scales in the Lepidoptera); and the insertion of the ventral diaphragm muscles on the

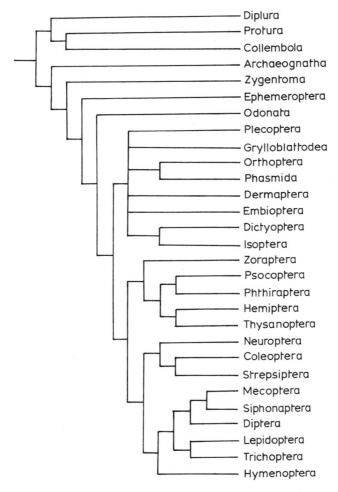

Fig. 102 Possible phylogenetic relationships of extant orders of insects
See text for discussion; note that not all branches of the dendrogram are supported by adequate cladistic evidence.

nerve-cord. The Mecoptera and Diptera, together with the Siphon-aptera, also seem to constitute a monophyletic group, though with fewer synapomorphies (such as the loss of the prothoracic spina and of some labial muscles). The Trichoptera + Lepidoptera form a sister-group of the Mecoptera + Diptera + Siphonaptera, the whole assemblage of five orders forming the monophyletic Panorpoid complex (also known as the superorder Panorpida). The affinities of the Coleoptera, however, are far from clear, though they may share a few specializations with the Neuroptera. Whether the Strepsiptera are really close allies of the Coleoptera is also undecided. The Hymenoptera, too, are an isolated group of uncertain affinities, though the eruciform larva of the Symphyta, with its single-clawed legs and silk-secreting labial glands, suggests a possible relationship with the Panorpoids.

Taxonomic implications. There is no compelling reason why a classification should reflect exactly all aspects of the phylogeny of a group, though many taxonomists believe that phylogenetic classifications are the most desirable ones. Whether this principle can yet be applied rigorously in practice to the higher classification of insects may be doubted in view of the many uncertainties in their phylogeny, some of which have been indicated above. However, there is some evidence that a number of supraordinal taxa found in many older classifications are not really natural, monophyletic groups and are probably best abandoned. Among wingless insects, for example, this is true of the 'Apterygota' and the 'Thysanura' (in the wide sense of Archaeognatha +Zygentoma). It is also true of the so-called Exopterygota (i.e. all non-holometabolous winged insects and their secondarily apterous descendants) and, within these, of the Palaeoptera (Ephemeroptera + Odonata). The Mallophaga is probably also a taxon that should be given up; it includes the biting lice, a group of Phthiraptera defined only by primitive features and not reflecting phylogenetic relationships within the Psocodea (Psocoptera + Phthiraptera). The same principle may be applied to other 'paraphyletic' taxa at various levels in the systematic hierarchy, and it is even possible that such familiar and apparently well-established taxa as the Dictyoptera, Psocoptera, Homoptera, Megaloptera and Symphyta may eventually have to be replaced or newly delimited if strictly phylogenetic classifications are required. The extent to which cladistic methods can be successfully applied at the lower taxonomic levels seems to be more debatable, but lies outside the scope of this chapter.

6

Some important modes of life in insects

In the course of their evolution the insects have become adapted to life in many very different habitats. This process of adaptive radiation has been accomplished through the establishment of intricate structural and functional relationships with the many different physical, chemical and biological features of the insects' environment, and includes the development of varied modes of behaviour which allow them to exploit these relationships to the full. A very wide range of terrestrial habitats has been occupied by insects, ranging over all of the major life-zones from the tropics to circumpolar regions. Within each of these a large proportion of the insect fauna is dependent directly on the many different species of flowering plants (the second most numerous group of organisms in terms of the species extant today) and close, often highly specific and obligate relationships have been evolved between the two groups. All the main niches offered by plants – foliage, flowers, fruits, seeds and subterranean structures – are exploited by one group of insects or another. The insects feed by chewing up the freely exposed parts of the plant or by sucking the sap from its vascular system or its cells, or by tunnelling into its tissues, or living on various plant products such as timber or harvested crops. Mutually beneficial relationships between insects and other organisms are commonly encountered, as in the diverse pollination mechanisms of Angiosperms or the symbioses with fungi and bacteria. Another major food resource has been exploited by those insects which are external or internal parasites of other animals, the great majority being parasitoids of other species of insects. The many different kinds of freshwater aquatic habitats have also been colonized repeatedly by the insects during their evolution, so that insects make up a major part of many freshwater communities. Decomposing plant and animal matter of the most varied kinds also provides habitats and food resources for large numbers of saprophagous and other insects which constitute important elements in the food-webs of many communities, both terrestrial and aquatic.

Two special features of the insects contribute in important ways to their adaptive radiation. Firstly, the very large number of insect species means that their adaptive radiation is evident not only in the broad terms indicated above, but also at much lower evolutionary levels within families or genera, where a characteristic mode of life may show many detailed variations on a single common theme. Secondly, the life-cycle of Endopterygote insects (and, to a lesser extent, of some Exopterygota) has allowed great divergence in form and habits between the larva and the adult, so increasing greatly the range of adaptive modification that the insects exhibit. Examples illustrating many forms of adaptive radiation will be found in the following discussion of some important modes of life encountered among the insects.

RELATIONSHIPS BETWEEN INSECTS AND PLANTS

Very many insect species live on plants or on plant products as diverse as pollen, nectar, stored grains or timber. Plants (and one is dealing here mainly with the higher vascular plants, especially the Angiosperms) provide the insects with food, shelter and sites for mating and oviposition, and in turn they suffer direct or indirect injury from the insects' attentions, though many flowering plants benefit from the close relationships that have evolved between their flowers and pollinating insects and a few plant species feed on insects (pp. 207 and 214). The herbivorous habit is widespread among some insect groups: most or all of the Acridoidea, Phasmida, Thysanoptera and Homoptera are phytophagous, as are almost all Lepidopteran larvae, a high proportion of the very numerous order Coleoptera, and some Hymenoptera (notably the larvae of sawflies (Symphyta) and the Cynipoidea). Many plants are utilized by a large number of insect species: some 1500 species of insects have been recorded from oaks, 600 from elms and 400 from apple, and insects of one species or another attack virtually all parts of plants. Many are mandibulate feeders, chewing up foliage and stems, others mine or roll leaves, induce galls, bore into stems, roots, tubers, bulbs, fruits or flower-heads or pierce the plant to suck up sap from its parenchyma or vascular system. The main adaptive features which insects show to their varied phytophagous habits concern: (a) the structure of their mouthparts and the mechanisms used to ingest food; (b) the sensory and behavioural processes used in selecting or recognizing their food; (c) their digestive physiology, including the complement of enzymes, the triturating mechanisms present, and the association with symbiotic micro-organisms involved in digestion and nutrition.

Their capacity for utilizing plant material is one of the major evolutionary achievements of insects, the more striking since plants generally provide food materials of lower nutritive quality than are available from animal prey and because phytophagous insects seem to be less efficient at converting their diet into their own body-substance than are predatory insects. Perhaps for these reasons it is not surprising that the phytophagous habit, although frequently encountered, is a predominant or major mode of life in only nine orders of insects, as against the 20 or so which feed mainly on animals or are scavengers among decaying organic matter or micro-organisms.

A striking feature of the relationships between insects and plants is the preference shown by many insects for a very restricted range of plants, sometimes amounting to a high degree of specificity in which related species of insects are associated with only a small number of related host-plants. For example, not one of the 40 000 or so described species of Homoptera has been recorded from even 1% of the 230 000 described species of vascular plants; over half of the species of aphids and Thysanoptera are specific to members of one genus of plant; and the leaf-mining Agromyzidae show a similar very high degree of specificity in their choice of host-plants. However, at the same time there are insects which can live and develop successfully on a wide variety of plants, though some of these polyphagous species may include several subspecific, genetically distinct biotypes. In other cases a single genus of insects may include several species which, though individually showing a high degree of specificity, are supported by a range of very diverse plants. Thus, the 21 British species of the Psyllid *Trioza* are distributed among hosts from 12 different families of flowering plants. The specificity shown in the relationship of plants and insects is only very partially explained in terms of the evolutionary history of the two groups. For instance, most host changes in aphids seem to occur through the capture of new, not necessarily closely related, hosts, and among Lepidoptera there appears to be a selection of host-plants based on chemical relationships which do not reflect phylogenetic affinities. On the other hand, some flowers and their pollinating insects show such striking instances of mutual adaptation in form and function as to imply very closely integrated processes of co-evolution.

Since insects can inflict injury on plants, the latter have often evolved defence mechanisms. These include physical deterrents such as the waxes, cutins and suberins which make the surface of a plant slippery, or thick cuticles and a high content of siliceous materials which make the leaf and stem physically tougher. Surface hairs may be used to deter insects, as in the bean plant *Phaseolus vulgaris*, whose hooked trichomes trap *Aphis craccivora*, or in *Nicotiana*, where the hairs secrete toxic alkaloids, especially nicotine. In other plants the flow of resins from injured tissues may drown the attacker, as in larvae of the Pine Shoot Moth *Rhyacionia buoliana* that feeds on pines. Many plants have evolved chemical deterrents against injurious insects. These defensive chemicals

197

may be permanently present in the plant or released in response to insect attack. They include nitrogen-containing compounds such as non-protein amino acids, cyanogenic glucosides, glucosinolates, alkaloids and lectins, as well as those substances which do not contain nitrogen and may be divided into terpenoid derivatives (mono-, di-, tri- and sesquiterpenes, cardiac glycosides and saponins) and phenolics, such as tannins and flavonoids. Some examples include the alkaloid tomatine of tomatoes which deters the Colorado Potato Beetle *Leptinotarsa decemlineata*, the sesquiterpenoid gossypol, which protects cotton plants from attack, and the tannins which form in oak leaves during the summer and which cause larvae of the Winter Moth *Operophtera brumata* to abandon feeding on oak after the spring and to turn their attention to other plants. Some of these substances are potent insecticides which have been extracted for commercial use: the pyrethroids are mono-terpenes from the flowers of *Chrysanthemum* spp., nicotine is an alkaloid from the tobacco plant and rotenone is an isoflavonoid extracted from the tuberous roots of *Derris elliptica*. A particularly effective deterrent, which inhibits feeding, and is therefore sometimes referred to as an antifeedant, is azadirachtin, a triterpenoid occurring in the neem tree, *Azadirachta indica*. In general, plants providing reasonably stable, long-term resources, such as woody perennials and the mature leaves of evergreen trees, tend to deter insects by means of resins, tannins and enzyme inhibitors which often occur in high concentrations and act by reducing the digestibility of the plant tissues. On the other hand, more temporary plant resources such as herbaceous plants and deciduous trees tend to produce lower concentrations of highly active toxins (alkaloids, cardiac glycosides, etc.) which exert pharmacological effects on the metabolism of insects and other animals consuming them. Some insects have turned these toxic materials to their own use; they are able to feed on toxin-containing plants and store the poisons in their own tissues so that they are then available in the insects' own defence against vertebrate predators. The habit has been recorded among Lepidoptera, Hemiptera, Coleoptera, Orthoptera and other groups and is associated with the development of warning (aposematic) coloration, so that predators may learn to recognize the toxic or unpalatable insects. Among the many examples are the swallowtail butterfly *Battus philenor*, which sequesters aristolochic acid-I from the *Aristolochia* plants on which the larva feeds; *Danaus plexippus*, the Monarch Butterfly, whose larvae feed on milkweeds (*Asclepias* spp.) from which they sequester a number of cardenolides; and the Cinnabar Moth *Tyria jacobaeae*, whose larvae obtain a number of pyrrolizidine alkaloids from ragwort (*Senecio vulgaris* and *S. jacobaea*).

Since a given species of insect feeds on only a very restricted range of plants (sometimes on only a single species) it needs to be equipped with sensory and behavioural mechanisms enabling it to locate the required plant or to choose it from among others available, or even to select that part of a plant on which it feeds preferentially. These host-selection mechanisms are numerous and show clear differences from one species to another, but the most important components involved are responses to the visual, olfactory and gustatory stimuli provided by the plants, some operating over distances of several metres, others at much closer range or becoming effective only after the insect has made a trial feed. It may sometimes be convenient to divide the process of host-plant selection into host habitat finding, host finding, host recognition and host acceptance. It is also necessary to bear in mind that host selection may be carried out by the ovipositing female as well as by the feeding stage.

The fact that many herbivorous insects respond positively to yellow surfaces suggests that visually mediated attraction to the yellow pigments found in leaves may be characteristic of foliage-feeding insects. However, some insects can also detect potential hosts at relatively short range on the basis of shape or size, responding positively to forms with a narrow silhouette like a tall stem, or to a vertical boundary between light and dark, or, in some butterflies, to plants bearing leaves of a characteristic shape. Obviously, insects with well-developed compound eyes are likely to make more effective use of visual stimuli than Endopterygote larvae which rely on their less efficient ocelli. Tephritids such as *Rhagoletis, Ceratitis* and *Dacus* use visual stimuli to select the fruits on which they mate, through their shape, size and the intensity of reflected light, while adults of the sawfly *Hoplocampa testudinea* locate apple blossoms for feeding and oviposition by their colour and reflectance rather than their shape.

The olfactory and gustatory recognition of plants involves chemo-receptor sensilla, especially those on the antennae and mouthparts. Olfactory stimuli are provided by specific chemical substances or, in many cases, by mixtures of substances with a specific composition. For example, the aphid *Rhopalosiphum padi* is specifically attracted by benzaldehyde; the Colorado Potato Beetle *Leptinotarsa decemlineata* responds to a mixture of unsaturated 6-carbon alcohols, aldehydes and esters; and the Cabbage Root-fly *Delia radicum* is attracted by propan-ethiol and dipropyl disulphide, and can be induced to oviposit by a variety of methyl and propyl sulphide esters. Larvae of the butterfly *Papilio ajax* can distinguish between the odours of six different essential oils through sensilla borne on the antennae. These sensilla contain in all 16 odour-sensitive receptor cells with spontaneous action potentials differing from one cell to another. When an odour is perceived, each cell may increase or decrease the activity with which it generates nervous impulses, so altering the pattern of sensory input to the brain. Coding of the stimulus is thus achieved through sensory cells with overlapping stimulus spectra (the so-called generalist chemoreceptors) and these should be distinguished from the more specialized receptor cells which respond to specific pheromones. The latency of response and the adaptation time are also characteristic of each receptor cell, and thus supplement the changes in impulse rate patterns. In ways such as this a very limited number of sensilla can detect very many subtle differences in the composition of the chemical stimuli. The maxillary palps of Lepidopteran larvae also bear olfactory sensilla (though of lower sensitivity) as well as styloconic gustatory receptors that are stimulated by contact with the plant or with juices exuding from it. There may be four sense-cells associated with each of the two gustatory sensilla on a palp, with each cell responding to a different substance, such as salts, amino acids, fructose, inositol or various secondary plant materials such as mustard oil glycosides, sàlicin or populin, according to the species of insect. Several cells may respond to a given substance but with different senstivities, and in a number of caterpillars there are deterrent-sensitive receptors which respond to the various chemically diverse feeding deterrents such as quinine, pilocarpine and azadirachtin. Further contact chemoreceptors occur on the maxillary galea, the inner face of the labrum, the hypopharynx and the labial palps of many insects, and in some there are additional chemoreceptors on the tarsi, as in some butterflies. In Orthoptera there may be several thousand chemoreceptor sensilla on the mouthparts, with tens of thousands of individual sensory cells.

If an insect has not been deterred by its initial sensory contacts it will start feeding. The plant juices so taken in will contain dissolved substances that stimulate receptors on the inner surfaces of the mouthparts and the pre-oral food cavity. Some of these substances, differing from one insect species to another, will act as phagostimulants, inducing the insect to continue feeding; others, as indicated above, may act as deterrents. Phagostimulants may be nutritionally important substances like sugars, amino acids and lipids, but they also include non-nutritional secondary plant substances comparable to those which act as olfactory attractants or as deterrents. In fact, a single substance may act as a deterrent to feeding in one species of insect and as a phagostimulant in another. For example, species of the plant genus *Hypericum* (St John's Wort) contain hypericin, which deters many insects from feeding on the plants but acts as a phagostimulant to a Chrysomelid beetle, *Chrysolina*, which feeds on the flower-heads and upper parts of the plant, where the concentration of hypericin is greatest. Thus, the chemical basis of host-plant selection by insects depends on an interaction between deterrent and phagostimulant or oviposition-stimulating substances, some also nutritional, but others providing only token stimuli. Their effect varies from one species of insect to another and depends not only on individual chemicals but also often on the proportions in which these occur in a mixture of substances and whether they inhibit or reinforce one anothers' action.

The resultant of all the various component responses involved in host selection is a pattern of behaviour that ensures whatever degree of specificity (or lack of specificity) is shown by the insect. The importance of the different modes of stimulation will differ considerably from one instance to another. Aphids, for example, are to a considerable extent passive migrants which are deposited on or near various plants by turbulent air movements. They probe the plant superficially with their mouthparts to detect whether it is a suitable host, and only if it is do they probe more deeply and begin to feed; if the plant proves unsuitable they take off again and the process is repeated. In a rather different kind of host-selection behaviour the Cabbage Root-fly *Delia radicum* responds over a distance of several metres to the odour of volatile compounds (allyl isothiocyanate and others) from *Brassica* plants and at closer range (<2 m) to visual stimuli. Conversely, the Greenhouse Whitefly *Trialeurodes vaporariorum* detects potential hosts at a distance by visual means and only uses chemical stimuli at very short range.

LEAF-MINING INSECTS

A distinctive and specialized phytophagous habit has been evolved by the leaf-mining insects, in which the larval stages live and feed between the upper and lower epidermis of a leaf-blade, causing a characteristic blister-like or worm-like appearance where they have fed. A very similar habit has also evolved in a much smaller number of species which live just beneath the surface of fruits, stems, petioles or flower stalks, and a few species can live both in these situations and as leaf-miners. True leaf-miners are found among the Coleoptera (some Buprestidae, Curculionidae and Chrysomelidae), in the Hymenoptera (a few Tenthredinidae), and especially among the Diptera (Agromyzidae, some Tephritidae and Anthomyiidae) and the Lepidoptera (especially the Nepticulidae and Gracillariidae, but also in several other families of smaller moths). The various leaf-mining species show a considerable degree of specificity in their choice of host-plants and this, together with the form of the mines themselves, may be sufficiently characteristic to identify the miners with some accuracy (Fig. 103).

The Agromyzidae are the principal family of leaf-mining Diptera. They consist of about 1800 species, mostly with leaf-mining larvae and a substantial proportion of them in the large genera *Phytomyza*, *Liriomyza* and *Agromyza*. The female insects insert their eggs into the plant tissue with the oviscapt, and the larva then usually forms a so-called upper-

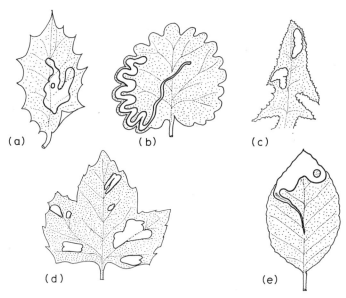

Fig. 103   Leaf-mining insects

(a) Blotch mine of *Phytomyza ilicis* (Agromyzidae) on holly leaf; (b) serpentine linear mine of *Phytomyza glechomae* (Agromyzidae) on leaf of *Glechoma hederacea* ((a) and (b) after Séguy). (c) Blotch mine of *Agromyza sonchi* on leaf of *Sonchus* (after Spencer); (d) *Phyllonorycter platani* (Lepidoptera: Gracillariidae) on *Platanus* (after Hering); (e) linear-blotch mine on beech due to *Orchestes fagi* (Coleoptera: Curculionidae) (after Eidmann).

surface mine, feeding on the layer of palisade tissue immediately below the upper epidermis of the leaf. However, some species have larvae that feed in the lower parenchymal layers of the leaf or in the middle layers, while a further group make 'full-depth' mines in which all the leaf parenchyma is eaten away. The shape of the mine is also characteristic: it may be linear or serpentine, or may form an irregular expanded blotch, and it may be near the margin of the leaf, along the mid-rib, or near the centre. The mine may show obvious broadening as the larva grows, and the deposition of frass may also be distinctive: some species deposit a regular line of frass along the middle or sides of the mine, others may deposit it all at the end of the mine. Some species form large blotch mines in which several larvae live together. The fully fed larvae of some species pupate in the mine, whereas others leave it by a small slit and pupate on the leaf or in the soil. A few Agromyzids mine the thallus of ferns and horse-tails, but the great majority are associated with flowering plants, especially the Compositae and Gramineae. A few familiar members of the group may be mentioned. *Phytomyza ilicis* has a larva which first feeds in the mid-rib of a holly leaf, then forms an irregular linear-blotch upper surface mine in which it pupates. *Phytomyza syngenesiae* and *P. horticola* are closely allied polyphagous species formerly confused under the single name *P. atricornis*; the first is found in many Composites, including chrysanthemums, *Sonchus, Taraxacum* and *Lactuca*, and is a horticultural pest. The common Celery Leaf-miner *Euleia* (= *Acidia*) *heraclei* is a Tephritid and the Mangold-fly *Pegomyia hyoscyami* is an Anthomyid; both form blotch mines.

In the Lepidoptera the majority of leaf-miners are to be found in the families Nepticulidae, Gracillariidae, Coleophoridae and Elachistidae, but other families include some species with this habit. Taken as a whole they show considerable diversity in the form of the mine, the methods of feeding, and the structural adaptations of the larvae. For example, *Elachista* forms linear mines, as do most species of *Nepticula*, but some form blotches and in the large genus *Phyllonorycter* (Gracillariidae) only blotches are found. These three genera are miners in all larval instars, but in some species the mining habit is confined to the earlier stages; the later larval instars of *Coleophora* and *Incurvaria*, for example, are case-bearers, while the older larvae of *Caloptilia* (= *Gracillaria*) live in a conical roll of leaves. The leaf-mining larvae of Lepidoptera may be tissue-feeders throughout their life or the first few instars may be sap-feeders, as in the Gracillariidae. These sap-feeding larvae are highly specialized with a rather flattened head and body, large labrum, reduced blade-like mandibles, no spinneret, an enlarged, hairy hypopharynx (with which the sap is collected), and no legs or abdominal prolegs. One or more normal, active, cylindrical, tissue-feeding instars may follow, though in some species these later instars do not feed and are concerned only with spinning a cocoon. Pupation may occur within the mine, or the fully-fed larva may leave it and pupate on the host-plant, on the ground, or in the soil, usually in a silken cocoon. Among some of the better-known Lepidopteran leaf-miners may be mentioned *Catoptilia azaleella*, a pest of indoor azaleas, and *C. syringella*, which forms conspicuous blotch mines on the leaves of lilac and privet. Various species of *Phyllonorycter* mine the leaves of many trees, including oaks, hornbeam, hazel, beech, birch, willow, apple, pear and hawthorn, as well as some herbaceous plants; all pupate in the mine. Many of the same host-plants are also mined by various species of *Nepticula*, most of which pupate in a silken cocoon on the ground.

INSECTS AND PLANT GALLS

Plant galls are masses of hypertrophied tissue, of very diverse form, produced by the plant in response to the presence of bacteria, fungi, mites, insects or other organisms. In insect-induced galls (Figs 104 and 105) this reaction of the plant appears to be due to substances secreted by the ovipositing female or the feeding larva; their chemical identity has not been established, though they may lead to localized overproduction

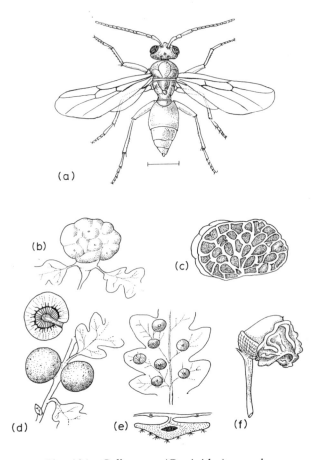

Fig. 104   Gall wasps (Cynipidae) on oak

(a) Sexual female of *Biorhiza pallida*; (b) oak-apple gall due to *B. pallida*; (c) section of same to show multilocular nature; (d) marble gall due to *Andricus kollari*, with section of a vacated gall; (e) button galls due to *Neuroterus lenticularis*, with section of same; (f) 'knopper gall' of acorn, caused by *Andricus quercuscalicis*. ((a)–(d) after Bernard, (e) after Houard, (f) after Kieffer.) Scale line = 1 mm.

of auxins or giberellins by the plant itself. The principal groups of gall-forming insects are the gall-midges or Cecidomyiidae (Diptera) and the gall-wasps or Cynipidae (Hymenoptera), most of whose larvae inhabit galls, together with some members of other groups such as the Aphidoidea, Coccoidea, Psyllidae, Thysanoptera, Tenthredinidae, Tephritidae and Agromyzidae. The gall-forming insects are usually highly specific in their choice of host-plant, and in the situation and form of the gall they produce. Galls may occur on virtually any part of a plant according to the species of insect involved – leaves, stems, roots, flowers and fruits may all be affected by one gall or another. The tissues

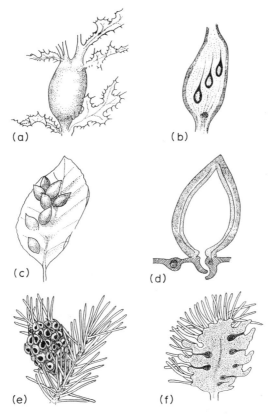

Fig. 105   Plant galls caused by insects
(a) *Urophora cardui* (Diptera: Tephritidae) in stem of the thistle *Cirsium arvense*; (b) longitudinal section of same, showing larva ((a) and (b) after Redfern). (c) *Mikiola fagi* (Diptera: Cecidomyiidae) on leaf of beech; (d) section through same; (e) pineapple gall of *Adelges abietis*; (f) section through same (c, d and f after Ross).

of the gall provide food for the gall-maker, which is also sheltered within it. Many galls enclose a single chamber containing one insect (usually a larval stage); others are compound structures containing many chambers and insects. In addition to the primary inhabitants, a gall may also contain a number of associated insects which either parasitize the gall-formers or are inquilines, using the gall simply for food and shelter.

Some of the characteristic galls of oaks in Europe, all caused by Cynipidae, include the large red and yellow, spongy, multilocular oak-apples due to *Biorhiza pallida*; the hard, green or brown spherical marble galls induced by *Andricus kollari*; the small, yellowish-brown button-shaped galls on the undersides of leaves, caused by *Neuroterus quercusbaccarum*; and the irregular woody deformations of the acorn and its cup due to *Andricus quercuscalicis*, a species recently introduced from continental Europe into Great Britain, and now spreading rapidly there. The Cynipidae show many examples of alternation of generations, a summer bisexually reproducing generation alternating with an over-wintering generation of parthenogenetic females. They show sexual dimorphism, the females of the two generations differ structurally and behaviourally, and the galls inhabited by the larvae of the two generations may be quite different in form and position. Thus, in *Biorhiza pallida* the larvae in the oak-apple galls give rise to winged males and to females that are apterous or almost so; these mate and the females lay eggs on the roots of the oak, producing galls there from which a generation of apterous parthenogenetic females emerges in the following spring to lay their eggs in the oak buds, forming oak-apple galls there once more. In *Neuroterus quercusbaccarum* the button galls overwinter on fallen leaves; in the spring they produce parthenogenetic females which induce grape-like galls among the oak catkins in early summer. *Andricus kollari* is unusual in that the bisexual generation emerges from galls on *Quercus cerris* while the marble galls that yield parthenogenetic females are produced on other species of oaks. A very distinctive Cynipid gall on roses is the conspicuous bedeguar or pin-cushion gall, about 5 cm across and covered with a mass of reddish filaments. It is caused by *Rhodites rosae*, which shows no alternation of generations and usually reproduces parthenogenetically, males being very rare. The yellowish or reddish bean-shaped galls commonly encountered on the leaves of willows are due to sawflies, *Pontania proxima* and related species, a largely parthenogenetic group with two broods a year; the mature larvae emerge and pupate on the bark or in the soil.

The Cecidomyiidae include a large number of gall-forming species, as well as others which have saprophagous or predacious larvae or attack plants without forming galls. The large genus *Dasineura* includes *D. ulmaria*, which forms reddish pustule-like galls on the upper surface of leaves of the Meadowsweet, *Filipendula ulmaria*; another species, *Dasineura crataegi*, causes rosette-like galls at the ends of hawthorn shoots. *Rhabdophaga rosaria* is another common Cecidomyiid, causing the 'camellia gall' of willows; each rosette contains a single larva which pupates in the gall. The upper surfaces of beech leaves often bear small yellowish galls, more or less egg-shaped or conical; those due to *Hartigiola annulipes* are hairy, while those caused by *Mikiola fagi* have a smooth surface. An unmistakable gall on Creeping Thistle (*Cirsium*) is the swollen egg-shaped stem gall caused by a fly of the family Tephritidae, *Urophora cardui*; at first soft and yellowish-green, it later becomes brown and woody and usually contains about four larvae, each in its own chamber, pupating in the gall.

Among the Aphidoidea a number of species cause thickening and rolling of the leaf-margins of their host-plants, leading to an open gall-like structure which shelters the aphids and allows them to feed and reproduce. A more distinctive structure is the hollow 'purse-gall' formed by *Pemphigus bursarius* on the petiole of poplars; these are the primary hosts and the aphids produced there migrate in the summer to lettuce and sow-thistle, on which they live without producing galls. Characteristic galls (Fig. 105) are formed by the Adelgidae, a family of aphids restricted to conifers and with complicated life-cycles involving migration from the primary host (some species of *Picea*) to various secondary hosts. In a typical case, that of *Adelges cooleyi*, a distinctive 'pineapple gall', or pseudocone, is produced on *Picea* through hyper-trophy of a group of adjacent needle-like leaves. Within the gall some of the larvae develop into apterous non-migratory forms which remain on the spruce, producing further pineapple galls there, while others give rise to migrants which colonize *Pseudotsuga* and there pass through several parthenogenetic generations before returning to *Picea*, where they give rise to sexual morphs which in turn eventually produce gallicolous forms there.

INSECTS AND THE POLLINATION OF FLOWERS

Though many flowering plants are capable of self-fertilization, the majority depend on pollination of their flowers from those of another plant in order to set fertile seed and maintain genetic diversity. This process of cross-pollination may be brought about by various agencies, including transfer of pollen by wind, water, birds and bats, but by far the most common method depends on the activity of insects which visit the flowers, usually to collect food in the form of pollen and nectar, and in doing so transfer pollen from one flower to another. The mutual advantages of this association have led to the evolution of a great variety of pollination mechanisms, some very complicated and highly specific and involving many structural, functional and behavioural adaptations in both insects and plants. Co-evolution of this kind has probably played an important part in the phylogeny of several groups of Angiosperms and insects.

Among the insects which commonly visit flowers are the following:

Coleoptera. Many families, especially the Mordellidae, Oedemer-idae, Malachiidae, Chrysomelidae, Cantharidae and Cerambycidae. Virtually all have short-tongued mouthparts and feed on pollen or on nectar from freely exposed nectaries.

Diptera. Tipulidae, Bibionidae, Chironomidae, Empididae and other families, especially the Syrphidae and Bombyliidae.

Lepidoptera. Many families, including the Papilionoidea and

Sphingidae; the long proboscis is adapted for feeding from deeply placed nectaries.

Hymenoptera. The majority of pollinators belong to the solitary and social bees (Apoidea), which are well adapted to collect pollen on special brushes or baskets after it has adhered to their characteristically plumose body hairs. The bees show various degrees of elongation in their mouthparts, adapting them to different depths of flowers. *Apis mellifera*, the honey-bee, is a most important pollinator, as are also bumble-bees (*Bombus*) and many solitary bees, some with short tongues (*Colletes, Halictus* and *Andrena*), others with longer ones (*Osmia, Megachile* and *Anthophora*). Wasps are not important pollinators, but there are some characteristic wasp-flowers such as *Scrophularia* and some species of *Cotoneaster*.

The Angiosperms emerged during the Cretaceous period, and their earliest members were probably pollinated by Coleoptera, a group of insects which had arisen much earlier and which are known to pollinate many of the more primitive flowering plants extant today. It is characteristic of insect-pollinated plants that their flowers are usually hermaphrodite and generally large, coloured and scented, often forming abundant pollen or alternative nutritive tissue or with nectaries. The evolutionary trends towards more specialized relationships with particular groups of insects may include: (a) reduction in the number of sepals and petals; (b) the formation of a tubular or spurred corolla, at the base of which the nectaries are concealed so that they are accessible only to long-tongued insects; (c) a tendency to develop irregular (zygomorphic) flowers that may be easier to recognize and can be entered by the insect in special ways that facilitate pollination; (d) the evolution of characteristic colours and scents attractive to insects and of guide-marks of contrasting colour (often only recognizable through the insects' perception of ultraviolet reflection) which direct the insect to a source of nectar in the flower.

Beetle-pollinated flowers tend to have variable, sometimes dull, colours, to produce strong, fruity odours, and are often flat or bowl-shaped, with abundant pollen or freely exposed nectaries. Many similar flowers are also pollinated rather indiscriminately by a variety of other insects (bees, flies and Lepidoptera). Those characteristically visited by bees are highly coloured (though not normally bright red, which appears dark to bees); they tend to have nectaries that are more deeply placed, especially when pollinated by long-tongued bees, and the petals are often modified to provide a landing platform and enclosed spaces which the bee enters. Flowers pollinated by hawk-moths (Sphingidae) are open at night or around dusk, when the moths are active, with strong, sweet scents, white or light-coloured flowers, and a long tubular corolla with basally concealed nectaries. Special pollination mechanisms

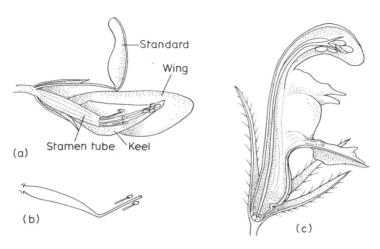

Fig. 106   Insect-pollinated flowers

(a) Flower of Bird's-foot Trefoil, *Lotus corniculatus* (Leguminoseae) in half-section;
(b) same, ovary and style after removal of stamen-tube, showing position of anthers on
long stamens; (c) flower of White Deadnettle, *Lamium album* (Labiateae) in half-section.
(After Proctor and Yeo.)

and close, sometimes highly specific relationships between flowers and
their pollinators are too numerous to discuss adequately here, but a few
examples will illustrate the diversity to be found.

The flowers of the Leguminoseae (Fig. 106) have a highly modified
corolla consisting of a conspicuous standard, a pair of lateral wings, and
two closely associated petals forming a boat-shaped keel, which
conceals the carpels and stamens. The latter are mostly fused to form a
tubular structure within which nectar collects. Though the details of the
pollination mechanisms vary somewhat, the arrival of an insect on the
flower forces down the wings and keel, exposing the anthers and
dusting the insect with pollen, while the stigma makes contact with the
ventral surface of the insect. Somewhat similar mechanisms operate in
the flowers of Monkshood (*Aconitum*), which are pollinated by bumble-
bees (*Bombus*). In Labiateae, such as the White Deadnettle (*Lamium
album*), the corolla is two-lipped. The lower lip is a landing platform and
the upper lip forms a hood which encloses the stamens and style. Long-
tongued bees probe into the lower tubular part of the flower to reach the
nectar while their dorsal side is dusted with pollen and also touches the
stigma. The strongly zygomorphic flowers of some Scrophulariaceae,
such as *Antirrhinum*, operate in a somewhat similar way; a honey-bee or
Bombus lands on the lower lip of the corolla, prises the lips apart with the
head while searching for nectar, and so brings its dorsal surface into
contact with the anthers and stigma.

Some flowers or inflorescences are modified to form traps which

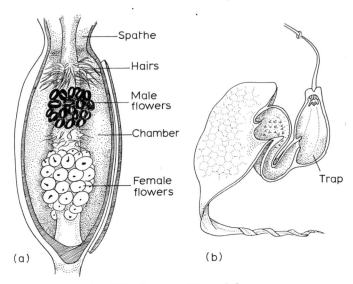

Fig. 107   Insect-pollinated flowers

(a) *Arum maculatum*, inflorescence with spathe partly cut away to show chamber in which insects are trapped (based on a photograph in Proctor and Yeo); (b) half-section of flower of *Aristolochia grandiflora* (after Cammerloher).

imprison the pollinating insects temporarily, as in the tubular flowers of *Aristolochia* or in many members of the arum family Araceae (Fig. 107). For example, in *Arum maculatum* there is a more or less tubular spathe enclosing the spadix or axis of the inflorescence. The female flowers are arranged at the base of the spadix, with male flowers above them, and above this the spadix is enlarged into a club-shaped structure. The lower part of the spathe is dilated to form a small globular chamber around the flowers, partially closed above by downwardly directed hairs. Small flies, mainly *Psychoda phalaenoides* in Britain, are attracted to the odour emitted by the club-shaped part of the spadix and slide on the greasy inner surface of the spathe into the chamber, where they are trapped for a day or so and effect cross-pollination with pollen they have brought from a previously visited inflorescence. They also pick up pollen from the male flowers before they escape when the hairs at the top of the chamber wither and cease to form a barrier. Other species of *Arum* trap different flies, including Ceratopogonidae and Simuliidae.

Some of the most remarkable pollination mechanisms occur in the Orchidaceae, where the pollen grains adhere together to form club-shaped pollinia, usually two to each flower, which need to be placed accurately on the stigma of another flower (Fig. 108). In some species, such as *Orchis mascula*, a bumble-bee or other insect will land on the lip of the flower and insert its proboscis into the spur, thereby detaching

210

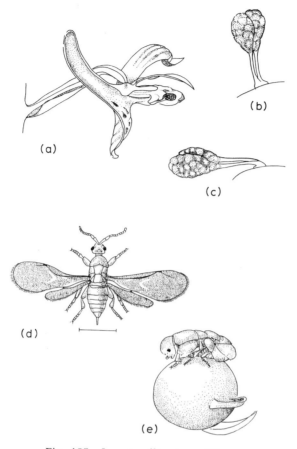

Fig. 108 Insect pollination of flowers

(a) Half-section of flower of Early Purple Orchid, *Orchis mascula* (after Proctor and Yeo);
(b) pollinia of an orchid after removal from flower; (c) same, after pollinia have swung
forward to pollinating position; (d) female of a fig-wasp, *Blastophaga psenes*; (e) male of
Blastophaga copulating with female concealed in fig (after Grandi). Scale line = 1 mm.

one or both of the pollinia, which stick to its head like horns. The
pollinia are erect at first, but they soon droop forward through about 90°
and are then in exactly the right position to come into contact with the
stigma of the next flower visited. In orchids of the genus *Ophrys* the
flower is modified so that part of it resembles an insect. A male insect,
initially attracted by the flower's scent, mistakes this special part of the
flower for a female and tries to copulate with it, thereby picking up or
transferring the pollinia. Different species of *Ophrys* have different
pollinators, which may be solitary wasps (*Gorytes* or *Campsoscolia*) or
bees (*Andrena*). The phenomenon is known as pseudocopulation and has
evolved independently at least three times among the orchids and their

211

insect visitors; Australian orchids of the genus *Cryptostylis* are pollinated in this way by an Ichneumonid, *Lissopimpla semipunctata*.

Among the figs (genus *Ficus*) one finds many complicated, highly specific, obligate and mutually beneficial relationships with their pollinators. The 900 or so species of *Ficus* are pollinated by Chalcidoid wasps of the family Agaonidae (fig-wasps). With few exceptions each species of fig has its own species of Agaonid and, broadly speaking, closely related species of fig tend to have closely related Agaonids. The 'fruit' of figs is actually a specialized inflorescence called a syconium, which forms a globular structure whose inner surface bears hundreds of small single-ovuled female florets (which may have long or short styles) and a lesser number of male florets. The fruit is provided with an apical opening (ostiole) protected by scales. In a typical species of fig, one or a very few of the winged female wasps of the relevant species, previously mated, enters the cavity of the syconium through the ostiole and lays an egg in each of a number of ovules by inserting its ovipositor into the styles of the short-styled female florets; the other female florets have styles that are too long to permit oviposition. In laying her eggs the female transfers pollen that she has brought on her body from another inflorescence. The female then dies, but the eggs she has laid give rise to larvae which consume the ovules in which they develop, and eventually produce males (which are wingless) and females. The males emerge first and fertilize the females before they have left the florets in which they develop. The newly emerged females then pick up pollen from the recently dehisced anthers of the male florets and escape from the 'fruit', either through the ostiole or through a special tunnel cut in the wall of the fruit by males. Each escaped female then visits another fig to repeat the process while the males die without leaving the fruit. The details of the life-cycle and the biology of the figs differ from one species to another, and in the edible fig, *Ficus carica*, the position is somewhat unusual. Some varieties have fruits with only female florets which do not require pollination as they develop parthenocarpically. Other varieties have inflorescences which show seasonal polymorphism: some have only long-styled female florets, in which the wasp cannot lay eggs but which it pollinates; such fruits produce seeds but no wasps. The other type of 'fruit' contains only short-styled female florets (sometimes called gall florets) which are used for oviposition; they thus produce wasps but no seeds, though they may yield pollen, in which case they are effectively male inflorescences.

The essential features of fig pollination, namely that the plant sacrifices part of its seed production in order to ensure cross-pollination, while the insect obtains food and shelter for its developing progeny, are also characteristic of another unusual relationship between species of *Yucca* and a few species of the small Prodoxid moth *Tegeticula* in

N. America. The maxillary palps of the female moth are produced basally into tentacle-like processes on which pollen is first collected. A pollen-bearing moth then enters another *Yucca* flower, and if it is suitable she lays an egg in its ovary and then presses some of the pollen into the tubular stigma, repeating the process until she has laid at least one egg in each of the three cells of the ovary. Some of the ovules are then eaten by the developing *Tegeticula* larvae, but the rest give rise to seeds.

Many orchard and field crops depend on cross-pollination to produce fruit or set seed. The conservation and augmentation of pollinating insects is therefore of considerable practical importance. In many cases the honey-bee *Apis mellifera* is an effective pollinator, but species of *Bombus* and of some solitary bees have been encouraged to nest in artificial containers with useful results. Under experimental conditions plant breeders often use blowflies and similar easily reared Diptera to ensure pollination.

INSECTIVOROUS PLANTS

Some flowering plants obtain supplies of nitrogenous compounds by trapping and digesting insects. The habit has evolved independently in about six plant families, and the 450 or so species of insectivorous plants show a variety of interesting adaptations (Fig. 109). For example, the aquatic bladderworts (*Utricularia* spp.) bear small water-filled vesicles on their divided leaves, each provided with a valve-like lid that opens inwards, allowing small aquatic insects and crustacea to enter, but preventing them from leaving again. The prey dies and its breakdown products are absorbed by the plant. Some terrestrial insectivorous plants trap small insects on the surface of their leaves with a sticky secretion. The butterworts, *Pinguicula*, are closely related to *Utricularia* but have a rosette of broad leaves clothed with glands that produce a sticky secretion. In the more specialized *Drosera* (sundews) the leaves are fringed with long glandular hairs ('tentacles') which bend over to enclose small flies caught on the sticky secretion which they produce apically. Within an hour or so the insect is drowned and it is digested over the course of a few days, after which the tentacles return to their erect position. The Venus' Fly-trap, *Dionaea muscipula*, is also a member of the Droseraceae, but its leaves, arranged in a rosette, are each divided longitudinally by a deep groove and their lateral margins are fringed with spines. The upper surface of the leaf bears several long 'trigger hairs' and when an insect (attracted by nectaries along the margins of the leaf) touches these hairs the two halves of the leaf close together quickly. The marginal spines fit between each other to ensure that the insect is trapped; glands on the leaf surface secrete a digestive liquid, and the

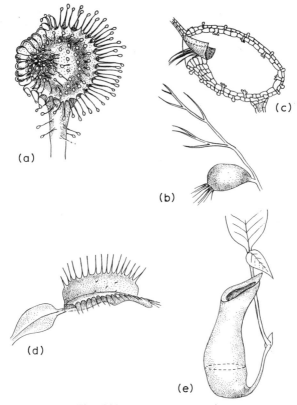

Fig. 109   Insectivorous plants

(a) Leaf of *Drosera rotundifolia*, showing tentacles curved over at left of disk; (b) *Utricularia vulgaris*; (c) section through bladder of *Utricularia*; (d) leaf of Venus' Fly-trap, *Dionaea muscipula*; (e) modified leaf of a pitcher plant, *Nepenthes*, with level of liquid indicated in pitcher (after Strasburger).

resulting solution is absorbed. Some of the most remarkable adaptations are shown by the pitcher plants, such as the N. American *Sarracenia* and the Malaysian *Nepenthes*. In these the leaves are modified to form tubular containers which are partly filled with liquid and may be covered by a lid-like structure. The inner surface of the container bears extrafloral nectaries which attract insects that then fall into the liquid, a process facilitated by the smooth inner surface of the pitcher and its downwardly directed hairs. The insects are digested by proteolytic enzymes secreted into the liquid and the products of digestion are absorbed by the plant. Curiously, the liquid contents of *Sarracenia* pitchers provide a habitat for the larvae of a blowfly, *Sarcophaga sarraceniae*, and a mosquito, *Wyeomyia smithii*, both feeding on the dead insect debris that has accumulated there. *Nepenthes* pitchers also have an insect fauna of their own.

INSECTS AND MICRO-ORGANISMS

Many insects have evolved close and sometimes complicated relationships with a variety of micro-organisms – viruses, bacteria, fungi and Protozoa in particular. In some of these associations the insect acts as a vector, transmitting micro-organisms pathogenic to other animals or to plants. Examples of these are discussed on pp. 294–7 and 313ff. In other associations the insect is itself parasitized by an injurious species of micro-organism, and some of these are also discussed elsewhere (pp. 337–8). This section is concerned only with cases in which the insect feeds on the micro-organisms or they have together formed a symbiotic relationship through which the micro-organism obtains shelter while it and the insect gain important nutritional benefits.

Filter-feeding on mud, debris and suspended particles, including zoo- and phytoplankton, is practised in many groups of aquatic insects and must often involve the ingestion of micro-organisms. Such habits have evolved on several occasions, as in the larvae of Ephemeroptera, Trichoptera and Diptera (especially the Simuliidae, Culicidae and Chironomidae). Adaptations to this mode of feeding include the development of setal sieves on the mouthparts or fore legs and the secretion of silken filtration nets for capturing food, though more needs to be known of the kinds and quantities of foods collected in these ways. Even detrivorous larvae, feeding on leaf-litter, may rely on the activities of micro-organisms to bring about the partial decay of plant material before it can be consumed. Bacteria, yeasts and other fungi may also be ingested by those insects which feed on fermenting fruits, carrion, dung and other decomposing organic matter. These include adults and larvae of dung-beetles and of Dipteran families such as the Muscidae and Calliphoridae. Yeasts on fermenting fruit and the sap-flows of trees provide essential components of the diet of Drosophilidae, and it is the presence of yeast sediments in crude potassium tartrate (argol) which accounts for the fact that the Ptinid beetle *Trigonogenius* sometimes breeds in such deposits. The large fruit-bodies of Basidiomycetes and other fungal hyphae under bark or in wood provide food for many families of Coleoptera such as the Mycetophagidae, Cisidae, Endomychidae, Erotylidae and Lathridiidae. The larvae of the Dipteran family Mycetophilidae are almost all fungus-feeders, occurring in fleshy Basidiomycete fruit-bodies or under decaying bark and in rotten wood. Larvae of the Platypezidae are found in agarics. Somewhat less normal fungus-feeders are found in the larvae of Footman moths (Arctiidae: Lithosiinae) which feed on lichens, and in the ambrosia beetles (some Scolytidae) which cultivate fungi in the burrows that they make in wood, the larvae feeding wholly or partly on the hyphae, which provide a source of essential sterols.

Highly specialized fungus-feeding habits are found in some of the

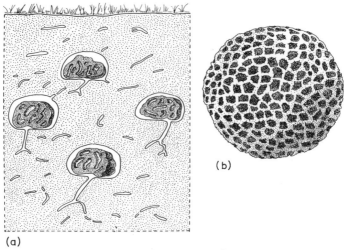

Fig. 110   Fungus gardens of termites

(a) Schematic section through underground nest of *Pseudacanthotermes spiniger*, showing four chambers containing fungus gardens. (b) A fungus garden of *Protermes minutus* in surface view. (After Grassé.)

higher termites (Isoptera) belonging to the Old World subfamily Macrotermitinae. Here genera such as *Macrotermes*, *Microtermes* and *Odontotermes* cultivate fungus gardens in the chambers of their large nests (Fig. 110). These gardens consist of firm, moist, spongy material produced by the worker termites as faecal pellets of partly digested plant material. The individual masses of this substrate vary in diameter from a few centimetres to more than 60 cm, each mass enclosed in a soil-lined cavity. The beds are permeated by hyphae of species of *Termitomyces*, each species of termite apparently cultivating its own species of fungus. So long as the termites tend the gardens the fungal mycelium does not produce mushrooms, though these grow when the termite nests have been deserted. The fungal mycelium and its substrate are eaten by the termites, and probably supply breakdown products of cellulose and perhaps some vitamins. It is not clear how the fungi are introduced into newly developing colonies, but this may be accomplished by the alate founders. It is a remarkable fact that a very similar fungus-growing habit has evolved independently in a mainly tropical group of New World ants, the Attini. The underground beds consist of spongy masses of leaf fragments, pollen and caterpillar frass, and are inoculated with fungal mycelium by the queen ant, which had stored it in her infrabuccal pouch before founding the colony. The gardens are maintained by workers, and the fungal hyphae produce knob-like bromatia which are grazed regularly, so preventing the fungus from developing fruit-bodies.

A curious symbiotic relationship exists between fungi of the genus *Septobasidium* and the scale-insects *Aspidiotus*. The female and immature scale-insects feed on a host tree, where they shelter among the mycelium of the epiphytic fungus. In turn the fungus derives its nourishment through haustoria which penetrate the bodies of a proportion of the young scale-insects and it is disseminated by the active first-instar larvae. Insects of various kinds also play a part in the dispersal of some fungal spores. The stinkhorns (*Phallus*, etc.) are specially adapted for this, forming spores on a freely exposed hymenium whose surface attracts flies through its odour and consistency. Other fungi exist which infect plants systemically and are specially adapted to this habit, since they sporulate only on the anthers of their hosts, from which the spores are transferred to the stigmas of other flowers by pollinating insects.

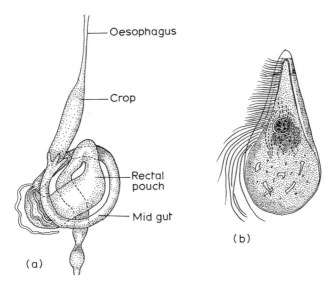

Oesophagus

Crop

Rectal
pouch

Mid gut

(a)

(b)

Fig. 111   Symbiosis between termites and Protozoa
(a) Gut of *Archotermopsis wroughtoni* (Termopsidae) (after Imms); (b) a flagellate Protozoan, *Trichonympha collaris*, from gut of *Zootermopsis angusticollis* (after Kirby).

A great variety of internal symbionts are known among different groups of insects. In all termites except the most highly specialized family Termitidae the rectum is enlarged to accommodate a rich symbiotic fauna of flagellate Protozoa belonging to the Trichonymphidae and other families (Fig. 111). These are able to digest the wood and other cellulose-containing material on which the termites feed, producing simple fatty acids which are absorbed and metabolized by the termites. The termites are thus enabled to utilize the cellulose in their diet even though the termite mid gut does not secrete celluloclastic

217

enzymes. Termites from which the Protozoa have been removed experimentally soon die. The Protozoa are lost with the cuticle of the rectum when an immature termite moults, but it can acquire a fresh supply of Protozoa by feeding on drops of liquid exuding from the rectal pouch of other members of the colony. Very similar flagellate Protozoa occur in a N. American cockroach, *Cryptocercus punctulatus*.

Most Homoptera, such as leafhoppers, Coccoidea and Aphidoidea, harbour bacterial or yeast-like symbionts in specialized cells (mycetocytes), which may occur scattered in the gut wall or fat-body (as they do also in biting lice) or are aggregated into more or less compact organs (mycetomes) in the haemocoel. The micro-organisms cannot be cultured *in vitro* and their function is uncertain, but they are transmitted through the mother's ovary to the next generation, and they seem necessary for normal growth and survival, perhaps because they supply essential nutritional factors such as sterols or are needed for the synthesis of amino acids. In many Heteroptera the mid gut is produced into small caeca, varied in form and number, which contain bacteria in their lumen or in the cells of their walls. Their function is again uncertain, but the fact that the micro-organisms are transmitted to the progeny suggests an essential role, perhaps a nutritional one. Mycetomes are found in many beetles; in *Stegobium* and *Lasioderma* they harbour yeasts which can be cultivated *in vitro* and are responsible for synthesizing B-vitamins and sterols. The symbionts are smeared on the surface of the eggs and the newly hatched larva acquires a supply when it eats the eggshell immediately after hatching. Larvae prevented from obtaining the symbionts need to be supplied with a dietary source of B-vitamins in order to develop normally, as do some other species which never contain symbionts.

PREDACIOUS INSECTS

Predacious or predatory insects are those which capture and feed on living animal prey, which often consists of other insects but may include a variety of small animals, usually invertebrates. Predatory habits are found in many different groups of insects (Figs 112 and 113). Some of these, such as the dragonflies (Odonata), the Mantodea, and the larvae of Plannipennian Neuroptera (lacewings and their allies), are exclusively predatory and the habit is common in many other orders. It occurs, for example, among some Orthoptera, such as the subfamily Saginae of the Tettigoniidae, and in the Gryllacrididae, and it is also found in some Plecoptera (Perlidae), Thysanoptera, Mecoptera and the larvae of some Trichoptera. The Heteroptera include a number of largely predacious families such as the Nabidae, Anthocoridae, Reduviidae and Phymatidae, as well as the aquatic families Gerridae, Veliidae, Naucoridae, Nepidae

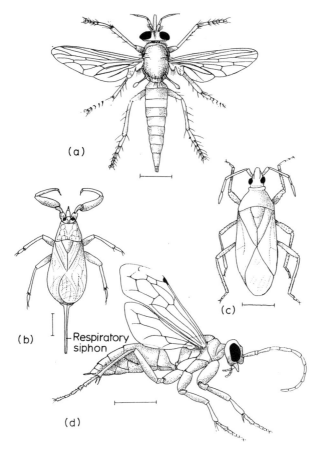

Fig. 112   Some predacious insects

(a) *Asilus barbarus* (Diptera: Asilidae) (after Séguy); (b) *Nepa cinerea* (Hemiptera: Nepidae) (after Poisson); (c) *Anthocoris nemorum* (Hemiptera: Anthocoridae) (after Poisson); (d) *Cryptocheilus* sp. (Hymenoptera: Pompilidae) (after Riek). Scale lines in (a), (b) and (d) = 5 mm; in (c) = 1 mm.

and Notonectidae. The Coleoptera probably contains more species of predator than any other order, including most or all members of such families as the Carabidae, Dytiscidae, Gyrinidae, Silphidae, Staphylinidae, Histeridae and Coccinellidae. Many Diptera are also predators, sometimes in both the adult and larval stages (as in the Asilidae, Rhagionidae and Dolichopodidae) or mainly as larvae (Tabanidae, many Syrphidae and some Cecidomyiidae), or largely in the adult condition (Empididae and Scatophagidae). The Hymenoptera include the ants (Formicidae), one of the most successful groups with largely predacious adults, as well as several other groups with more specialized predatory

219

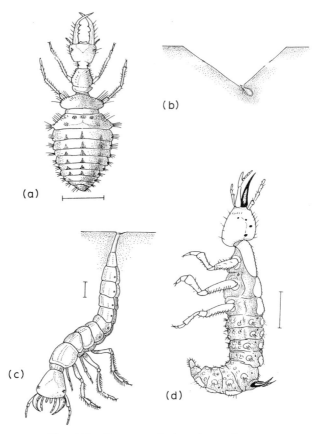

Fig. 113   Some predacious insect larvae
(a) *Myrmeleon formicarius* (Neuroptera: Myrmeleontidae) (after Berland and Grassé); (b) section through pit of *Myrmeleon* larva (after Doflein); (c) *Dytiscus marginalis* (Coleoptera: Dytiscidae) (after Engelhardt); (d) *Cicindela hybrida* (Coleoptera: Carabidae) (after Jeannel). Scale lines = 5 mm.

habits, which provision their nests with living insects or spiders that have been paralysed, in order to provide fresh food for their young (Pompilidae, Eumenidae and Sphecoidea). Even the Lepidoptera include some species with predatory larvae, more especially in the family Lycaenidae ('blues'). Along with the parasitoidal insects discussed on pp. 232–7, the predacious species exert an important controlling influence on populations of other insect species. Their biology and habits are therefore of great significance in understanding the population dynamics of insects and some are important agents in the control of pest species.

Some predatory insects are generalized feeders, living on a variety of species of suitable size which happen to be abundant locally at various times. Others, however, show varying degrees of specialization. For example, Silphid beetles feed mainly on Dipteran larvae, Lampyrids live on snails and earthworms, and Coccinellids feed predominantly on aphids, scale-insects and whiteflies. The larvae of Tabanidae often feed on those of other Diptera, some Bombyliid larvae attack the egg-masses of Acridid grasshoppers, and Syrphids feed largely on aphids and other small Homoptera. The specialized predators among the aculeate Hymenoptera tend also to provision their nests with a restricted range of prey species: Pompilid wasps hunt spiders, Eumenids store Lepidopteran larvae, and Sphecoids show a variety of preferred prey, mostly various insects though some take spiders. The borderline between predator and parasite is not always clear: some Hymenopteran families, for example, have larvae that are commonly considered as ectoparasites of other insects (Thynnidae, Tiphiidae and Scoliidae), but could perhaps be regarded equally as rather highly specialized predators.

The adaptations shown by predacious insects relate in general to the legs, mouthparts, sensory structures and, of course, their behavioural patterns. Many predators use their legs for seizing their victims and for holding them while they are being devoured. Thus, in dragonflies and adult Diptera of the family Asilidae all three pairs of legs are used for this purpose, these limbs being notably elongate and spiny. In the water-bugs (*Notonecta*, etc.) the fore legs alone are adapted for seizing and holding the prey; they are held well in front of the head and terminate in sharp prehensile claws. In the Mantidae, and in the Neuropteran family Mantispidae, the prey is caught and impaled by the combined femora and tibiae of the fore legs. The femur bears a ventral channel flanked by a double series of spines and the tibia is adapted to close in this groove like the blade of a pocket-knife, its sharply toothed edge acting in conjunction with the femoral spines in impaling the prey. In these two families, and in various others that use the fore legs for capturing their prey, the coxae of the limbs concerned are notably elongated (Fig. 5c) so as to throw the legs forward and also allow increased freedom of movement. Other predators have projecting sharply pointed mandibles for seizing their victims, as is well shown in larvae of ground beetles, of *Dytiscus* and of most Neuroptera (Figs 82 and 113). In dragonfly nymphs, as already noted, the labium is modified into a prehensile organ or mask (Fig. 66c).

The sensory organs of many predators are highly developed, especially the compound eyes – a feature well seen, for example, in the Mantidae, Odonata, some Carabidae and Asilidae. When the prey are few and far between, and therefore require agile search, the legs of predators are adapted for running (Carabidae); or the predators are strong rapid fliers (Odonata, Asilidae). In cases where the prey is abundant and sedentary the legs and sense organs of the predators are not specially developed, since in such cases very little searching may be required. Larvae of Neuroptera, Syrphidae and Coccinellidae come under this category as they develop from eggs laid in close proximity to the aphids and other small insects that form their food.

The mandibles, and sometimes also the maxillae, of predators are sharply pointed and adapted for piercing; they may also be toothed as in Odonata, being thus adapted for lacerating and tearing. In the Asilidae, together with other predacious flies, and also in many waterbugs, the mouthparts are developed into a rigid horny proboscis.

Many predators lie in wait for their prey, pouncing on it suddenly when it is within reach. This adaptive behaviour is well seen in dragonfly larvae and in mantids; the members of both groups are often protectively coloured to match their backgrounds, thus allowing the unwary prey to come within easy reach. In most cases this involves cryptic coloration, but the mantid *Hymenopus coronatus* is bright pink to match the colour of the flowers on which it sits in wait for its prey. Another mantid species, *Idolium diabolicum*, from Africa, goes further; it does not sit among flowers, but its highly coloured appearance and the foliate expansions of its legs and body give the whole insect the appearance of a flower. The larva of the Neuropteran family Myrmeleontidae (ant-lions) constructs a conical pit in sandy soil, at the bottom of which it lies concealed, emerging to seize with its enormous mandibles the insects which fall into the pit and are unable to escape (Fig. 113). Very similar habits have evolved quite independently in the larvae of the Rhagionid flies *Vermileo* and *Lampromyia*. The larvae of the tiger-beetles *Cicindela* and its allies (Carabidae: Cicindelinae) are provided with a heavily sclerotized head capsule and prothorax, stout projecting mandibles and a pair of strong hooks on the dorsal surface of the fifth abdominal segment (Fig. 113). They live in burrows in the soil and, when waiting for prey, the head lies at the entrance to the burrow, to the walls of which the larva anchors itself by its legs and dorsal hooks. The larvae of some Trichoptera, such as *Polycentropus, Plectrocnemia* and *Hydropsyche*, differ from the usual caddis flies in not forming a portable case. Instead, they construct silken nets of various forms, in which small insects, Annelids and other planktonic organisms are ensnared and caught. The nets may be sac-like, funnel-shaped or more irregular, with branching galleries, and they may be spun in still or running water according to the species concerned.

INSECT PARASITOIDS

The term 'parasitoid' denotes a special form of parasitism which is characteristic of very many insect species and which differs from the more typical forms of parasitism in three main ways: (a) it is only the

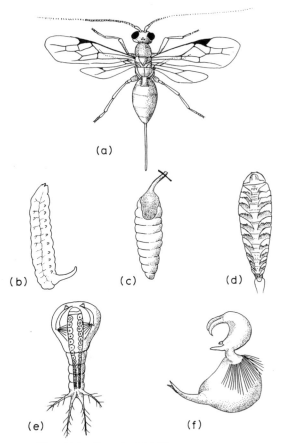

(a)

(b)   (c)   (d)

(e)   (f)

Fig. 114   Parasitoidal Hymenoptera

(a) *Opius fletcheri* female (Braconidae) (after Willard); (b)–(f), first-instar larvae. (b) poly-pod larva of *Figites anthomyiarum* (Cynipidae) (after James); (c) *Encyrtus infidus* (Chalcidoidea: Encyrtidae), showing larva attached to egg-shell with respiratory duct (after Clausen); (d) ventral view of planidium of *Perilampus hyalinus* (Chalcidoidea: Perilampidae) (after Smith); (e) cyclopiform larva of *Platygaster* (Proctotrupoidea: Platygasteridae) (after Clausen); (f) teleaform larva of *Scelio fulgidus* (Proctotrupoidea: Scelionidae) (after Noble).

larval stages of the parasitoid which may be regarded as parasitic and show distinctive adaptations to this mode of life – apart from their oviposition behaviour the adults do not differ fundamentally from those of entirely free-living species; (b) the larva eventually kills its host, which is usually another species of insect, less often some other small invertebrate; and (c) the parasite is relatively large in relation to the host species. The parasitoidal mode of life is especially characteristic of several large groups of Hymenoptera (Fig. 114), occurring in all Ichneumonoidea and most Chalcidoidea, as well as smaller groups such as the Proctotrupoidea, Scoliidae and Dryinidae. Among the Diptera

(Fig. 115) the large family Tachinidae is the predominant parasitoidal group, but the habit occurs in other families such as the Sarcophagidae, Nemestrinidae, Pipunculidae and Cyrtidae. All members of the small and aberrant order Strepsiptera can be regarded as parasitoids, though in almost all of them the sexually mature female also remains internally parasitic. The parasitoidal habit is rarely found among the Coleoptera and Lepidoptera. As mentioned previously, the distinction between parasitoids and specialized predators is sometimes difficult to establish, especially among those species which are sometimes treated as ecto-parasites of other insects. Even among the more typical internally feeding parasitoids the larva, after first feeding mainly on the blood and fat-body of the host, goes on to devour the other viscera in a way that might entitle it to be called an 'internal predator'.

Although some species such as the Tachinid *Compsilura concinnata* attack a wide range of hosts, most parasitoids show well-defined host preferences, exemplified both by the host ranges of parasitoidal families or larger groups and by those of genera and species. For example, among the Hymenoptera most of the very large numbers of Ichneumonid species are primary parasites of Lepidopteran larvae, though some also attack Lepidopteran pupae and a smaller number are parasites of Coleopteran and Hymenopteran larvae: *Rhyssa* and its allies are external parasites of the larvae of Siricid and Xiphydriid sawflies. Many groups of Braconidae are exclusively parasites of Lepidopteran larvae, but some attack Coleopteran larvae; *Alysia* and *Opius* (Fig. 114) occur in Dipteran larvae, and *Aphidius* is found in aphids. Among the parasitoidal Chalcidoidea there is a wide range of preferred hosts within the Lepidoptera, Coleoptera, Diptera and Hymenoptera, while the Aphelinidae and Encyrtidae parasitize Homoptera. The Trichogrammatidae and Mymaridae are two Chalcid families of egg-parasites, as is also a Proctotrupoid family, the Scelionidae. Other Proctotrupoids include the Platygasteridae in Cecidomyiid larvae and Homopteran nymphs. Among the parasitoidal families of Diptera the Pipunculidae (Fig. 115) are all internal parasites of Homoptera (Cicadellidae, Cercopidae and Delphacidae), but the host preferences of the Bombyliidae are very wide, though individual species show much greater specificity; they attack the egg-pods of locusts, the immature stages of various aculeate Hymenoptera and, in a few instances, the soil-inhabiting larvae of beetles. The Tachinidae are parasitoidal on various hosts, especially larval Lepidoptera and adult Coleoptera, but *Gymnosoma* and its allies attack Heteroptera and the Dexiinae are parasitoidal on Scarabeid larvae. Relatively few Diptera are parasitoids of other Diptera.

Several forms of parasitoidal infestation have been noted. Primary parasitism involves attack on a free-living host, whereas hyperparasites attack the immature stages of species which are themselves parasitic and

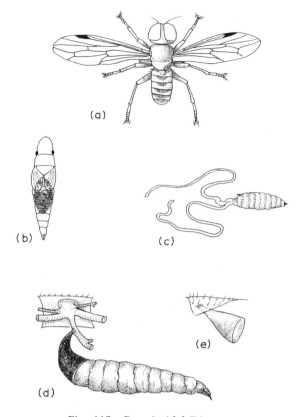

Fig. 115   Parasitoidal Diptera

(a) Adult of *Pipunculus cruciator* (Pipunculidae) (after Perkins); (b) larva of the leafhopper *Hecalius* containing a larva of *Pipunculus cruciator* (after Perkins); (c) third-instar larva of *Cryptochaetum grandicorne* (Agromyzidae) (after Thorpe); (d) larva of *Prosena sibirita* (Tachinidae), showing respiratory funnel attached to tracheal trunk of host (after Clausen); (e) larval respiratory funnel of *Dexia ventralis*, arising from puncture in integument through which the first-instar larva entered the host's body.

may therefore be secondary or even tertiary parasites. Hyperparasitism is rare in the Braconidae, whose members are therefore largely beneficial when their hosts are pests of crop plants. Hyperparasitism occurs more often in the Ichneumonidae, especially in the subfamily Cryptinae and some Ophioninae such as *Mesochorus*; *Gelis* parasitizes the exposed cocoons of various Braconidae, and *Hemiteles* is either an obligate or facultative secondary parasite. The Chalcidoidea include some families that are exclusively primary parasites and others, such as the Eulophidae, Aphelinidae and Encyrtidae, which include some species that are hyperparasites, often of other Chalcidoids. Most hyperparasites live external to the immediate host and show less restrictive host ranges than do primary parasites. The number of parasitoidal larvae that can survive within an individual host insect varies appreciably. Many species are solitary, with only a single parasite in each host, but in some species two or more larvae of the same parasitoid can complete their development successfully in one host. This condition is known as superparasitism and in a few species, which show a characteristic form of multiple twinning known as polyembryony (Fig. 48), many hundreds of larvae are formed by the repeated division of a single early embryo, as in some Encyrtidae and Platygasteridae.

The oviposition habits of parasitoidal insects have been much studied and often show a variety of adaptive features intended to ensure that the young larva is able to develop in its normal host. In some Hymenoptera with internally parasitic larvae the egg is laid in the egg of the host, but more often it is deposited in the larval host's body cavity or, in some species, it is regularly placed within a host organ such as the brain, a ventral ganglion or the intestine. The long ovipositor of many parasitoidal Hymenoptera is well adapted to this habit, and the females of some species show remarkable host-seeking behaviour, as in *Rhyssa* and its allies, in which the ovipositor is inserted through the bark and wood of a tree so as to deposit the egg on the wood-boring sawfly larva which is being parasitized. In other species the egg of the parasitoid is laid inside or on the outer surface of the host's integument, the latter situation being common where the parasitoidal larva lives external to its host. In other external parasitoids the egg may be laid near the host, in its burrow or cocoon or cell. Only in the Chalcidoid families Eucharitidae and Perilampidae are the eggs laid apart from the hosts; they are deposited in or on plants, where they give rise to young larvae which then search for their hosts. Some Tachinidae lay eggs or, in the viviparous species, deposit their larvae on the host or its food, but in others the terminal abdominal segments of the female are modified into a piercing oviscapt enabling the egg to be inserted into the host's body.

The larvae of parasitoidal Hymenoptera show a considerable range of form in the early instars, though the later ones tend to be much more uniform in appearance. The most commonly encountered first-instar larva, like those of later instars, is more or less spindle-shaped, apodous, with 12 or 13 body segments, a soft integument that is bare or provided with sensory setae, and a somewhat reduced head capsule. Other first-instar larvae may be degenerate, sac-like forms, or are provided with tail-like appendages or vesicles that are sometimes described as respiratory, though their real function is often obscure. A few species have polypod larvae bearing paired secondary limb-like appendages on many of the body segments (Fig. 114). A highly characteristic first-instar form is the so-called planidium which hatches externally and is specially adapted to searching for its host. Such free-living larvae have evolved independently in several parasitoidal families and are fusiform, with a strongly sclerotized integument bearing spines or other processes that assist locomotion and with a terminal adhesive disc (Fig. 114). Planidium-like first instar larvae also occur in other groups of parasitoidal insects such as the Strepsiptera and Rhipiphorid beetles, where they are known as triungulinid larvae. Planidia also occur among some of the parasitoidal Diptera (Cyrtidae, Bombyliidae, Nemestrinidae and some Tachinidae) and a few Diptera have larvae with caudal appendages, but as a rule the larvae of Dipteran parasitoids, especially the mature larvae, tend towards a common form that does not differ greatly from that of their free-living relatives.

Two features of parasitoidal larvae are worth emphasizing. First, in many families the larva changes appreciably in form and habits as it develops, thus displaying various degrees of hypermetamorphosis. Secondly, because of their situation within the body of the host, many have developed special respiratory adaptations. Most parasitoidal Dipteran larvae and some Hymenoptera have an open tracheal system and establish contact with the atmosphere by perforating the body wall or a tracheal trunk of their host (Figs 114 and 115). In those forms with a closed tracheal system gaseous exchange occurs through the thin cuticle, beneath which the tracheae may branch extensively so as to increase the area over which diffusion occurs. In early instars the tracheal system may be absent or filled with liquid, and in these cases oxygen diffuses directly into the haemolymph. The richly tracheated tail filaments of *Cryptochaetum* larvae (Diptera: Agromyzidae; Fig. 115) act as gills, but the blood-filled outgrowths from the body of other parasitoidal larvae are probably not respiratory.

Because they are generally responsible for the death of their hosts, parasitoids, together with predators, exert a considerable influence on the growth of insect populations and often provide effective biological control of insect pests. These topics are discussed on pp. 272–6 and 335–7.

ECTOPARASITIC INSECTS

The ectoparasitic habit has evolved several times within the Insecta (Fig. 116). Two related groups, probably with a common origin, are the sucking lice (Siphunculata) of mammals and the biting lice (sometimes grouped into the separate order Mallophaga) which are mainly parasitic on birds but include some species that infest mammals. All stages of the life-cycles of these insects occur on the warm-blooded host, and together they make up the majority of insect ectoparasites, with the Mallophagan species far more numerous. The fleas, or Siphonaptera, constitute a further group, distinguished by the fact that only their adults are ectoparasitic (on birds and mammals), the larvae living freely

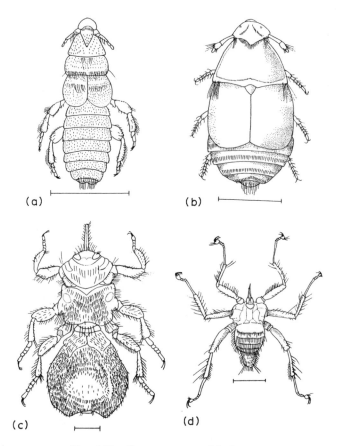

Fig. 116   Some ectoparasitic insects

(a) *Androctenes horvathi* (Hemiptera: Polyctenidae) (after Jordan); (b) *Platypsyllus castoris* (Coleoptera: Leptinidae), occurring among fur of the beaver, where it probably preys on mites (after Jeannel); (c) Sheep Ked, *Melophagus ovinus* (Diptera: Hippoboscidae) (after Imms); (d) *Penicillidia jenynsi* (Diptera: Nycteribiidae), an ectoparasite of bats (after Imms). Scale lines = 1 mm.

in the host's nest or lair. In addition there are ectoparasites to be found among the Diptera (Hippoboscidae and a few other families), in the Hemiptera (the Cimicidae, or bed-bugs, and the Polyctenidae, found on bats) and in the Dermaptera (Hemimeridae; Fig. 71), together with a few others from various orders, some of whose claims to be considered parasites are perhaps doubtful.

Ectoparasitic insects tend to show a number of features in common – all adaptations to their unusual mode of life. They are all small in relation to the sizes of their hosts, with which they tend to remain closely associated. They also tend to have a reduced sensory equipment, with short antennae and the compound eyes reduced or absent. They are mostly wingless – all lice and fleas, for example – or with greatly reduced wings (Cimicidae and Polyctenidae), or with the habit of shedding their wings after settling down on a host, as in some Hippoboscidae which, as a family, show a range of reduction from fully winged to completely apterous species. As a rule ectoparasitic insects are provided with various devices which help them to grip the host's fur or feathers and so to resist dislodgement when the host grooms itself. Examples of these structures include the strongly developed claws, specially modified for gripping individual hairs in the mammal-infesting lice, as well as rows of backwardly directed bristles on the body, and the comb-like ctenidia of fleas, the projections of which lock on to the host's hairs or feathers when the flea is dragged backwards during grooming. The ectoparasitic habit has also encouraged the evolution of specialized methods of feeding and nutrition. The Siphunculata, Siphonaptera and ectoparasitic Diptera and Hemiptera have all independently acquired highly specialized mouthparts that enable them to penetrate the host's skin and feed on its blood, while the biting lice feed on feathers or hair and epidermal secretions. Finally, since many ectoparasites can survive for only a short time away from the body of their host, they tend to display characteristic host-seeking behaviour and to react positively to warmth, darkness and the odour of their hosts.

One of the interesting biological features of ectoparasitic insects is the host specificity they show, which is displayed most clearly by the sucking and biting lice. Each group of related hosts tends, with few exceptions, to have related parasites. Thus, among the biting lice the Trichodectidae tend to occur mainly on the Carnivora, the Gyropidae on rodents, and the Boopidae on marsupials. Fleas tend to show a lesser degree of specificity and the distribution of bird fleas may be more closely associated with the nesting habits of the host than with its evolutionary relationships. When a single host is infested with several species of ectoparasites they tend to be distributed over its body in a characteristic fashion, each species of ectoparasite being more or less restricted to a particular region of the body and thus providing an interesting example of the ecological principle of resource-partitioning (cf. p. 271). A remarkable instance of the close physiological relationship between the life-cycle of an ectoparasitic insect and its host is provided by the rabbit flea, *Spilopsyllus cuniculus*. The fleas found on adult rabbits do not copulate and for much of the time the female fleas have undeveloped ovaries. However, when the doe becomes pregnant sexual maturation of the fleas begins to take place and this is caused by the increased concentration of corticosteroids in the rabbit's blood. When the doe bears young the fleas leave her and move to the nestlings, where they feed. The high concentrations of corticosteroids and growth hormone in the nestlings' blood now induces the fleas to copulate. Eggs are then laid in the nest and the adult fleas return to the doe to await another pregnancy.

Because of their blood-sucking habits, ectoparasitic insects are well adapted to transmit diseases of man and other animals; examples of this are described below and on pp. 313ff.

BLOOD-SUCKING INSECTS

The habit of piercing the integument of another species to feed on its body fluids through specialized mouthparts has evolved on many occasions in the insects. The best-known examples of this are found among those species of Diptera which feed on birds and mammals, such as the mosquitoes or horse-flies, but other groups of insects have acquired the habit, some of them feeding exclusively in this way. Many insects feed similarly on the body fluids of invertebrates (usually other insects), but most of these are essentially predators which kill the species they feed on, whereas true haematophagous insects feed repeatedly on their hosts without necessarily causing serious direct injury.

The main insect groups with blood-sucking representatives are as follows:

Diptera. Adults of most mosquitoes (Culicidae, subfamily Culicinae); Simuliidae (Black-flies); many Ceratopogonidae (Biting midges); most Tabanidae (horse-flies); Glossinidae (tsetse flies); Hippoboscidae; some Muscidae.

Siphunculata (sucking lice). All stages of all species.

Heteroptera. All stages of Cimicidae (bed-bugs), Polyctenidae (on bats) and some Reduviidae.

Siphonaptera (fleas). Adults of all species.

In the Diptera it is usually only the females which take blood, this normally being required to provide the protein for maturation of the eggs. So far as is known, the females also feed on nectar, honey-dew and other similar sugary secretions of plant origin, which are the normal foods of the males. However, in *Glossina, Stomoxys* and the Hippoboscidae both sexes take blood-meals, as do those of the other insect orders. The hosts are usually mammals and birds; some blood-sucking insects show considerable specificity in this respect, whereas others will feed on a variety of hosts. In ecological and epidemiological studies, where it is important to determine the host species on which a haematophagous insect is feeding, this may require serological tests on blood from the recently engorged insect. A few Culicinae, Ceratopogonidae and Psychodidae feed on amphibians and reptiles, and some Cerato-pogonids take blood from much larger insects; species of *Forcipomyia* feed through the wing-veins of Lepidoptera, Neuroptera and Odonata,

230

and *F. anophelis* has even been recorded to obtain blood by puncturing the abdomen of a recently engorged female mosquito, though it also feeds on cattle.

The most striking adaptive modifications of all these insects concern the mouthparts, which differ greatly from one group to another in their detailed structure, but are all adapted for piercing and sucking (Figs 91, 117, 154 and 158). Some account of the feeding mechanisms is given in the systematic sections of this book (pp. 118–81), and illustrates how the same essential function is accomplished by structurally diverse organs. Two main modes of feeding are known. The more generalized

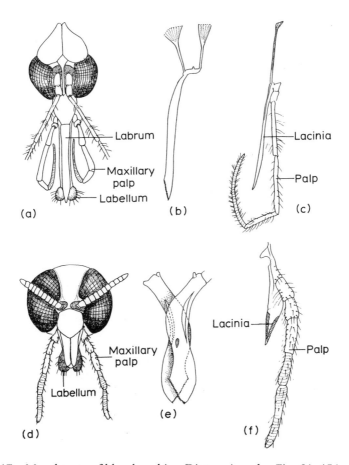

Fig. 117   Mouthparts of blood-sucking Diptera (see also Figs 91, 154 and 158) (a) *Phlebotomus* (Psychodidae), head and mouthparts, anterior view; (b) *Phlebotomus*, mandible; (c) *Phlebotomus*, maxilla; (d) *Simulium* (Simuliidae), head and mouthparts, anterior view; (e) *Simulium*, mandibles, crossed in scissors-like position; (f) *Simulium*, maxilla. (After Snodgrass.)

forms such as the Tabanidae and Ceratopogonidae are pool feeders, which pierce or abrade the skin and then suck up the blood that exudes from the wound. A more specialized mechanism, found in the Heteroptera, sucking lice, mosquitoes and fleas, takes the form of vessel feeding, in which a stylet-like structure or a bundle of stylets pierces the skin and probes until its tip encounters a capillary, from which the blood is then imbibed. In some mosquitoes feeding involves cycles of salivation and ingestion, while in the Reduviid *Rhodnius prolixus* salivation is continuous during probing. In some, but by no means all, haematophagous insects the saliva inhibits coagulation of the host's blood. The insects engorge to an extent that is controlled by abdominal stretch-receptors. In some blood-sucking Heteroptera and in the Siphunculata a single large blood-meal is taken during each larval instar, but other species may take several smaller meals between successive moults. In most mosquitoes and in many other haematophagous Diptera the adult female undergoes a number of gonotrophic cycles, in each of which a blood-meal is followed by the maturation and deposition of a batch of eggs, a condition known as anautogeny. In some species, however, one or even all egg-batches may be laid without a blood-meal, and in completely autogenous species the female mouth-parts are reduced and she does not bite.

Apart from their characteristic feeding habits, haematophagous insects show varying degrees of closeness in relation to their hosts. Many of those listed above are permanent or temporary ectoparasites, and their special adaptations to this mode of life are discussed briefly on pp. 227–30. Others, such as the mosquitoes, horse-flies and tsetse flies, are attracted to their hosts only for the relatively short feeding periods, and they are often mainly active at certain seasons or times of day. The basis of this attraction to the hosts has not always been clearly established, though suitable conditions of wind, light, temperature and humidity may be necessary. Some blood-sucking insects appear to find their hosts by visual perception of their movement, but others seem to depend on responses to carbon dioxide, convection currents of warmer air, unidentified body odours or specific chemical substances like lactic acid. Probably a combination of stimuli is involved, at least in those cases where some individual hosts are much more readily bitten than others.

The ability of blood-sucking insects to transmit micro-organisms pathogenic to man and other animals is discussed on pp. 313–25.

AQUATIC INSECTS

Despite some theories to the contrary, the insects are primarily terrestrial and their early forms almost certainly evolved on land. In the course of their evolution, however, many insect groups have secondarily and independently invaded a variety of aquatic habitats, to which they have often become highly adapted. Thus, the immature stages of virtually all Ephemeroptera, Odonata, Plecoptera and Trichoptera are entirely aquatic, as are all stages of several Heteropteran families, such as the Gerridae and Hydrometridae, which live on the water surface, and the Naucoridae, Notonectidae and Corixidae which swim below it. Among the Coleoptera one finds many aquatic families, notably the Dytiscidae, Haliplidae and Hydrophilidae, which live within the water as larvae and adults, whereas the Gyrinidae have surface-dwelling adults ('whirligig beetles') and submerged larvae. A substantial number of Dipteran families also have aquatic larvae and pupae, though the adults are terrestrial; among them are well-known groups like the Chironomidae, Culicidae and Simuliidae, as well as the less familiar Blephariceridae, Dixidae, and other families which include species whose larvae are aquatic as well as others which are terrestrial. Even among such predominantly terrestrial groups as the Orthoptera, Lepidoptera and Hymenoptera, or the Curculionid and Chrysomelid beetles, there are species which have adopted aquatic modes of life.

The habitats which these insects occupy are also very varied, ranging from small temporary pools to large permanent lakes, and from rapid mountain brooks and trickles to broad slow-flowing rivers. Within many of these there are species adapted to life on or just below the surface film, and others which swim actively in the main body of the water, burrow in the bottom sediments or live in close association with aquatic vegetation. The great majority are restricted to freshwater habitats, though some live in brackish water or inland salt lakes. Curiously, there are very few fully marine insects, though some Chironomid larvae live in shallow coastal waters or in the littoral zone, and in *Pontomyia natans* from Samoa the wingless adult females also live beneath the surface and the males can swim. The surface-dwelling Gerrid *Halobates* occurs near coasts and also far from land, where it is associated with floating seaweed.

The main adaptive features of aquatic insects concern the external form of the body, the relationships of the insect to the surface film, the food and feeding mechanisms, locomotion, and the processes of osmoregulation and respiration (Fig. 118).

The highly polished, smooth, elliptical contour of many water beetles serves to reduce resistance to the water during swimming. The nymphs of some mayflies, and the larvae of certain Diptera and Coleoptera that inhabit torrential streams, assume a greatly flattened form. This feature, coupled with the provision of special anchoring devices (spines and suckers), helps to prevent such insects from being swept away by the current.

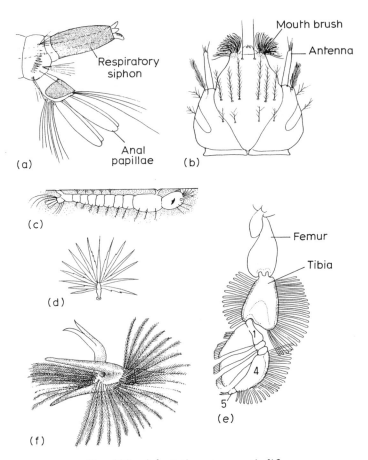

Fig. 118   Adaptations to aquatic life

(a) Terminal region of abdomen of larva of *Aedes aegypti* (Diptera: Culicidae), showing respiratory siphon and osmoregulatory anal papillae (after Macfie); (b) head of larva of *Anopheles*, showing mouth-brushes (after Evans); (c) larva of an Anopheline mosquito in position below surface film (after Marshall); (d) palmate hair from abdomen of *Anopheles maculipennis* larva (after Séguy); (e) hind leg of *Gyrinus natator* (Coleoptera: Gyrinidae); (f) last tarsal segment of mid leg of *Rhagovelia* (Hemiptera: Veliidae) showing plumose hydrofuge hairs (after Poisson).

Many aquatic insects have to pierce the surface film in order to maintain their posterior spiracles in contact with the atmosphere and, at the same time, prevent water from entering the trachea. In some cases (e.g. mosquito larvae) perispiracular glands provide an oily secretion that imparts hydrophobe properties to the surrounding cuticle, i.e. the water retreats from such areas, leaving the surface dry. In other cases special devices achieve the same object. Thus, when the larva of *Dytiscus* is supported at the tail extremity by the surface film the entry of water into the tracheal trunks is prevented by a circlet of hydrofuge hairs around the posterior spiracles. These hairs are so closely set that water is unable to penetrate between them when they pierce the surface film; their outer surfaces show strong hydrophile properties, whereas the inner surfaces of these hairs are hydrophobe in character. In the Collembolan *Podura aquatica* and in the pond skaters (Gerridae) a coat of fine hydrophobe hairs covers the body and holds the water at a distance so that these insects cannot be wetted.

The food and feeding mechanisms of some aquatic insects do not differ greatly from that of their terrestrial counterparts. Aquatic predators, for example, may have raptorial fore legs (as in *Naucoris* or *Nepa*) or sharp, piercing mandibles (as in the larvae of *Dytiscus*). The characteristic prehensile labial 'mask' of Odonate larvae is restricted to this group of aquatic predators, but the characteristic piercing and sucking mouthparts of the aquatic Heteroptera are not fundamentally different from those found in terrestrial members of the order. Many aquatic insects feed on coarsely divided organic matter such as leaf fragments, which they shred with relatively unmodified mandibulate mouthparts (e.g. some Trichopteran and Plecopteran larvae). Others feed on more finely divided organic materials, including bacteria, which they may gather with their mouthparts or obtain by filtration. Filter feeding is particularly characteristic of some aquatic groups, which may spin silken nets through which water flows, as in some Trichopteran larvae, or draw a current of water through the burrow or tube in which they live among the bottom sediments, as in some Chironomid larvae. Larvae of *Simulium* and of mosquitoes are provided with vibrating mouth brushes that set up water currents and thereby waft microscopic food particles into their mouths. Other aquatic insects feed by scraping off the algae and bacteria that adhere to stones and other surfaces beneath the water, and may have specially modified mandibles with cutting edges or grinding surfaces; such insects are often also adapted to cling to exposed surfaces in rapidly flowing water. A few aquatic insects, such as the larvae of the small Hydroptilid caddis-flies, feed by piercing the individual cells of the submerged parts of larger algae, mosses or flowering plants.

Movement through the water or on its surface or among the bottom sediments occurs in various ways. In many aquatic insects the third pair of legs, or the second and third pairs, are specially modified for swimming. Thus, in *Dytiscus* the hind legs are long and much flattened from side to side so as to function as oars. The tibia and tarsus bear closely set fringes of swimming hairs along their upper and lower edges. These hairs become spread during the swimming stroke and fall back when the leg is drawn forward. The tarsus rotates on its axis in a way which allows the swimming stroke to be made by its broad surface, while its edge cuts through the water in reaching the return position; in

235

other words the rotation is comparable with a sculler 'feathering' his oars. *Notonecta* and its allies swim, like *Dytiscus*, by means of their oar-like hind legs which operate simultaneously. *Hydrophilus*, on the other hand, uses its hind legs alternately while swimming in much the same sequence as a walking insect. The Dytiscidae consequently swim a long straight course, whereas *Hydrophilus* exhibits a somewhat wobbling and less efficient mode of progression. Whirligig beetles (*Gyrinus*) perform their rapid gyrations on the surface of ponds or slowly moving streams and swim by means of their greatly modified second and third pairs of legs (Fig. 118e). Some fly larvae, notably those of *Chironomus* and mosquitoes, swim by vigorous muscular action of the abdomen that results in side-to-side wriggling movements through the water. Certain minute Chalcids (*Caraphractus*, etc.), that parasitize the eggs of various aquatic insects, swim beneath the water by means of their wings.

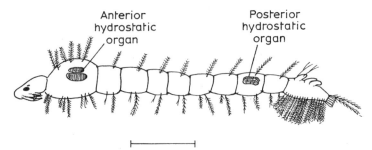

Fig. 119   Larva of *Chaoborus* (Diptera: Culicidae)
Scale line = 2 mm.

Associated with locomotion are the variations in buoyancy shown by some aquatic insects. Those in which a large respiratory air-bubble is trapped beneath the elytra or among hair-tracts on the body will tend to float up unless they propel themselves actively downwards, and in the 'backswimmers' (*Notonecta* and its allies) the ventral position of the bubble is associated with the insect floating ventral side uppermost beneath the surface. The transparent 'phantom larva' of *Chaoborus*, which is a close ally of mosquitoes, has its tracheal system mainly represented by two pairs of bean-shaped sacs that act as hydrostatic organs (Fig. 119). This larva is able, by a chemical process which contracts or expands their walls, to vary the size of the sacs so that its buoyancy can be adjusted to the pressure of the water at different depths.

The aquatic mode of life may be associated with important adaptive modifications in the processes of excretion and osmoregulation. Since there is no longer a pressing need to conserve water, some fully aquatic forms like the larvae of *Sialis* and *Aeshna* have reverted to excreting the nitrogenous products of protein breakdown as ammonia which, though toxic if it were allowed to accumulate, can now be eliminated in dilute solution. On the other hand, the continuous excretion of water in aquatic insects is liable to lead to the loss of essential inorganic ions such as sodium, potassium and chloride. This may be prevented by the evolution of a cuticle which is particularly impermeable to inorganic ions (as in the larva of *Sialis*) and to the development of mechanisms for re-absorbing these ions through the wall of the hind gut. Some aquatic insects are also able to absorb inorganic ions actively from the water in which they live. This occurs through specially modified areas of integument where the epidermis contains mitochondrial ion pumps. In mosquito larvae these occur on the tubular anal papillae which are larger when the ionic concentration of the external medium is lower (Fig. 118a). Some of the external gill-like structures of other aquatic insects have a similar osmoregulatory function.

The respiratory adaptations of aquatic insects are dealt with in the section on respiration (pp. 76–7).

PROTECTIVE COLORATION AND MIMICRY

The body, wings and other appendages of insects vary greatly in shape and colour, often providing the means whereby defenceless species can protect themselves by cryptic (concealing) coloration or camouflage, and noxious insects can advertise their presence by bright colour patterns (Figs 120 and 121). Mimicry, in the sense employed here, is the resemblance of two or more species of insects to one another.

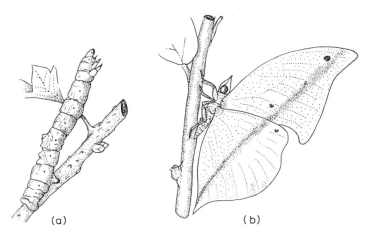

(a)   (b)

Fig. 120   Protective resemblance
(a) Twig-like larva of Early Thorn Moth, *Selenia dentaria*; (b) Indian Leaf Butterfly, *Kallima inachus* (after a photograph by C. Halgren).

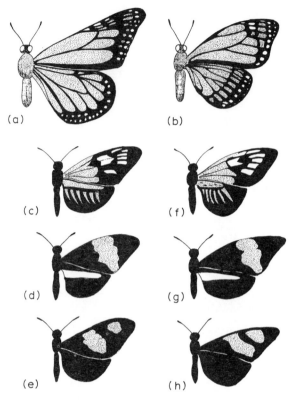

Fig. 121   Batesian and Müllerian mimicry in butterflies (semi-schematic)
(a) *Danaus plexippus* (Danainae), the model; (b) *Limenitis archippus* (Nymphalinae), the Batesian mimic; (c)–(e) three forms of the distasteful polymorphic *Heliconius melpomene*, each with a characteristic geographical distribution; (f)–(h) three forms of *Heliconius erato*, also distasteful, with each occurring in the geographical region occupied by the corresponding form of *H. melpomene*. ((c)–(h) after Turner.)

Insects provide many examples of cryptic coloration which in most cases is believed to have evolved through natural selection by vertebrate predators which seek their insect prey by sight. In some insects the concealment occurs as a general resemblance to the colour or other features of the insects' habitat. Species found on fresh vegetation tend to be green, while those occurring on darker backgrounds such as soil may be brown or black. Many Lepidopteran larvae active in the daytime show counter-shading, with a darker upper surface and a lighter lower surface (reversed in species which feed or rest upside-down). Disruptive colour patterns, tending to break up the outline of the insect, are also widespread. Many insects show more detailed resemblances to specific features of their environment. The larvae of many Geometrid moths, such as the Early Thorn, *Selenia dentaria*, are remarkably twig-like in appearance, with brownish irregularly cylindrical bodies, held out at an angle to the twig on which they rest, attached only by the more posterior prolegs (Fig. 120). Some long-horned grasshoppers (Tettigoniidae) like the Pseudophyllinae have broad, green, leaf-like fore wings, and the resemblance of many Phasmida (Stick and Leaf Insects) to twigs, stems and leaves is well known, culminating in genera such as *Phyllium*, where the fore wings, flattened body, foliaceous expansions of the legs, and green colour all help to convey a close resemblance to foliage (Fig. 70a). The Indian leaf butterfly *Kallima inachus* and its allies have wings with a brownish under-surface, exposed when the insect closes them at rest and showing a striking resemblance in shape and colour to a dead leaf, with indications of the leaf-veins and spots that imitate signs of fungal decay (Fig. 120b). In this, as in many other cases, the posture and behaviour of the insect is an essential feature of the camouflage. Cryptic coloration and behaviour have also evolved in some predacious insects, which are thus presumably less visible to their prey; many examples occur in the praying mantids (Mantodea), of which some such as *Hymenopus* resemble brightly coloured flowers, while others look like twigs or foliage.

Some instances of cryptic coloration have been analysed experimentally and shown to reduce the chances of the insect being attacked by predatory birds, but many others require fuller investigation. Some of the most detailed studies, demonstrating clearly the selective value of camouflage, have been made on the phenomenon of industrial melanism. Many species of moths are normally concealed by the irregular speckled pattern of brown, grey or greenish colour on their wings when they settle on the trunks of lichen-covered trees. During the past 150 years, however, in some industrial areas of Europe and N. America with smoky, polluted air, the tree trunks have become black and bare, and in such areas the typically coloured moths have been replaced by melanic varieties, more uniformly dark grey or blackish in colour, which are then better concealed from predatory birds than the original lighter-coloured forms. The phenomenon has occurred in many species and direct evidence of selective predation and genetic determination of colour has been obtained for some of these, such as the Peppered Moth, *Biston betularia*, where the typical form may be replaced by a melanic variety (f. *carbonaria*) which differs in a single dominant allelomorph. More recently, reduced air pollution has resulted in a reversal of these events, with normal forms tending to replace the melanic varieties.

Insects which are cryptically coloured while resting sometimes also display warning colours when they move quickly, and so are thought to alarm, confuse or divert predators. Areas of bright colour ('flash coloration') may be revealed suddenly, as in the Yellow Underwing moth *Noctua pronuba*, whose yellow-banded hind wings are concealed at rest, or the grasshopper *Oedipoda caerulescens*, whose blue and black barred hind wings are hidden at rest by the cryptically coloured fore wings, but are displayed when it takes to flight. Large, brightly coloured eye-spots are also displayed in a warning fashion by a number of insects such as the Eyed Hawkmoth *Smerinthus ocellata* or the Owl butterfly *Caligo* and other Brassolinae of tropical S. America. The smaller eye-spots on the wings of many Satyrid butterflies are thought to be protective in another way, encouraging birds to strike at the wing and so deflecting an attack away from more vulnerable parts of the body.

Typical warning (aposematic) colours are usually bright, simple patterns displayed by noxious insects to warn vertebrate predators of their distasteful character. After the predator has learned to associate the colour pattern or appearance with unpalatability it will avoid feeding on the aposematically coloured species. Examples include the bright red or yellow and black lady-bird beetles (Coccinellidae) or the larva of the Cinnabar Moth (*Tyria jacobeae*) which is broadly banded in black and orange-yellow.

Mimicry is a special form of protective resemblance, in which two or more species of insects (often not closely related) have evolved very similar colour patterns and behaviour (Fig. 121). Though several complicated classifications of mimicry have been proposed, only two main forms are distinguished here: Batesian and Müllerian mimicry. In Batesian mimicry (named after the naturalist H. W. Bates, who first described it among other examples) one species, the model, is unpalatable or injurious in some way and advertises this fact by a distinctive colour pattern so that predatory birds or mammals learn to avoid it. Another species, the mimic, is palatable but is protected because it has evolved a colour pattern very similar to the unpalatable model and is therefore mistaken for it by predators that have learned to associate the pattern with distastefulness. A good example is provided by two Nymphalid butterflies from N. America. The Monarch (*Danaus plexippus*) is a Danaine whose larva feeds on milkweeds (Asclepiadaceae) and sequesters a cardiac glycoside which makes the adult unpalatable. It is mimicked by the Viceroy (*Limenites archippus*) which is a palatable species from a different subfamily (Nymphalinae). In a somewhat more complicated example, the Blue Swallowtail butterfly (*Battus philenor*) of North and Central America is the distasteful model for four different mimics: two are species of another swallowtail genus, *Papilio*, and the others are the females of two sexually dimorphic Nymphalids.

In typical cases of Batesian mimicry one expects that the mimic is less abundant than the model, that the model tends to resemble its close relatives while the mimics tend to differ from theirs, and that the model alone is protected by its unpalatability. In contrast to this, typical

Müllerian mimicry occurs when two or more unpalatable species have evolved the same appearance, so that losses due to the attacks of inexperienced predators, which have not yet learned to associate the pattern with distastefulness, are shared between the two species. The distinction is useful even when it is not clear-cut, as when several species differ in relative edibility. Many mimetic associations involve several species in a complicated way, with a group of distasteful Müllerian mimics whose appearance is closely copied by several edible Batesian mimics. In some cases a given species may be polymorphic or sexually dimorphic in colour pattern with the different morphs entering into different mimetic relationships. The mainly Central and South American Nymphalid butterflies of the subfamily Heliconiinae are distasteful, with bright colour patterns of red, orange, yellow and blue. There are many mimetic associations between different Heliconiine species and between Heliconiines and equally unpalatable species from the sub-families Danaiinae, Ithomiinae and Acraeinae, while these in turn are mimicked by supposedly edible species from the Pieridae and Nymph-alidae. Again, *Heliconius erato* exists in many colour forms, each matched by a colour form of the equally polymorphic *Heliconius melpomene* (Fig. 121). Remarkable mimetic resemblances are also shown by the various colour forms of the female swallowtail *Papilio dardanus*, each mimicking species of *Danaus* and *Amauris*, while the males of *P. dardanus* are non-mimetic. The genetic, evolutionary and behavioural aspects of such complex mimetic associations present many problems, some now being clarified by experimental research.

SOCIAL INSECTS

Many insects form temporary aggregations, often containing very large numbers of individuals. The mating swarms of mayflies and Chironomid midges, the migratory swarms of locusts, and the hibernating associa-tions of some Coccinellid beetles are cases in point. However, these are not regarded as social insects and true social life occurs only in the Isoptera (termites) and in a relatively few groups of Hymenoptera. The latter include the ants (Formicidae), all of which are social, some groups of bees (e.g. *Bombus, Apis* and *Melipona*) and the social wasps (Vespidae). All these are sometimes said to be eusocial, living in well-defined colonies and showing three distinctive biological features: (a) they are polymorphic, each species consisting of some reproductive individuals and others which belong to sterile castes (workers or soldiers); (b) the parental generation overlaps one or more generations of progeny; (c) the members of the colony show co-operative brood care, some individuals feeding and looking after the progeny of others. These features are thought to have evolved from a solitary ancestral condition through the development of parental care, such as occurs among several groups of solitary insects, especially in the aculeate Hymenoptera. Social organization arose independently in the Isoptera and in several groups of Hymenoptera, and some indications of the transition from solitary to social forms may be seen among a few species which show only one or two of the three attributes listed above. Such forms are known as quasisocial or semisocial; examples occur among the bees and wasps and shed an interesting light on the evolution of the eusocial condition.

The Isoptera, discussed more fully on pp. 138–9, have sterile castes (workers and sometimes also soldiers) which are genetically of both sexes. In the Hymenoptera, however, the workers are females, the development of whose gonads has been more or less fully arrested, and though they sometimes lay some eggs they are never fertilized. Like the

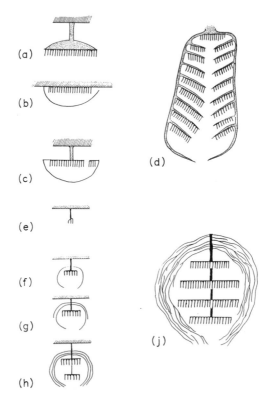

Fig. 122 Nest construction in social wasps (Vespidae): semi-schematic sections through different nest types

(a) *Polistes*; (b) *Metapolybia*; (c) *Charterginus*; (d) *Chartergus*; (e)–(h) stages in construction of a *Vespula* nest, (j) mature *Vespula* nest. (Based on Wilson and others.)

queens which lay most of the eggs, they are derived from fertilized eggs, the males or drones being produced from unfertilized ones.

In the Vespidae of temperate regions the colonies are annual and come to an end in the autumn, the sole survivors being the young fertilized females. The workers are not sharply differentiated from the fertile females, but are distinguishable by their smaller size and sometimes by certain colour differences. The larvae are fed by the workers on sugars and masticated fragments of insects. The nest is either subterranean (*Vespula vulgaris* and *V. germanica*) or arboreal (*Dolichovespula norvegica* and *Vespa crabro*). It is composed of wood particles mixed with saliva and worked up by means of the jaws into a substance which, when dry, has a paper-like consistency. The first-formed cells are a small group suspended by a central pedicel. New cells are added, resulting in the formation of horizontal tiers or layers, and the whole is enclosed in several layers of covering that protect the colony from wetness and sudden changes of temperature (Fig. 122e–j). The first-laid eggs develop into worker wasps after about 4–6 weeks from oviposition. These individuals take on the care of the brood and nest, leaving the female parent to devote herself to egg laying. At the end of the summer larger cells are constructed and in these develop the females of the next generation. Males develop about the same time, but perish soon after mating, while the females hibernate separately and become the foundresses of the next season's colonies.

Among tropical Vespidae there are wasps that form perennial colonies and a nest may be the combined effort of a number of females and workers. The initiation of new colonies is by a band of females and workers which have issued as a swarm from the parent colony. In temperate regions the colony is founded by a single fertilized female and is said to be haplometrotic. It may be argued that if conditions had been favourable the colony would have been perennial and the young females would have remained within the nest, thus giving rise to the pleometrotic condition found in the tropics. There is some evidence for this in the gigantic colonies – 425 cm across – of the *V. germanica* introduced to New Zealand.

The social bees show two major distinctions in their economy when compared with wasps: (a) they often use wax for comb-building, producing it as a secretion of glands located between the plates of the abdominal segments where it hardens into lamellae; (b) they have forsaken a carnivorous diet and have come to use the surer and more easily procurable food supplies afforded by nectar and pollen. Most of the structural peculiarities of bees are consequently adaptations for obtaining these two commodities. Those affecting the mouthparts are alluded to on p. 176. The nectar passes into the crop, where its cane-sugar (sucrose) becomes changed into invert sugars (glucose and

243

fructose). When fed to the larvae it is regurgitated as honey. Pollen adheres to the plumose hairs on the body of the worker. It is combed off by spines on the inner side of the first segment of the hind tarsi and then transferred to the corbicula or 'pollen basket'. The latter is either formed by special hairs on the ventral side of the abdomen or, more usually, by the hind legs, where the outer surface of the tibia is smooth, depressed, and flanked by long hairs for holding the pollen in a compact mass (Fig. 97c).

In the Bombini or bumble-bees the nest is commonly located in some cavity in the ground and its walls are constructed of fragments of grass or moss. It is provisioned with pollen mixed with honey, and upon this mass the female constructs a cell of wax within which she deposits her first eggs. The wax is secreted (by the queen and workers) beneath the dorsal and ventral plates of the second to fifth abdominal segments. A waxen receptacle or 'honey-pot' is also constructed and this the queen fills with honey that functions as a food reserve when she is confined to the nest. After about 4 days the larvae hatch, and when the stored food is consumed the female opens the cell and regularly supplies the brood with pollen and honey. On the 22nd or 23rd day after oviposition the first workers appear, and when sufficient have emerged they assume the functions of their caste, thus releasing the female for egg laying only. The workers construct further brood cells, together with receptacles for storing honey and pollen. When at full strength a colony numbers from about 100 to 500 bees. The rest of the economy resembles that of *Vespula* and only the young mated females survive the winter. There appears to be no evidence that special food plays any part in queen production, as happens in the honey-bee, and the differences between queens and workers are probably attributable to the quantity rather than the quality of the food received. The size difference between these two types of individuals is less constant than in *Vespula* and they tend to intergrade.

As representative of the Apini the honey-bee (*Apis mellifera*) shows a higher stage of social development than is found in the Bombini, and the queens, unlike those of the latter group, are sharply differentiated from the workers. The abdomen, for instance, is longer; there is no pollen-collecting apparatus on the hind legs; and both wax and pharyngeal glands are absent. She has become a highly specialized egg-laying machine and also produces the 'queen-substance' which the workers lick from her integument; this inhibits their ovarial development, and in its absence they begin building new queen cells. The nest is composed of vertical combs of hexagonal cells placed back-to-back. The drone cells are larger than those of the workers, and the cells used for queen rearing are irregular and more or less sac-like in form, vertical instead of horizontal, and attached near the edge of the comb. The young larvae are first nourished on so-called 'royal jelly' which is produced by the pharyngeal glands of worker bees. Larvae destined to grow into queens are fed with this substance until pupation, whereas with drone and worker larvae it is replaced from the fourth day onwards by a mixture of honey and predigested pollen. Experiments in which eggs or very young larvae are transferred from worker to queen cells, and vice versa, indicate the paramount influence of food in production of these two types of individuals. In this way an egg from a worker cell can be made to develop into a queen, and similarly one from a queen cell will grow into a worker bee. The colonies are perennial and, unlike those of bumble-bees, are of great numerical strength; a flourishing hive may contain 50 000–80 000 bees, of which the vast majority are workers.

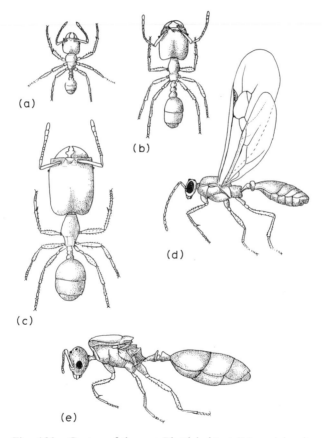

Fig. 123   Castes of the ant *Pheidole kingi* (Myrmicinae)
(a)–(c) Minor, media and major workers (selected from a continuous series of forms, the larger-headed ones often referred to as soldiers); (d) male; (e) queen (fertile female) after wings have been shed. (After Wheeler.)

245

All species of ants are social in behaviour, and it is among these insects that caste differentiation reaches its greatest extent (Fig. 123). Thus, in some there are two forms of queen, in others it is the male that is dimorphic, and in such cases one form is winged and the other apterous. The workers are wingless with reduced eyes; these individuals are alike in some primitive groups, but in other ants they may be highly polymorphic. In certain species they present a graded series with major workers at one extreme and minor forms at the other (Fig. 123a–c). Alternatively, there may be two contrasted types only: large-headed forms with powerful jaws, termed soldiers, that aid in the defence of the colony, and minor forms or true workers. The majority of ants construct cavity nests in the soil or mound nests composed of various materials; in tropical lands there are species that utilize cavities in plants or construct nests of carton or silk attached to trees. In any case no comb is built, the brood being dispersed in groups along the galleries and chambers of the nest. At times swarms of winged males and females leave the colony. After a brief aerial existence they mate and the females cast off their wings. The young queen forms the beginnings of a new nest in which she produces the first batch of worker ants. These soon take charge of the colony, thus leaving the parent free to devote herself to oviposition.

A major problem in the study of social insects concerns the physiological and behavioural factors that determine caste differentiation and the maintenance of social relationships within the colony. There is little doubt that these will be found to differ considerably from one group of social species to another, though certain common features may be noted. Communication between members of the colony clearly plays an important part, at least some of it involving the distribution of pheromones such as the queen substance of the honey-bee *Apis mellifera* (p. 56) and the morphogenetic factors whose activity has been demonstrated in some termites. Trophallaxis, the mutual exchange of nutritive materials between adults and young, has also been regarded as an important bond maintaining social life, occurring both in the Isoptera and in some Hymenoptera. Thus, wasp larvae exude saliva in exchange for food supplied by the workers, who imbibe this secretion eagerly and may even demand it without reciprocal exchange of food. While the larvae of some ants similarly exude saliva which is attractive to their attendants, others produce an integumentary exudate for the same purpose, and in one tropical group the desired secretion is the product of special larval organs. Trophallaxis does not occur in bees, perhaps because the ready availability of nectar and pollen makes the exploitation of larval secretions unnecessary. The functions of trophallaxis are not fully understood, however, and apart from its nutritive role it may play a part in the transfer of pheromone-like substances.

It had already been recognized by Darwin that the existence of sterile castes among social insects presents difficulties for the theory of natural selection. More recently it has been argued that the evolution of workers in the Hymenoptera could be a consequence of 'kin selection'. Because of the haplo-diploid method of sex determination in this order of insects, females will, given certain assumptions, have three-quarters of their genes in common with their sisters but only half in common with any progeny they might have. The inclusive fitness of a female (i.e. the differential survival of her own and her relatives' genes) may therefore be favoured by promoting the reproductive success of her sisters rather than by reproducing herself. However, it must be pointed out that though all Hymenoptera have a haplo-diploid sex-determining mechanism, social organization is still a rare phenomenon among them, and that other organisms with haplo-diploidy have not evolved sterile castes. Moreover, the termites, which are all social, have a normal diploid form of sex determination.

7

The biology of
insect populations

Many features of the biology of insects are related to the fact that they occur not as isolated individuals, but as members of populations. These populations tend to occupy more or less restricted parts of larger habitats, they change in density from time to time and from one place to another, and they show varying degrees of spatial or reproductive isolation from other similar populations. They also interact with populations of other species (including other insects) and many such interacting populations may be integrated to form more or less well-defined communities. Populations are also subject to changes in genetic constitution and therefore evolve at various rates – mainly, it seems, under the influence of random genetic mutations and variously directed pressures of natural selection, though random processes of 'genetic drift' may also occur. Studies of the behaviour of insect populations and the environmental factors that influence them are not only of intrinsic ecological and evolutionary interest, but are also needed to understand and control those pest populations which are injurious to man, crops and domesticated animals.

This account of insect population biology begins by considering methods of estimating population size, discusses the growth in numbers of single populations and their fluctuations, then goes on to describe the uses of life tables and key-factor analysis in studying population dynamics. Some theoretical aspects are then dealt with, including the natural regulation of population sizes, competition and its consequences, and the quantitative study of host–parasitoid and predator–prey systems. This is followed by an account of the ways in which populations of different species may be regarded as forming a community and of the problems presented by attempts to analyse diversity, stability and succession in insect communities. Finally, there is a discussion of some aspects of genetic variation in insect populations and its role in evolution. If, at times, some of these sections seem unduly speculative or oversimplified, this is because of the great variability among and between different insect species and the great difficulty of ascertaining the ways in which a multiplicity of interacting processes operate in field conditions.

ESTIMATION OF INSECT POPULATION SIZE

Any account of changes in insect populations must be based on reliable estimates of their size or population density. Estimates of relative size are sometimes easily available, as from the numbers recorded by standardized traps or collecting methods on different occasions, or for different species or stages of the life-cycle. Although such methods have their importance, they do not in general provide accurate estimates of the absolute size of populations since the effectiveness of the collecting or trapping method will usually vary with environmental conditions or the activity and behaviour of the insects. Estimates of absolute population density, expressed as numbers per unit area or volume of habitat, are generally more difficult to obtain, but are necessary if one is to make censuses of the numbers present at each stage of the life-cycle and to estimate the effects of mortality, reproduction or migration.

When a habitat is relatively homogeneous and its area or volume can be accurately calculated, direct counts of the insects present in standardized samples may be possible. This can be done for habitats such as soil or turf, from which the insects are extracted mechanically in various ways from samples of known volume and are then counted. The atmosphere may be sampled for flying or drifting insects by specially constructed suction traps, and comparable methods have been devised for sampling some aquatic habitats or for bulk grain, wood or the ectoparasites of vertebrate hosts. Such methods need to be designed so as to minimize bias in taking the samples or in extracting and counting the insects. They should also be suitable for statistical analysis so as to assess the accuracy with which the estimates of population size have been made. Populations of sedentary insects, such as female Coccoidea or Aleyrodid larvae, can be measured by direct counting of standardized samples (e.g. leaves or whole plants), followed by statistical analysis and adjustment to yield estimates of absolute density. Population estimates of parasitoidal larvae may be based on dissections of host samples of known density.

For more mobile insects in less homogeneous habitats direct sampling of units of the habitat is more difficult and the estimation of absolute population density is then usually carried out by mark and recapture techniques. In their simplest form, that of the 'Lincoln index', this first entails collecting a sample of the living insects, marking each one (with a spot of quick-drying paint or by labelling with a radioactive isotope), and releasing them. After a suitable interval to allow the marked individuals to become dispersed among the population, a second sample is taken and the number of marked and unmarked insects in it is recorded. If n_1 is the number of insects in the first, marked sample, and n_2 and n_3 are the numbers of marked (i.e. recaptured) and unmarked specimens in the second sample, then the estimated population size N is given by $N = n_1(n_2 + n_3)/n_2$. Moreover, if the numbers of individuals in the first and second samples are approximately the same, then the variance of N is given by $\mathrm{Var}(N) = n_1^2 n_3(n_2 + n_3)/n_2^3$. The Lincoln index method obviously involves a number of assumptions: the viability and behaviour of the insects is supposed to be unaffected by marking, the marked insects are assumed to disperse uniformly, there should be no changes in population size due to births or mortality during the interval between samples, and the population should not be affected by emigration or immigration of individuals. Various modifications and elaborations of this method have been developed; some of these are based on a single marked sample and a single recapture sample (as described above), whereas others entail repeated marking and recapturing. Some methods are strictly deterministic whereas others are based on stochastic models which allow for various probabilities of survival of the insects over a given interval and may involve complicated calculations that are best done by computer. Since each method entails different assumptions it may be instructive to apply two or more of these techniques to obtain reliable estimates of population size and perhaps also to infer some of the processes occurring in the population.

The ways in which estimates of absolute population density are used in further analysis of the dynamics of insect populations are described below, but the following figures will help to give some general impression of the very wide range of variation encountered in the density of different natural populations of insects. In southern England the grasshopper *Chorthippus parallelus* has been recorded at adult population densities of 0.23–2.76 per m². By comparison, swarms of young locusts (members of the same family, the Acrididae) contain millions of individuals at densities of 100–1000 per m². Small insects such as the Thysanoptera may be especially numerous: larvae of *Thrips angusticeps* overwintering in the soil down to 70 cm occur at densities of up to 6000 per m², while adults of *Aptinothrips rufus* have been recorded at 300 per m² on roadside verges and larval populations of *Thrips tabaci* in onion fields have been estimated at 160 000 per m². Compared with these numbers, the populations of wireworms (larvae of *Agriotes* spp.) in British arable farmland seem relatively small, though the much larger size of the individuals accounts for a greater total biomass; populations of over 180 per m², such as are recorded in old grassland, are much too high for many crops to be grown successfully. Tsetse flies (*Glossina* spp.) are injurious at what, by the standards of many insect populations, are very low densities. *Glossina morsitans* was estimated in one study to occur at the rate of about 0.02 per m², and even where it was regarded as abundant *Glossina pallidipes* populations contained only up to 0.2 non-teneral males per m². Populations of social insects are usually recorded as the numbers of adults (mostly workers) in a colony, and some representative estimates are as follows: *Vespula* spp. from about 100 to 5000; *Bombus* spp., 100–400; *Melipona* spp. (stingless bees) 500–4000, and domesticated colonies of the honey-bee *Apis mellifera* around 50 000. Ant colonies vary greatly in size according to the species: an average colony of *Myrmica ruginodis* contains about 1200 individuals, whereas large colonies of the wood ant *Formica rufa* consist of over 100 000 and those of the army ant *Eciton burchelli* have been estimated to contain over 700 000 insects.

MODELS OF INSECT POPULATION GROWTH

The growth of an insect population may be described by mathematical models which depend on various more or less realistic assumptions about the insects' net rates of reproduction and the way in which these are affected by various factors. A very simple model, that of exponential growth, assumes only that the rate of increase at any time is proportional to the size of the population (Fig. 124). For a population

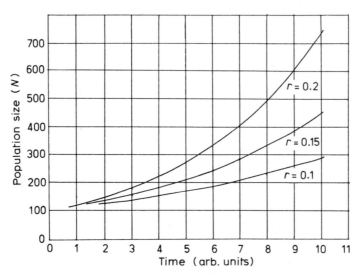

Fig. 124   Exponential population growth curves

The curves show the growth of three populations, each with an initial value of $N = 100$, but values of r (intrinsic rate of increase) equal to 0.1, 0.15 and 0.2. Note the increasing divergence of the curves as time increases.

with overlapping generations and a stable age-structure this is given by the differential equation

$$\frac{dN}{dt} = rN \tag{1}$$

where N is the population size and r the constant of proportionality. This equation may be solved to give the more familiar form

$$N_t = N_0 e^{rt} \tag{2}$$

where N_0 is the initial population size, chosen for convenience at a time denoted by $t = 0$, N_t is the size of the population at time t, and e is the base of natural logarithms (2.71828. . .). For most insect species, in which the generations are discrete (i.e. do not overlap), a more useful form of the same model is provided by the equivalent difference equation

$$N_{t+1} = e^r N_t \tag{3}$$

in which N_t is the population size in the t-th generation, and N_{t+1} is the size in the following generation. Given an initial population density for the first generation, the density for each successive generation can then easily be calculated for any given value of r.

A population growing exponentially according to (2) or (3) would increase in size indefinitely, growing in numbers during each generation or unit period of time by the constant factor e^r. The parameter r is therefore a measure of the rate at which the population increases and is commonly known as the intrinsic rate of increase, though it should be remembered that the same equation will describe an exponential decrease if $r < 0$.

In practice no insect population increases without limit in this way, though the early stages of population growth in an environment with abundant food and no external constraints will approximate to an exponential form. More usually, as a population grows in size various factors will operate to reduce the rate at which its numbers are increasing. This situation may be represented by a simple modification of the exponential growth equation (1) to give

$$\frac{dN}{dt} = rN\left(\frac{K - N}{K}\right) \tag{4}$$

where the factor $(K-N)/K$ is introduced to express in a simple way the notion that the rate of increase declines as the population approaches a constant value K, a parameter which represents an equilibrium population density that is usually called the carrying capacity of the environment in which the population is growing. Equation (4) is the differential form of the so-called logistic growth equation which, as in the previous case, may be solved to give a more explicit form, of which one is

$$N_t = \frac{N_0 e^{rt}}{1 + N_0(e^{rt} - 1)/K} \tag{5}$$

An equivalent difference equation, applicable to the case of a population with discrete generations, is given by

$$N_{t+1} = \frac{e^r N_t}{1 + (e^r - 1)N_t/K} \tag{6}$$

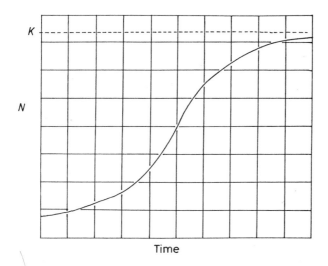

Time

Fig. 125   Diagram of logistic population growth curve

Note the sigmoidal shape of the curve and the way in which the maximum rate of growth (i.e. the steepest slope of the curve) occurs when the population size is one-half of the carrying capacity K.

Typical exponential and logistic growth curves are shown diagrammatically in Figs 124–126 and indicate the S-shaped or sigmoidal form of the logistic model. This model has several interesting properties, of

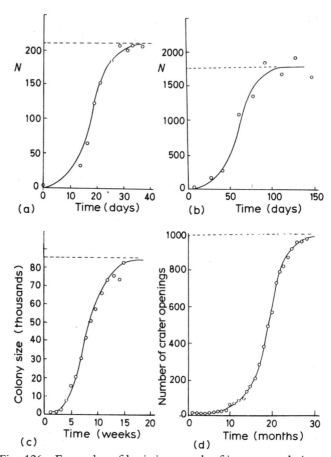

Fig. 126　Examples of logistic growth of insect populations
(a) *Drosophila melanogaster* (after Pearl); (b) *Tribolium confusum* (after Gause); (c) *Apis mellifera* (after Bodenheimer); (d) workers of the ant *Atta sextens* (as measured by number of craters in a colony) (after Britancourt).

which two may be noted especially: (a) in the early stages of growth, when the population size N is small relative to K, growth will approximate to an exponential form; and (b) the maximum rate of growth occurs when the population size is one-half of the carrying capacity; this can be seen from Fig. 125, where the slope of the curve is greatest at $N = K/2$, but can also be proved analytically by maximizing the expression for growth rate given in (4). Above this population size the rate of growth will gradually decline until it becomes very small as the carrying capacity is approached and the population nears saturation level.

　　Although the assumptions underlying the logistic growth model are unlikely to reflect all the factors that control population size, it provides

254

a satisfactory description of the way in which some insect populations increase, as illustrated by the examples for *Drosophila, Tribolium, Apis* and *Atta* in Fig. 126. Moreover, the parameters r and K provide a basis for interesting relationships between the population growth of a species and other features of its biology and life-history. Some species, described as '*r*-selected' or '*r*-strategists', tend to occur in unstable or temporary habitats, to which they are adapted through a capacity for rapid multiplication under favourable conditions (i.e. they have high *r*-values). They are often rather small species, tend to lay many eggs, develop quickly, have a short life-span and may produce several generations in a season. Their survivorship curve (p. 258) shows high juvenile mortalities and their population density varies greatly from time to time, not only because of their high intrinsic rate of increase, but also because they often have high powers of dispersal. Populations of *r*-selected species sometimes show catastrophic mortalities, and density-dependent processes (p. 262) probably play a less important role in the regulation of their population size. Many insect pests of crop plants are *r*-selected, notably aphids, whiteflies, locusts and Lepidoptera like *Spodoptera exempta*. At the other extreme are the *K*-selected species, occupying more stable, permanent or predictably seasonal habitats in which they tend to reproduce less rapidly to attain population densities that fluctuate less and are usually near the carrying capacity of the environment. Such insects tend to be larger, produce fewer progeny and develop more slowly, with life-cycles that are univoltine or even spread over two or more years. Their survivorship curves show lower juvenile mortalities and their population size tends to be regulated by density-dependent processes. Typical *K*-strategists are the tsetse flies (*Glossina*) and the Codling Moth (*Cydia pomonella*). Although this distinction into *r*- and *K*-selected species is useful, it should not be imagined that there is a sharp demarcation between them; rather, they should be looked upon as extremes between which broad transitions occur or in which a species may show some characteristics of *r*-strategists combined with others more usually found in *K*-selected forms. The selective pressures imposed by the environment and the consequent responses made by insects in evolving adaptive life-cycles may be more complicated than simple r/K hypotheses would suggest.

The logistic model of population growth is not the only one which yields a sigmoid curve when numbers are plotted against time. Other equations, embodying different assumptions and entailing different relationships between growth rate and population size will also lead to sigmoid curves, and the available laboratory and field data may be quite inadequate to discriminate between them. Furthermore, a smoothly increasing sigmoid curve may not provide a satisfactory fit to observed data, which often show considerable fluctuations about an equilibrium

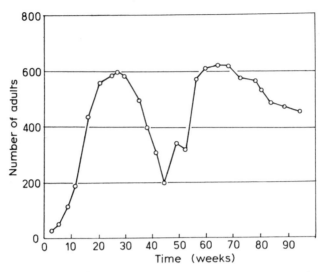

Fig. 127 Adult population curve of *Sitophilus oryzae*, cultured on 12 g of wheat, renewed every 2 weeks. (After Varley *et al.*, from data of Birch.)

value, as in Fig. 127. Fluctuations of this kind can be represented by a variety of mathematical models, in which special interest attaches to those which are simple extensions of the logistic model, incorporating a term which allows for a time-lag or delay in the response of the population to changing density. In its differential form the lagged logistic equation may be written

$$\frac{dN_t}{dt} = rN_t \left(\frac{K - N_{t-L}}{K} \right) \tag{7}$$

where the subscript L denotes the duration of the delay in units of time. The corresponding difference equation for discrete generations is then

$$N_{t+1} = \frac{e^r N_t}{1 + (e^r - 1)N_{t-L}/K} \tag{8}$$

where L is now the delay measured in number of generations. According to the values assumed by the various parameters, populations that grow according to (7) or (8) may show either a smooth approach to the equilibrium density K or an approach by damped oscillations. Alternatively, they may oscillate regularly about this level or show irregular fluctuations that could even lead to extinction. Such models therefore appear to be more versatile and realistic descriptions of the kinds of changes in population size that are found in many insects, though again it needs to be borne in mind that other mathematical formulations can yield rather similar patterns and that empirical data may be inadequate to distinguish between alternative models.

POPULATION FLUCTUATIONS

Insect populations do not usually remain almost constant in size over many years. Repeated measurements of population density show that the numbers of any particular stage in the life-cycle may vary in an apparently more or less erratic manner from season to season. This is clearly shown by the long series of records (extending over a century or more) for some Lepidopteran pests of coniferous forests in C. Europe (Fig. 128). Expressed in the number of pupae per square metre of forest floor, populations of the Geometrid moth *Bupalus piniaria* show fluctuations with periodic peaks when the insects may be some 10 000 times more numerous than they are in the years of their greatest scarcity. Comparable large-scale fluctuations occur in other species and shorter-term studies of many species confirm the tendency of insect populations to vary in density with time about some general long-term average, which may remain relatively stable over fairly large areas.

The factors or processes that cause populations to fluctuate in size do so by influencing the rates of reproduction or of mortality; they are likely to be numerous, to vary in relative importance from one species to another or from time to time, and to interact in relatively complicated and unpredictable ways. Broadly, however, it is possible first to distinguish between *extrinsic* (exogenous) factors or processes, operating on the population from outside, and *intrinsic* (endogenous) processes,

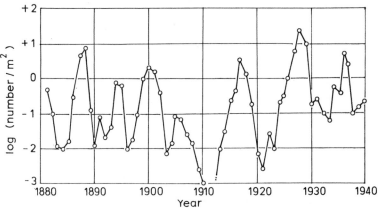

Fig. 128   Fluctuations in population density of the Pine Looper Moth, *Bupalus piniaria* (Geometridae)

Population density is expressed as number of pupae per m² of forest floor in Germany from 1880 to 1940. (After data of Schwerdtfeger.)

which arise within the population. Among the more important extrinsic processes are likely to be the effects of parasites and predators, the availability of resources such as food or sites for oviposition, competition with other species for resources (interspecific competition), and the favourable or adverse effects of weather (especially temperature, humidity and rainfall). Important intrinsic factors include intraspecific competition for various resources, dispersal of individuals to other habitats as the population density increases, and genetic changes in developmental or reproductive rates and in viability.

An alternative distinction may be made between processes whose action is affected by the population density and those which do not depend on density. Thus, weather conditions might normally be expected to exert a density-independent effect: the influence of adversely high temperatures, for example, is not likely to be different in dense populations than in sparse ones. On the other hand, the effects of predators or parasites are likely to be greater in dense populations, when they might be expected to find their prey or hosts more readily than they can when these are scarce. Sufficient food and living space will also be more difficult to find when the population is dense, and these factors will therefore exert their effects in a density-dependent manner. Conversely, when the population density is low, the effects of predation, parasitism and competition for food and space will be relaxed and the population will respond by more rapid growth. Density-dependent processes have therefore been regarded as the principal or sole agents for regulating population size, inhibiting the further growth of large populations and promoting the growth of small ones. The observational evidence for this and other theories of the natural regulation of insect populations is discussed in greater detail below (pp. 262–6).

LIFE TABLES

The essential information needed to understand and interpret the factors affecting population density may be summarized in a life table. For a species with discrete generations (i.e. those which do not overlap) such a table sets out the population sizes at each of a number of successive stages in the life-cycle, thus enabling the mortality (which may be attributable to various causes) to be ascertained at each stage. When plotted against time the progressively declining numbers of individuals constitute a survivorship curve, whose shape may convey useful information about the biology of a species. Two categories of survivorship curves may be recognized among insects. In some species, such as *Chorthippus brunneus*, discussed below, the heaviest mortality occurs in the early stages of development, after which there is a lesser and more gradual decline in numbers. In other species the opposite tendency is shown, with relatively low mortalities during the first part of the life-cycle, followed by a later, more abrupt decline in the size of the population. There are, however, many transitional forms between these extremes. Table 1 gives a life table for the Acridid grasshopper *Chorthippus brunneus* in southern England for a single season (1947–8). From this it may be seen that of the initial population of 200 eggs per 10 m², fewer than six adults finally escaped all the successive deaths that are tabulated for each of the immature stages. Obviously the estimates of population size and the other quantities that are derived from them will generally be based on samples of varying reliability, and tables such as this may be constructed for each of several successive generations. In this way it may be seen whether a particular stage of the life-cycle is always accompanied by a high mortality or whether the different causes of mortality exert effects which vary in relative importance from season to season.

Table 1　Life table of *Chorthippus brunneus* (1947–8) (simplified, from Richards and Waloff, 1954)

Stage	Numbers per 10 m²	Percentage mortality	Survival ratio	k
Egg	200.75	–	–	–
Instar I	15.86	92.1	0.079	1.102
Instar II	11.42	28.0	0.720	0.145
Instar III	8.68	24.0	0.760	0.119
Instar IV	6.60	24.0	0.760	0.119
Adult	5.80	12.1	0.879	0.056

N.B. The percentage mortality expresses the deaths occurring between a given stage and that which precedes it. The survival ratio is the proportion of insects which survive into that stage from the preceding one. The quantity k is discussed below (p. 260).

A somewhat more detailed life table for the knapweed gall-fly *Urophora jaceana* (Tephritidae) is presented in Table 2. Here the larval instars are not separately distinguished, but records of the population size were kept following each of a series of events (parasitism, predation, etc.), the effects of which on survival could be assessed quantitatively. It is clear from the table that 'winter mortality' and 'predation by mice' had the greatest relative effect on survival.

The two life tables given are representative of most insect populations in which there is one generation per year. Life tables can also be constructed for populations where several generations overlap so that all developmental stages are present at the same time, as in some species infesting grain stored in bulk. They can also be compiled for those

Table 2 Life table of *Urophora jaceana* (after Varley *et al.*, 1973)

Stage/event	Number per m^2	Percentage mortality	Survival ratio	k
Eggs laid	209.0	–	–	–
Eggs hatching	190.0	9.1	0.909	0.041
Larvae forming galls	148.0	22.1	0.779	0.108
Young larvae surviving	144.3	2.5	0.975	0.011
Parasitism by *Eurytoma tibialis*	63.2	56.2	0.438	0.359
Effects of other parasites	53.8	14.9	0.851	0.070
Predation by Lepidopteran larvae	44.5	17.3	0.827	0.082
Winter mortality	17.1	61.6	0.384	0.416
Predation by mice	6.1	64.3	0.357	0.447
Predation by birds	5.9	3.3	0.967	0.015
Larval deaths	4.3	27.1	0.729	0.137
Parasitism by *Habrocytus*, etc.	3.6	16.3	0.837	0.077
Pupae drowned	2.0	44.4	0.556	0.255

populations in which a cohort of identifiable individuals is followed throughout the life-span of its members. However, such tables are often difficult to prepare for insects, and simpler ones of the kind already discussed are more usually encountered. Indeed, they may be more informative than the kind of formal life tables modelled on those used in human demography and actuarial practice, since they generally include references to the incidence of specific forms of mortality such as that due to parasitism, predation or the adverse effects of physical factors.

KEY FACTOR ANALYSIS

A detailed analysis of the information provided by a life table enables the identification of certain key factors, of major importance in determining changes in population density. If, as in the life table, we define m_i, the mortality during the i-th stage of the life-cycle as the proportion of those individuals entering the stage which have died by the end of the stage, then the proportion surviving during that stage is $(1 - m_i)$. If the stages succeed each other, then the survival over the whole generation will be the product of the survivals $(1 - m_i)$ during each stage. Moreover, if each of the successive mortalities is due to some identifiable factor, whose killing power, k_i, is defined as $k_i = -\log_{10}(1 - m_i)$, then we can represent the combined killing effect K of all factors over the whole generation by

$$K = k_1 + k_2 + k_3 + \ldots + k_n$$

The magnitude of each of the n k-values can be calculated from the data provided by a life table as shown in the two tables given above. We can then assess the contribution of each factor to the total mortality in a particularly direct way since the k-values are additive. By repeating this kind of analysis over several generations it is possible to ascertain which of the factors are of major importance, i.e. which are the key factors controlling population changes.

An example is provided by the population of the Winter Moth *Operophtera brumata* studied by Varley and his co-workers over 13 generations. Six causes of mortality operated successively in each generation and for each causal factor a k-value could be calculated:

k_1 'winter disappearance', i.e. loss from all causes between census of females and that of full-grown larvae

k_2 parasitism of full-grown larvae by the Tachinid *Cyzenis albicans*

k_3 parasitism by other insects (Tachinidae and Ichneumonidae)

k_4 parasitism by a microsporidian, *Plistiophora operophterae*

k_5 predation on pupae, mainly by the Carabid beetle *Pterostichus madidus*

k_6 parasitism of pupae by *Cratichneumon culex*

The k-values over the 13 generations, together with the generation mortalities represented by $K = \Sigma^6_{i=1}k_i$ and the population densities of

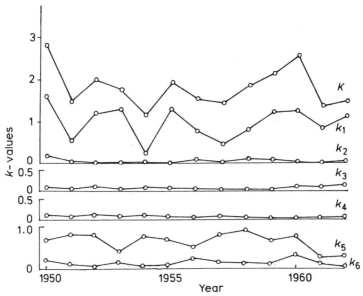

Fig. 129   Key factor analysis for the Winter Moth, *Operophtera brumata* (Geometridae) over 13 years (1950–62)

The uppermost graph shows K-values, the six lower graphs depict corresponding values of k_1–k_6 (p. 000). It is clear that k_1 (winter disappearance) contributes most to the observed mortality. (After Varley *et al.*)

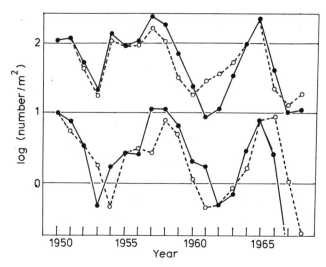

Fig. 130 Observed and calculated population densities of the larvae of the Winter Moth *Operophtera brumata* (Geometridae) and its pupal parasitoid *Cratichneumon culex* over 20 years

Full lines connect observed values, broken lines connect calculated densities. Upper graphs refer to *Operophtera*, lower ones to *Cratichneumon*. Ordinate: log (numbers/m²). (After Varley *et al.*)

adults and full-grown larvae are depicted graphically in Fig. 129. From this figure it can be seen that the complex of factors represented by k_1 constituted the most important agent of population change and could be regarded as the key factor, whereas the factors represented by k_5 and k_6, though of lesser importance, were more significant than those identified with k_2 to k_4. Comparison of the k-values with the population densities over several generations may also enable one to interpret the mortalities as due to density-dependent or other processes. The effects may then be incorporated in a model which aims at describing the changes that have occurred over the period of investigation and which, it might be hoped, could be used to predict future population changes. The results of one such model for *Operophtera* are indicated in Fig. 130. However, it must be emphasized that there are considerable difficulties in validating particular models empirically or in choosing between a number of alternative models. This is hardly unexpected when one recalls the very many complicated and interacting processes that control changes in population density.

REGULATION OF POPULATION SIZE; DENSITY-DEPENDENT PROCESSES

In general, populations of insect species persist for long periods without suffering extinction or increasing beyond all bounds. They are therefore, as we have already seen (p. 257), subject to regulation, or natural control, fluctuating more or less widely about a long-term average value. Several theories have been put forward to account for regulation and corresponding efforts made to identify and measure the processes occurring in natural populations. A major controversy has centred on the occurrence and extent of density-dependent processes. On the one hand it is argued that only density-dependent processes can allow populations to increase when they are below some equilibrium value and then to decrease after they have exceeded this level. There is considerable logical force in this argument, though it may be difficult to demonstrate the effective operation of the processes under field conditions. On the other hand, climatic factors, which might have been expected to operate in a density-independent manner, exert effects that are, in fact, sometimes closely correlated with population size. For example, it has been argued that variations in the density of *Thrips imaginis* populations on roses in Australia can, to a large extent, be accounted for by preceding variations in weather conditions (temperature and rainfall) and that these leave no room for the operation of density-dependent changes. However, a statistically significant regression of population size on climatic factors does not in itself provide a test for density-dependence, and when suitable tests are carried out on the same body of data they reveal the operation of density-dependent processes. In a general sense, of course, any form of intraspecific competition for a limited resource (such as food, shelter or oviposition sites) will operate in a density-dependent manner and may therefore be expected to regulate population size, even in the absence of classical density-dependent control by parasitoids and predators. A fuller discussion of density-dependent effects is therefore desirable.

The growth of a population is said to be density-dependent if the growth rate per individual decreases as population density increases. Such a decrease in the growth rate may, of course, be due to increasing mortality or decreasing fecundity. It has already been pointed out that population growth may follow a sigmoid relationship for reasons which may imply quite different relationships between the growth rate per individual and the size of the population. Thus, although a sigmoid growth curve indicates that a density-dependent effect is operating at the higher population densities, it by no means follows that this is true at lower densities. More refined analytical methods may therefore be necessary to ascertain whether a process is density-dependent, whether it is inversely density-dependent (so that the growth rate per individual increases with increasing population density) or whether it is density-independent.

If the growth of a population were independent of its density it might

263

be expected that the population size in the t-th generation would be directly proportional to its size in the $(t + 1)$-th generation, that is

$$N_{t+1} = \lambda N_t$$

from which $\log N_{t+1} = \log \lambda + \log N_t$, so that a plot of $\log N_{t+1}$ against $\log N_t$ would give a straight line of unit slope. On the other hand, a relationship of the form $N_{t+1} = \lambda N_t^b$ (where the exponent b is less than unity) would indicate a density-dependent relationship and would reveal itself in a double-logarithmic plot as a straight line with a slope less than unity. In this way density-dependent processes are claimed to have been demonstrated in populations of the spruce budworm *Choristoneura fumiferana* in Canada, though there are statistical reasons for doubting such an inference when, as in this case, the points being plotted are very scattered. Another more direct method of demonstrating density-dependence relies on plotting mortalities (or the equivalent k-values discussed on p. 260) against population size, as shown generally in Fig. 131 and for the specific cases of the Colorado Potato Beetle, *Leptinotarsa decemlineata*, and the Winter Moth, *Operophtera brumata*, in Fig. 132.

Though it is widely considered that regulation of an insect population must depend on density-dependent processes, the converse is not true.

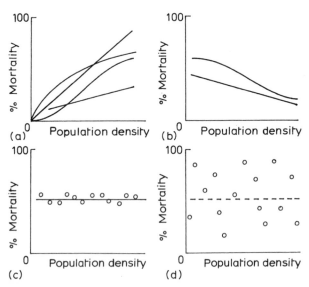

Fig. 131   Diagrams to illustrate various relationships between population density (abscissae) and percentage mortality (ordinates)

(a) Density-dependent; (b) inversely density-dependent; (c) density-independent (almost constant mortalities); (d) density-independent (large random variations in mortality). (After Varley *et al.*)

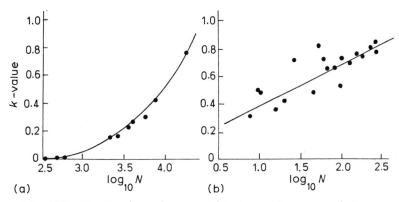

Fig. 132 Density-dependent mortality in two insect populations
(a) Colorado Potato Beetle, *Leptinotarsa decemlineata* (after Harcourt); (b) Winter Moth, *Operophtera brumata* (after Varley and Gradwell). Note that in both cases the *k*-values increase with population density.

A more detailed investigation shows that such processes may be able to exert a variety of effects on population size over a period of time. Thus, depending on the slope of the line relating *k*-values to population density (Fig. 133), a constant level of density may be attained in a single generation, gradually approached over a longer period, or brought about as the result of damped oscillations in population size. It is even possible (cases (d) and (e) of Fig. 133) for the population never to reach a constant size, but for it to show repeated uniform or irregular oscillations about a long-term mean. A delayed response to increased population size – sometimes referred to as a delayed density-dependent effect – will also generate oscillations in a population.

It may be seen from this very brief outline of some aspects of the problem that density-dependent processes may be difficult to identify and assess quantitatively in individual cases, and that they may produce a variety of different results in the population concerned. There is also evidence that the intensity of a density-dependent process in a given species may vary from time to time and over different parts of its range, and that quite different key-factors may be involved. It is therefore most unlikely that there is one simple theory of the natural control of insect populations: which factors operate in each case, and how they exert their effects, will require detailed field and laboratory investigation.

COMPETITION

For at least part of their time the members of an insect species are likely to be competing with one another or with members of another species for limited resources such as food, mates or suitable sites for oviposition, hibernation or pupation. Such competition does not

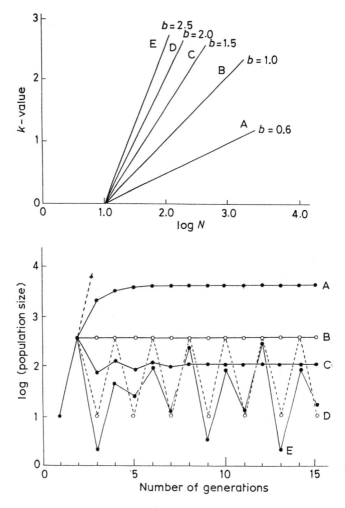

Fig. 133 Diagrams illustrating effect of different density-dependent relationships on the stability of a population

Upper figure shows five different linear relationships between log (population density)
and mortality (expressed as k-values). Lower figure indicates the consequences of these
for stability. (a) Gradual attainment of stability; (b) stability attained in one generation;
(c) damped oscillations leading to stability; (d) fluctuations of constant amplitude;
(e) irregular fluctuations. (After Varley *et al.*)

necessarily operate at all times; there may be abundant food or plenty of
available space, but whenever resources are limited and the population
is increasing it is likely to occur. To demonstrate competition it is
necessary to show that as the population density per unit of resource
rises, so the mortality (or, more appropriately perhaps, its equivalent
k-value, defined on p. 260) will rise, as in Figs 134 and 135. It is usual to

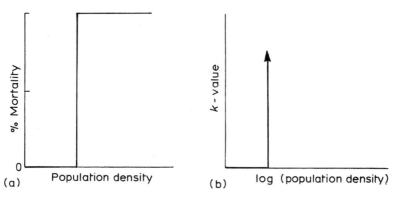

Fig. 134   Pure scramble competition

(a) indicates the way in which the percentage mortality increases abruptly from zero when the population density exceeds a certain threshold. (b) illustrates the same relationship in terms of log (population density) and k-values. (After Hassell.)

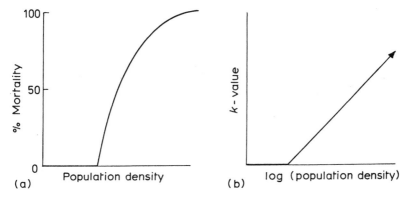

Fig. 135   Pure contest competition

(a) and (b) correspond to the two illustrations of Fig. 134. (After Hassell.)

distinguish between two forms of competition: intraspecific competition, which occurs between members of the same species, and interspecific competition, which occurs between members of two or more species. Both kinds can, and commonly will, occur together.

Intraspecific competition is of two kinds. In scramble competition each competing individual receives an approximately equal share of the diminishing resource, as in Fig. 134. It is therefore revealed as an abrupt increase in k-values as resources become limited or, when competition is well below the level at which all the individuals die, as a decline in body weight or fecundity or some similar measure of vigour. In contest competition, on the other hand, the limited resource is unequally divided between the competing individuals so that some are satisfied

267

while others receive none (Fig. 135). This can occur, for example, where there are a discrete, limited number of pupation or oviposition sites or of territories within which mating can occur. If the resources are approximately constant in amount or number, then contest competition will tend to produce stability of population size and it may generally be distinguished from scramble competition by the smaller slope of the curve relating k-values to the population size.

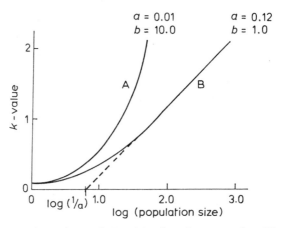

Fig. 136   Density-dependent relationships based on equation (9) for different values of the parameters a and b

Curve (a) approaches scramble competition and curve (b) contest competition. (After Hassell.)

The effect of intraspecific competition is to replace an exponential form of population growth by a logistic relationship or, more satisfactorily perhaps, by one which incorporates a delayed density-dependent effect. This may be expressed explicitly, as in (7) and (8) on p. 256, or implicitly, as in Hassell's equation which, for a population with discrete non-overlapping generations, is given by

$$N_{t+1} = e^r N_t (1 + aN_t)^{-b} \qquad (9)$$

By varying the value of the parameter b in (9) it is possible to describe the density-dependent effects of both scramble and contest competition (Fig. 136). Moreover, as pointed out above (p. 265) the effect of delayed density-dependent processes operating in accordance with models (8) or (9) will be to simulate the kind of regular or irregular fluctuations in size that have actually been observed in populations of single species competing for food (as in the well-studied examples of the blowfly, *Lucilia cuprina*, or the beetle *Callosobruchus chinensis*). Low rates of increase and/or weak competition result in a smooth gradual approach to an equilibrium population density, whereas higher rates of increase and scramble competition induce rapid changes and oscillations about the equilibrium density.

Experimental studies of interspecific competition, in which populations of two competing species have been maintained for many generations, have demonstrated two kinds of outcome. In some cases only one of the species eventually survives and the unsuccessful competitor is eliminated. This has been shown, for example, in mixed populations of the two flour-beetles *Tribolium confusum* and *T. castaneum*, where, at lower temperatures and relative humidities, only *T. confusum* survives. However, the balance is a delicate one because at higher temperatures and relative humidities *T. castaneum* supplants *T. confusum*. The competition between the two species is also affected by the presence of a Protozoan parasite *Adelina; T. confusum* succeeded in cultures containing the parasite, *T. castaneum* when it was absent.

However, replacement of one species by the other is not the inevitable outcome of interspecific competition. Mixed populations of *Tribolium confusum* and another beetle *Oryzaephilus surinamensis* can occur in which the two species coexist at equilibrium levels (which do not, incidentally, depend on the initial densities). Coexistence does, however, depend on the presence within the culture medium of small tubular refuges within which *Oryzaephilus*, but not *Tribolium*, can pupate. Without such refuges *Tribolium* will eliminate *Oryzaephilus*, which illustrates again how the outcome of competition between two species may depend on particular features of the habitat they occupy.

The classical mathematical description of simple two-species competition is provided by the Lotka–Volterra model, which represents an extension of the logistic growth model (p. 252) by including extra terms to express the adverse effect of each species on the other. In differential form the Lotka–Volterra equations may be written as

$$\frac{dN_1}{dt} = r_1 N_1 \left(\frac{K_1 - N_1 - \alpha N_2}{K_1} \right)$$

$$\frac{dN_2}{dt} = r_2 N_2 \left(\frac{K_2 - N_2 - \beta N_1}{K_2} \right)$$

(10)

where the subscripts 1 and 2 refer to the two species and the additional parameters α and β are the so-called competition coefficients: α is the coefficient indicating the effect which the presence of species 2 has on the population growth of species 1, while β measures the converse effect of species 1 on species 2. At equilibrium, when dN_1/dt and dN_2/dt are both zero, then $N_1 = K_1 - \alpha N_2$ and $N_2 = K_2 - \beta N_1$. Plots of N_1

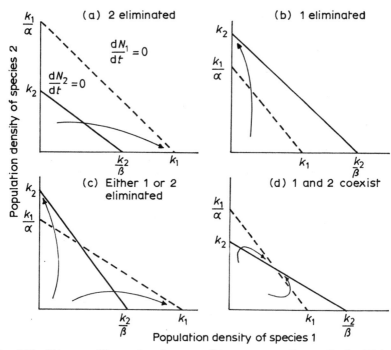

Fig. 137   Diagram illustrating four possible outcomes from a Lotka–Volterra
model of competition between two species
Symbols as given in equation (10). (After Hassell.)

against N_2 then give straight lines ('zero growth isoclines') which may
or may not intersect. The four possible cases are illustrated diagrammatically in Fig. 137, and show that the outcome of Lotka–Volterra
competition may be the progressive elimination of one or the other
species or the coexistence of both at a point of stable equilibrium. As in
the case of single-species (intraspecific) competition discussed above,
however, this equilibrium is approached asymptotically in the Lotka–
Volterra model and a more realistic description of interspecific competition, with fluctuations about the equilibrium population densities, is
provided by other models which incorporate delayed density-dependent
effects. The Hassell equation (9) may be extended to cover this situation
rather as the unlagged logistic model (4) was extended to give (10).

Models of competition – and those just mentioned are not the only
ones available – are not easy to test under experimental conditions and
are even more difficult to validate in the field. Their usefulness lies
rather in the unified conceptual framework that they aim to provide and
in the possibilities that they offer in helping to decide between
alternative interpretations of observational data. Through such models
it is possible to link competition with the study of interactions between

an insect population and its predators and parasites (pp. 272–6), and to suggest interpretations of some other aspects of competition discussed below.

COMPETITIVE EXCLUSION; RESOURCE PARTITIONING; THE ECOLOGICAL NICHE

The theory of interspecific competition suggests that if two or more species have identical ecological requirements they will not be able to exist together; one will oust the others so that only the successful species eventually occupies that particular ecological niche. This view, sometimes known as Gause's principle or the principle of competitive exclusion, is difficult to establish conclusively since the differences in the ecological requirements of the species may be very slight or subtle. Nevertheless, there is a good deal of indirect evidence that the principle holds in some cases. It is likely, for instance, to explain the phenomenon of competitive displacement, in which the artificial introduction of a species into a habitat occupied by a closely related species leads to the latter being supplanted by the newcomer. The repeated introduction of the parasitoidal Chalcid *Aphytis* into California to control the Citrus Red Scale *Aonidiella aurantii* illustrates this phenomenon. Originally, from about 1900, *Aphytis chrysomphali* had established itself, but it was then almost completely replaced by another species, *Aphytis lingnanensis*, introduced in 1948. This, in turn, was very largely replaced by a third species, *Aphytis melinus*, introduced in 1956. A similar sequence of events occurred as a result of the successive introduction of three species of the Braconid *Opius* into Hawaii to control the Oriental Fruit Fly, *Dacus dorsalis* (Tephritidae): *Opius longicaudatus* was largely replaced by *O. vandenboschi* which, in turn, was succeeded by *O. oophilus*.

A corollary of the principle of competitive exclusion is that when two or more species appear to coexist in the same general habitat it will be found that they occupy more or less distinct ecological niches, so that the resources of the habitat are in fact partitioned out between its various occupying species. Many examples of resource partitioning are now known among insects. Three species of the Ichneumonid *Megarhyssa* parasitize larvae of the Siricid sawfly *Tremex columba* in N. America. They all possess a long ovipositor which is used to bore to its full extent into the wooden logs in which the host lives, and to deposit an egg there. However, the ovipositor of *M. greenei* is only 40 mm long, whereas that of *M. macrurus* is 80 mm long and that of *M. atrata* is 120 mm in length. The three species of *Megarhyssa* are therefore not really in competition, since they are parasitizing different host populations, found at successively deeper levels as the logs become older and the *Tremex* larvae burrow more deeply into them. Three species of

Scolytid beetles attack the white pine, *Pinus strobus*, in the N.E. United States. *Dendroctonus valens* is restricted in its attack to the base of the tree, the smaller *Ips pini* to the upper trunk and large branches, while the smallest species, *Pityogenes hopkinsi*, only enters the bark of the smaller branches. In other cases the differences between two related species may be much less obvious. *Mesopsocus immunis* and *M. unipunctatus* are two species of Psocoptera that occur together on larches in the north of England. They have virtually identical food preferences and occur at the same time, but *M. immunis* lays its eggs mostly in the axils of small side-shoots, whereas *M. unipunctatus* oviposits mainly on leaf-scars and girdle-scars. In this case oviposition site rather than food is the limited resource; interspecific competition is avoided by the different choice of egg-laying sites, and intraspecific competition within both species is reduced by the insects' habit of dispersing from populations of high density. Another way in which competition is avoided and the resources partitioned among related species is through their geographical separation: several of the eight species of the leaf-hopper *Erythroneura* that live on sycamore in N. America show clear differences in abundance according to latitude, though they also tend to feed on different parts of the leaf. Separation in time is another way in which interspecific competition is avoided and the resources of a habitat utilized successively throughout the season or over some shorter period. Different species of skipper butterflies (Hesperiidae) have been shown to have different flight periods, each associated with the appearance of different flowers; two species of Corixidae occupying the same pond have different periods of maximum abundance; and two species of the solitary bee *Andrena* visit flowers of the Evening Primrose, *Oenothera*, either when they are newly opened or when they are old.

By reducing or eliminating competition, situations like those described above have enabled larger numbers of species to be supported by a given habitat than would otherwise be the case. Such considerations indicate the way in which the diversity of a community is related to competition among the species present. They also lead to a fuller understanding of the concept of the ecological niche, defined quantitatively in terms of the ranges of different factors (food, space, light, moisture, temperature, etc.) which allow a given species to survive and which may overlap to different degrees with the requirements of related species or those occurring in the same general habitat. In these respects the study of population ecology approaches that of communities, a topic discussed briefly below (pp. 276–85).

HOST–PARASITOID AND PREDATOR–PREY RELATIONSHIPS

The general biology of predacious and parasitoidal insects has already been described on pp. 218 and 222). Both there and also in relation to practical methods of pest control (pp. 335–7) it has been emphasized that predators and parasitoids exert important effects in determining and regulating the population densities of the insects which they attack. Many examples of this have been cited; here we need to discuss in rather more detail some of the quantitative aspects of the interaction between insect predators and their prey, or parasitoids and their hosts. There are, of course, many differences in biology and behaviour between typical predators and typical parasitoids. In parasitoids, for example, it is only the adult female which searches for the host, whereas in predators the males and often the juvenile forms also seek out and kill their prey. Also, in parasitoids the number of progeny is closely determined by the number of hosts parasitized, whereas the reproductive capacity of predators is likely to depend in more complicated ways on the number of prey attacked. Further, the parasitoid–host systems can often be more effectively modelled by assuming discrete non-overlapping generations in which changes can be described by difference equations; predator populations, on the other hand, may have a more complicated age-structure that exerts important effects and is better modelled by differential equations. Nevertheless, despite these differences the quantitative analysis of interactions between these two groups of insects and the species they attack can often be considered within the same general framework of theory.

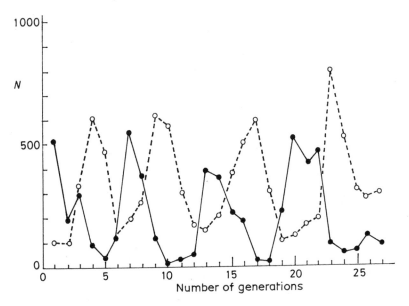

Fig. 138 Fluctuations in population density in a host–parasitoid system consisting of the bean weevil *Callosobruchus chinensis* (full lines) and its Braconid parasitoid *Heterospilus prosopidis* (broken lines). (After Uchida.)

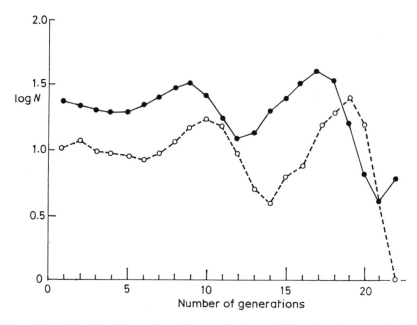

Fig. 139 Unstable fluctuations in populations of the Greenhouse Whitefly *Trialeurodes vaporariorum* (full lines) and its Chalcidoid parasite *Encarsia formosa* (broken lines). (After Burnett.)

The objective of this theory – that is, to describe mathematically the variations in the numbers of predators and prey or parasitoids and hosts – is, of course, a very ambitious one, since there are considerable differences between species. Some predators seem to have little effect on their prey density, whereas others maintain it at very low levels; some systems show more or less regular cyclical fluctuations over long periods, while in others the fluctuations are unstable and the prey may become extinct (as does also the predator, unless it can attack alternative prey species). Examples of both the latter alternatives are shown by the stable oscillations, for more than 100 generations, in a laboratory population of the bean weevil *Callosobruchus chinensis* parasitized by the Braconid *Heterospilus prosopidis* (Fig. 138) and the unstable fluctuations of the whitefly *Trialeurodes vaporariorum* parasitized by the Chalcid *Encarsia formosa* (Fig. 139).

All of these effects are the ultimate result of the various component activities involved in predation or parasitism: the success of searching for prey or host, the time required to search, the way in which prey density affects the numbers attacked by each predator, the mutual interference of predators, and so on. Studies of these processes may enable their effects to be represented by parameters in mathematical models of predator–prey interactions, though simpler models with fewer assumptions can often simulate successfully some of the effects observed in simplified laboratory systems. Extensions of the theory to natural field populations is much more difficult, since population levels and fluctuations in the prey are likely to be affected by many factors besides the activities of predators (which may, in any case, consist of several species, perhaps with alternative prey, all linked in a complicated food web).

One of the earliest mathematical models of predator–prey interactions, proposed by Lotka and Volterra, may be formulated as a pair of differential equations:

$$\frac{dN}{dt} = (r - C_1 P)N$$

$$\frac{dP}{dt} = (C_2 N - d)P$$

$$(11)$$

where N and P are the numbers of prey and predator, respectively, r is the intrinsic rate of increase of the prey, and d is the death rate of predators in the absence of prey; C_1 and C_2 are two parameters expressing, respectively, the rate at which prey is attacked and the extent to which prey is, in effect, converted into more predators. These equations describe a system with complete overlap of generations and non-seasonal reproduction in both populations. They yield smooth, stable oscillations about equilibrium population levels, with the prey and predator oscillations out of phase, the amplitude of the oscillations depending on the initial numbers of prey and predators. As such, they do not account for the instability shown by some predator–prey systems, nor do they reflect adequately the way in which the generations of many such systems are discrete, with strictly seasonal reproductive periods. The Lotka–Volterra equations may, however, be expressed in a modified form as difference equations, which depict a system with discrete, non-overlapping generations and which incorporate a delayed density-dependent effect. Such a model, in which the equilibrium levels are unstable and lead, when disturbed, to oscillations of increasing amplitude, may be represented as

$$N_{t+1} = e^r N_t (1 - a P_t)$$

$$P_{t+1} = N_t (a P_t)$$

$$(12)$$

where the subscripts t and $t+1$ denote two successive generations and a is a parameter called the area of discovery (actually the proportion of the total area of the system which is searched by one predator).

In this form there is a considerable similarity between the Lotka–Volterra equations and an alternative model originally proposed by Nicholson and Bailey as especially appropriate for insect host–parasitoid systems. This may be expressed as

$$N_{t+1} = e^r N_t \exp(-aP_t)$$

$$P_{t+1} = N_t[1 - \exp(-aP_t)]$$

(13)

It will be seen that the Lotka–Volterra equations and the Nicholson–Bailey model are special cases of the more general system

$$N_{t+1} = e^r N_t f(N_t, P_t)$$

$$P_{t+1} = N_t[1 - f(N_t, P_t)]$$

(14)

where the function $f(N_t, P_t)$ takes the form $1 - aP_t$ for the Lotka–Volterra model and $\exp(-aP_t)$ for the Nicholson–Bailey equations.

Neither of the models discussed takes into account some of the biologically important factors that are likely to operate in predator–prey or host–parasitoid systems. However, the general form (14) provides a family of models by allowing other alternative expressions to be chosen for the function $f(N_t, P_t)$. In this way it has been possible to incorporate parameters that allow for the 'handling time' (i.e. the time required for the predator to subdue, kill and consume its prey), for the effects of aggregation or mutual interference of predators, or for the existence of some kind of 'refuge' – spatial or temporal – that permits the survival of protected prey. In such ways it may be possible to model a system with unstable oscillations and then show how various factors can act to stabilize them. This is far from taking into account all the varying and interacting environmental conditions that affect both predator and prey, or host and parasitoid, but it does at least help one to understand the influence of some of these factors when their effects are not obscured by the others.

FOOD WEBS AND THE TROPHIC STRUCTURE OF COMMUNITIES

Previous sections have considered populations of a single species, or simple systems such as those where two species compete for similar resources or in which a predator attacks a single species of prey. In nature, however, populations of many species of plants and animals may occur in a given area, often interacting in complicated ways that are only partially understood. A first step in analysing such a state of affairs is to recognize the existence of more or less well-defined and discrete communities occupying spatially delimited habitats. The boundaries between habitats may sometimes be indistinct, a given habitat may change appreciably with time, and some relatively distinct communities may nevertheless be linked through common species. Despite these general difficulties of definition, it is obvious that the assemblages of insects found in, say, different mountain streams tend to resemble one another in many respects and that they differ from comparable assemblages found in large, permanent lakes or those encountered in small, temporary pools. All these, in turn, will differ even more from the assemblages found in adjacent areas of undisturbed deciduous woodland or those from grazed pasture-land; each type of habitat tends to have its own characteristic species, or its specially abundant or highly adapted forms, at least within broad geographical limits.

How far interspecific interactions, especially competition, are responsible for producing highly integrated, true communities, or how far, on the other hand, the assemblages are really only collections of relatively independent species, united by common habitat preferences, are still debatable matters. Within a relatively well-defined habitat, however, it is evident that the most important relationships between the individual species are those based on food requirements, the so-called trophic relationships of a community. Some of these may be expressed in the oversimplified form of a food chain, as in the following example:

Oak-tree (*Quercus robur*) → Winter Moth larva (*Operophtera brumata*) → predacious beetle (*Philonthus decorus*) → Shrew (*Sorex araneus*)

where each successive species feeds on the one which precedes it in the chain. A more complete, though still simplified, picture – of which the simple chain given above forms a part – is provided by the food web illustrated in Fig. 140. This begins to show the complexity of the trophic relationships and indicates how insects may occur at two or more of the levels in the web. Of such levels the lowest will always consist of the primary producers such as green plants, which can use solar energy to carry out photosynthesis and therefore employ as food only such simple substances as water, carbon dioxide and mineral salts. A second level, that of the primary consumers, consists in this case of herbivores like the larvae of *Operophtera brumata* and *Tortrix viridana*, which feed on the oak leaves. These in turn are fed on by the secondary consumers, including

277

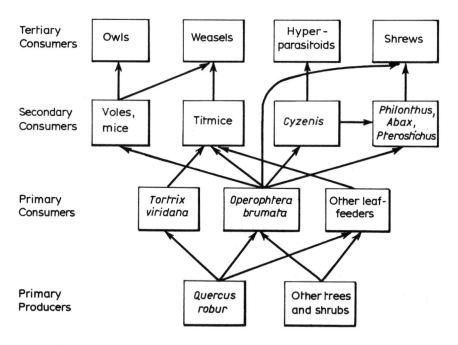

Fig. 140 Food web, showing parasites and predators associated with the
Winter Moth *Operophtera brumata* (Geometridae). (After Varley.)

the predators and parasites of the phytophagous insects (*Cyzenis*,
Philonthus, *Abax* and *Pterostichus* in the figure). Finally, these predators
are themselves attacked by tertiary consumers such as the hyper-
parasitoids of *Cyzenis* or the shrews (*Sorex*), which eat the beetle
predators. Even when the community under consideration is that
associated with a single species of plant, the food web may assume a
formidable complexity (as in Fig. 141) with scores or even hundreds of
insect species involved, including omnivorous species which operate at
more than one trophic level. The situation in the larger and more
complex ecosystems can be imagined; it is likely to defy anything
approaching a full qualitative description, let alone an understanding of
exactly how all the species interact with one another in terms of
population dynamics. At best one might hope to identify and
concentrate attention upon some of the more important components of
these complex communities.

Merely to recognize the trophic relationships may be a task of some
difficulty: direct observation of feeding habits provides a partial
understanding, but needs to be supplemented by other techniques. The
analysis of gut contents (often difficult because it involves the

identification of fragments of plant or animal tissue) provides some additional information. Plants or other organisms at one trophic level may be labelled with radioactive isotopes which can then be detected in the bodies of those feeding on them. Serological tests have sometimes also been applied: an antigen is prepared from each of the likely species of prey and is injected into a rabbit to yield a specific antibody, which may then be used to give a precipitin reaction with the gut contents of the predators. In this way the sources of the blood meals taken by biting flies (mosquitoes, tsetse flies, etc.) can be identified and the method has also been used to identify the insect predators of other insects.

In general, and with exceptions that are sometimes easily explicable, the insects or other organisms in a food web show characteristic differences in biology as one passes towards the higher levels. There are usually fewer species among the higher levels, their populations are smaller, the individuals are larger, they can search more effectively for their food, they utilize it more efficiently, and they have lower reproductive rates. However, many phytophagous insects are very large

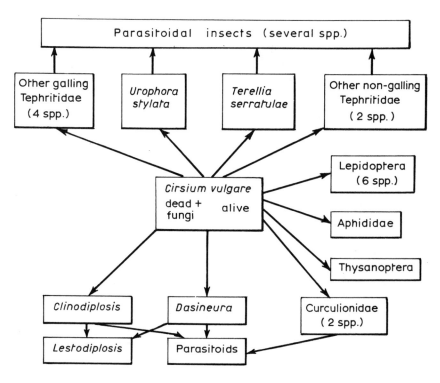

Fig. 141   Food web involving some of the insects commonly associated with the thistle *Cirsium vulgare* in Britain. (After Redfern.)

for their class, and parasitoids, on the other hand, are smaller than their hosts.

Insects with very similar trophic relationships may be quite different taxonomically and in respect of some other biological features. However, the trophic similarities may enable them to be grouped into 'guilds' – assemblages of species that exploit similar resources using similar foraging habits, and therefore with similar ecological roles. On thistles (*Cirsium arvense* and *C. vulgare*), for example, there are several distinct guilds of insects, each associated with a particular microhabitat provided by the plant: the flower-heads are inhabited by the larvae of several species of Lepidoptera, Cecidomyiid midges and Tephritid flies; the stems of the plant are bored by internally dwelling larvae of another species of Tephritid, an Anthomyid, and several species of Curculionids and Lepidoptera; the larvae of another group of insects mine the leaves (Diptera, Lepidoptera and Coleoptera), while still other species of insects feed externally on the leaves or are detritus feeders in the decomposing flower-heads of the dying plant. In each case the phytophagous species have associated predators and parasitoids so as to constitute miniature communities within the larger habitat offered by the plant. However, apart from their common dependence on the plant and their susceptibility to a few polyphagous predators, these smaller communities show a substantial degree of autonomy.

DIVERSITY, STABILITY AND SUCCESSION IN INSECT COMMUNITIES

Insect communities or, to use a more neutral term, the assemblages of species found in a particular habitat or locality, differ greatly in diversity. The ecological concept of diversity is not easy to define exactly, as is shown by the number of different indices that have been advocated for measuring it. In general, diversity denotes both the richness of the fauna (as indicated by the total number of species present) and the equitability of their distribution. An assemblage containing equal proportions of each of a given number of species is regarded as more equitably distributed, and therefore more diverse, than one in which a few of the species are more numerous than the others. Many attempts have been made to identify special characteristics of the community, or of its habitat, that might promote or limit its diversity. There are probably too few well-analysed examples to generalize confidently on this subject, but a number of interesting aspects may be mentioned. It is for example, well established for many insect groups that the number of species in areas of about the same size is greatest in the tropics and decreases in the higher latitudes. That the age of a habitat may also be associated with the number of species occupying it is shown by the data depicted in Fig. 142. Those trees which were more abundant throughout the Quaternary period (Pleistocene and Recent) in Britain are associated with more insect species than are trees which were less frequent or which are known to have been introduced recently. Again, the area occupied by a habitat is important: if host-plants of similar life-form are compared, the more widespread plant species are found to support a greater variety of insect species than do the host-plants with a restricted distribution. In the special case of island faunas this 'species area relationship' has been found for Carabid beetles, ants and other animals to follow the relationship $S = CA^z$, where S is the number of species and A is the area of the island, C is a parameter that depends on the taxon and the geographical area, and z commonly has a value of about 0.3. A similar relationship also holds for sample areas within continents, though the value of z is then closer to about 0.15. The spatial heterogeneity of the habitat is another factor related to diversity, as indicated, for example, by the fact that a structurally complex tree, such as birch (*Betula pubescens*), may support ten times as many insect species as do otherwise comparable but structurally simpler herbaceous plants.

Fig. 142 Relationship between numbers of Quaternary remains of British trees (abscissa) and the numbers of insect species associated with them (ordinate). (After Southwood.)

More generally, the richness of the associated insect fauna decreases in a sequence from trees, with the richest fauna, through woody shrubs down to perennial herbs and weeds, a sequence of decreasing size and structural complexity of the plant. The occurrence of interspecific competition may also be expected to affect diversity. Keener competition should yield niches that are more restricted, allowing more species to be packed into the habitat. On the other hand, it has also been argued that intense attack by polyphagous predators will depress the density of prey populations, thus reducing competition between them and allowing the addition of new prey species which, in turn, support more predators. There can be little doubt that the various factors influencing diversity will differ in importance from one case to another, even when the communities concerned have much in common. For example, in one study of the numbers of species of leaf-mining insects on British trees, in which almost 70% of the total variation was accounted for, the taxonomic structure of the tree genera (and therefore presumably their evolutionary history) was of much greater significance than the geographical range of the trees or their maximum sizes, though other studies of similar communities in Britain and in N. America suggested that host-range had a considerable effect.

It has often been held on theoretical grounds that the more diverse a community is, the more stable it will be, in the sense that the sizes of the various populations present will vary less from time to time. There is some observational support for this view: populations of flea-beetles, aphids and caterpillars on a pure stand of *Brassica oleracea* reached higher densities than did those on *Brassica* plants growing as part of an old-established and very diverse field system. The stability of a community is also thought to be related to the number of links in the food chains which it contains. The more complex the food web is, the more effectively a community will be buffered against the environmental changes which cause populations to fluctuate in size. The empirical evidence from insect populations is hardly sufficient to support or refute the general validity of these arguments. If diversity causes stability, then populations of phytophagous insects feeding on a large number of different host-plants should behave in a more stable fashion than those with restricted diets; in fact, the opposite is true for the Lepidoptera of Canadian forests. On the other hand, the insect species with the most competitors showed the greatest stability, as the theory suggests.

Some insect communities may appear to change little over many years because they occupy stable habitats. Others, however, are subject to changes that form part of the processes of biological succession such as have been more fully documented for the plant communities on which they depend. Successions of this kind may be seen in the slow transitions which occur when an area of bare ground is colonized successively by lower plants, herbs, shrubs and trees wherever climatic and other factors allow such a climax vegetation to develop. Much more rapid successions occur among the transient communities associated with obviously temporary habitats. For example, during the summer a rapid succession of insects is associated with cattle dung, in which a series of Diptera lay eggs and undergo larval development, as well as many Coleoptera such as *Aphodius*. The dominant species change as the dung dries and the succession may involve 50 or so species and be largely completed in about one month. Relatively rapid successions of species also occur in the communities that accompany and assist in the decomposition of carrion. About 280 species of insects are associated with carrion in Britain, almost all Coleoptera and Diptera. Among the beetles there is a sequence of dominant forms from families like the Silphidae, Histeridae, Staphylinidae and, in the later stages, Dermestidae. Among Diptera the Calliphoridae and Muscidae predominate, with species of *Lucilia, Phormia* and *Calliphora* well represented. The sequence of insect species accompanying the decomposition of a human cadaver is sufficiently well defined to be of some use in forensic medicine to determine the time elapsed since death. Dying and dead wood, in the form of standing trees, fallen trunks, branches, stumps and logs, offers an extensive habitat for a rich and diverse association of insect species, wood-rotting fungi and other organisms, which appear in succession as decay proceeds. About 1000 species of insects occur in such sites in Britain, the details of the succession depending greatly on the species of tree. Scolytid and Cerambycid beetles are among the early colonists, accompanied by their parasitoids and predators. After the bark has been loosened there are further invasions by small beetles and Dipteran larvae, many probably feeding on microscopic fungi. The rotting wood may then be tunnelled by a number of species, such as beetles of the genera *Sinodendron, Dorcus* and *Ptilinus*; stumps may have their own characteristic species, such as the pine weevil *Hylobius abietis*, whose larvae burrow in the roots of dying conifers. A great variety of other species are found in the later stages of decay, mainly Coleoptera, Dipteran larvae and Collembola, including some which use the dead wood temporarily for shelter and hibernation.

The successions which occur among the plant species that make up larger and more varied communities have often been described. These must obviously be accompanied by changes in the associated insect fauna, though the ecological principles which underlie such changes are not yet fully understood. However, phytophagous insects can affect the course and the rate of successional changes in plant communities, as can be demonstrated by excluding them experimentally. The insects, in turn, are influenced by the changes in the vegetation, and this is reflected by differences in the life-cycles and habits of species from different stages of the succession. Early successional insect faunas tend to include species with a greater number of generations per year, the proportion of bi- and multivoltine species declining as the succession proceeds. A higher proportion of fully winged species is also found in the earlier stages of succession, with more species overwintering as adults and therefore ready to disperse and colonize the habitat more fully in the spring. The greater structural complexity of vegetation in the later stages of succession permits a higher proportion of insect species occupying specialized niches. As a plant succession develops towards a climax there may be a decline in its taxonomic diversity. The diversity of the associated insect community does not, however, decrease to the same extent; its persistence at a relatively high level is correlated with the greater structural complexity of the later vegetation.

GENETIC VARIATION IN INSECT POPULATIONS

Although only a small fraction of the very large number of insect species has been studied genetically, there is no doubt that most if not all of their observable characteristics are influenced by their genotypes. In some cases simple Mendelian inheritance at single genetic loci accounts for clear-cut qualitative differences between individuals. Many of the very numerous mutant forms of *Drosophila* are of this kind, as are also the colour varieties of some Lepidoptera. For example, the yellow variety of *Pieris napi* and the black variety of *Papilio machaon* are both due to simple recessive alleles; in the Scarlet Tiger Moth *Callimorpha dominula* the normally coloured form *dominula* results from a homozygous dominant condition, the form *limacula* is the homozygous recessive, and the form *medionigra* is the heterozygote. Other, more complicated forms of Mendelian inheritance are also known to cause well-defined variations in colour pattern: those of the Asiatic Coccinellid beetle *Harmonia axyrides*, for instance, are explicable in terms of the action of five alleles at a single locus, while the pattern of spots on the underside of the wing of the Lycaenid butterfly *Lysandra coridon* is determined by several genes. However, genetically determined variation in insects is not confined to such simple structural or pigmentary differences. Continuously varying and biologically important characteristics such as size, viability, fecundity, longevity, rate of development and duration of diapause have all been shown to have a genetic component, often polygenic in nature. So also have various behavioural features such as courtship patterns, pheromone secretion, the choice of food or host-plant preferences in phytophagous insects or the oviposition preferences of parasitoids. Resistance to insecticides is also inherited, sometimes in a simple Mendelian fashion, sometimes in ways that are more complicated. In *Drosophila melanogaster*, for example, a single gene on the second chromosome is responsible for DDT-resistance, with cross-resistance to γ-hexachlorocyclohexane (γ-HCH) and parathion, and also confers susceptibility to thiourea.

It is generally supposed that under natural conditions each species of insect normally exists as a set of more or less spatially restricted populations, with individuals able to mate and reproduce freely, both within and between such populations. This occurs even though the populations are, to varying degrees, genetically different. This variation takes the form of differences in the frequencies of various alleles in different parts of the species' range or at different seasons. A high degree of heterozygosity may be present, as may sometimes be seen from variations in the proportions of different genetically determined and phenotypically obvious structural or colour differences. The cuckoo-spit insect *Philaenus spumarius*, for example, is well known for its many colour varieties. In Finland these are due to a set of seven multiple alleles at a single locus, and the frequencies of these differ among different island populations in a way that depends on variations in the host-plants found in small meadow communities. Often, however, the polymorphism is less evident, as in the well-studied case of some *Drosophila* species (especially *D. pseudoobscura*) where the banding pattern of the larval salivary gland chromosomes shows great intraspecific variation, with different chromosomal forms occurring in different proportions at different sites and seasons, and associated with genetically determined differences in viability and fecundity. Modern electrophoretic techniques, which enable genetic differences to be detected without resort to breeding, have considerably extended our knowledge of genetically determined variation within and between insect populations.

Genetically controlled intraspecific variation is responsible for at least some of the so-called 'biotypes' which have been recorded among phytophagous or parasitoidal insects, where different strains of a species are associated with particular host forms. In the Hessian Fly, *Mayetiola destructor*, for example, many genetically determined biotypes occur, differing in the virulence of their attack on various cultivars of wheat, the resistance of which is in turn also controlled genetically, so that the genotype of the fly tends to match that of the host variety which it attacks most seriously. The Delphacid planthopper *Nilaparvata lugens* is another economically important insect in which several biotypes have been described, differing among other things in the severity of their attack on different varieties of rice.

Where genetically distinct populations of a species occupy well-defined geographical areas and display relatively well-defined phenotypic differences, the groups concerned are often recognized as taxonomic subspecies, indicated by an additional subspecific name. For example, the Large White butterfly *Pieris brassicae* is represented in North Africa and Europe by the subspecies *Pieris brassicae brassicae*, in the Canary Islands by the subspecies *cheiranthi*, and on Madeira by the subspecies *wollastoni*. However, it should be noted that most subspecies of insects have been based on phenotypic differences without much direct knowledge of any underlying genetic differences; it is usually assumed that consistent and virtually constant phenotypic distinctions reflect genetic differentiation. The trinomial system has, moreover, been abused by employing it to denote almost any kind of variant, including those of purely environmental origin or the individual forms in a polymorphic population. Not all geographical variation takes the form of subspeciation however. Sometimes, in place of subspecies occupying discrete areas one finds continuous variation in one or more characters along an environmental gradient, forming a so-called cline, as has been well demonstrated in some Scandinavian butterflies, in which about half the investigated characters showed some form of clinal variation. Clines are also the basis of the 'ecogeographical rules' such as Gloger's Rule, which states that among insects the pigmentation is greatest in cool, humid regions and decreases as the climate becomes warmer and drier. Relatively distinct sets of populations such as subspecies may be isolated (as in many island forms) or they may occupy contiguous areas of territory, with or without some overlap of the different forms at a zone of intergradation. When mating between distinct but contiguous or overlapping populations is restricted the forms may be regarded as incipient species ('semispecies'), as among the various strains of *Drosophila paulistorum* in S. America.

In all these and many other forms of geographical variation, the genetic structure of the populations may be incompletely known and the relative importance of genetic and environmental factors in determining the observed variation may be difficult to assess. Even the phenotypic variation itself may be only partially characterized; often it is only some superficial features which have been recorded while biometric differences or variations in viability or fecundity are neglected. That such differences exist is well shown by work on the moth *Lymantria dispar*, which revealed that different Japanese populations differ in rates of development, in their response to temperature changes, and in the extent to which mating between populations produces intersexual and sterile hybrids. It is not surprising that the relative importance of the evolutionary forces which have led to the diverse forms of geographical variation are incompletely understood. It is however, probable that natural selection plays an important role in establishing populations adapted to local environmental conditions, in controlling polymorphism, and in maintaining clinal variation. It is also possible in small populations for random sampling effects to result in genetic change in the absence of selection. This 'genetic drift' has been demonstrated in small laboratory colonies of *Drosophila* and may be responsible for differentiation in species that form small, partially isolated populations under natural conditions. Whether there are phenotypically obvious characters that are adaptively neutral and must therefore always depend for their spread on genetic drift rather than selection is not established; it is perhaps more likely that an apparently non-adaptive feature is associated with a genotype that is also responsible for attributes that are less obvious, such as differences in viability or fecundity, which are of definite selective value. However, it has been argued strongly, that at the molecular level (i.e. in respect of mutations affecting the sequence of nucleotides in the triplets that make up the genetic code of the DNA and therefore of the amino acids that these encode) most evolutionary change and most of the variability within species depend on the random drift of mutant alleles with little or no selective advantage. Even if true, this would still be compatible with a major role for natural selection in determining changes in the frequencies of genotypes with overt phenotypic effects, as in the accepted neo-Darwinian manner.

The occurrence of genetically distinctive populations or groups of populations, especially those ranked as subspecies or semispecies, is clearly related to the processes whereby new species arise. These processes, which lie at the heart of modern theories of evolution, can be understood best if we have an agreed definition of the species. The biological species concept, now widely accepted, defines a species as a group of potentially or actually interbreeding populations which are reproductively isolated from other such groups. Gene flow occurs between the populations within such a group, but not between the groups that constitute distinct species. In practice it may be difficult or impossible to know whether two recognizably distinct populations are capable of interbreeding successfully under natural conditions, and the occurrence of consistent structural, physiological, behavioural or cyto-logical differences is widely accepted as evidence of reproductive isolation. There must, however, be instances where speciation is currently in progress and which are therefore impossible to accom-modate in a rigid definition of the species. Moreover, it is well established that many insect groups contain sibling species, which are reproductively isolated from one another but are virtually indistinguish-able by the kinds of structural characters generally employed by systematists. Bearing these facts in mind, four possible modes of speciation have been proposed, differing mainly in the roles which they attach to geographical separation as a prior condition of the reproductive isolation which evolves. These four possible modes are known as allopatric, sympatric, parapatric and stasipatric speciation. Allopatric speciation occurs when some members of a single, undifferentiated ancestral species become geographically isolated, either through their

287

own powers of dispersal or from extrinsic environmental causes. This is followed by the evolution of genetic differences between the isolated population (or populations) and those from which it arose. These differences eventually become sufficiently marked to prevent successful hybridization between the two forms, so that they thus achieve the status of separate species and will thereafter remain permanently distinct, even if their areas of distribution subsequently expand and come to overlap. Allopatric speciation is probably common in insects and in other organisms; whether it is the only important mechanism of speciation is not clear. Sympatric speciation – i.e. the formation of new species within the geographical range of a parent species – is thought by many to be an unlikely mode of evolutionary divergence on the grounds that without some kind of geographical (or at least microgeographical) separation between populations, dispersal and interbreeding will maintain sufficient gene flow to prevail over local selection pressures, so that a new, reproductively isolated form could never arise. On the other hand, many phytophagous insects have 'host-races' or 'biotypes' which are confined to different plant species growing in the same area and which may represent cases of incipient sympatric speciation. Reproductive isolation might also evolve sympatrically if different populations of a species were to breed at different seasons. In N. America two species of the green lacewing *Chrysopa* occur sympatrically: *C. carnea* and *C. downesi*. They differ in only a few alleles and are interfertile in the laboratory, but they are already isolated reproductively because *C. carnea* breeds in the winter and summer, whereas *C. downesi* breeds in the spring. It is possible that the two forms arose sympatrically and their present reproductive isolation by breeding season will certainly ensure that they will now diverge increasingly. Speciation has been described as parapatric when differentiation occurs between populations that occupy distinct but contiguous territories rather then those which are geographically isolated from each other, as in allopatric speciation. It resembles sympatric speciation in that gene flow would be expected across the boundary between the populations and is therefore subject to theoretical objections. Finally, stasipatric speciation is envisaged as a process that might account for evolutionary divergence among some species of the Australian grasshoppers of the subfamily Morabinae. Here semispecies with different chromosomal arrangements occupy adjacent territories with very narrow areas of overlap in which hybrids of reduced viability occur, suggesting that the new form arises as a small colony at the edge of the range of the ancestral species and subsequently expands its territory. It could perhaps be regarded as a special case of one of the other postulated modes of speciation.

It is of interest that, given certain assumptions, it is possible from electrophoretic data on the frequencies of members of polymorphic enzyme systems to calculate the extent of the overall genetic divergence between different populations. The so-called genetic distance between various members of the *Drosophila willistoni* complex increases from about 0.03 for local interbreeding populations to 0.23 for subspecies and semispecies, 0.58 for sibling species, and 1.06 for morphologically distinct species. Values of the same order occur in other quite unrelated groups of animals and may provide a guide to the amounts of genetic divergence that is to be expected among and between speciating populations of other insects.

8

Biology and control
of injurious insects

Although many insect species are well-known pests of agricultural crops
or play a part in the spread of human disease, it is by no means easy to
measure the extent of the injury which we suffer. Because of the
operation of market forces, the financial loss to crop producers may not
reflect the real damage done by pests, while the importance attached to
an insect-transmitted disease will depend to some degree on the
incidence of other forms of mortality in the population concerned. The
status of an insect as a pest may also change relatively quickly, as when it
is introduced accidentally into a geographical area from which it was
previously absent, or when changes in human activities and habits
expose society to species which are then able to develop their previously
unrealized potential for injury. Some insects are injurious over wide
areas, others may be of very minor importance in some parts of their
range or only occasionally reach levels of population density high
enough to cause damage. Insects which are important pests under given
forms of agricultural practice may become much less important when
techniques of cultivation change, or may then be replaced by 'new'
pests. These dynamic relationships between insect populations and
human activities have an underlying ecological basis that needs to be
studied carefully by those engaged in the control of injurious insects.
Despite the need for caution in interpreting crude figures of crop losses
due to insect pests, there are many statistics to illustrate the serious
nature of the damage they cause, often most severe in tropical countries
that are less well able to resist such injury. In West Africa cocoa pests of
the single family Miridae have caused losses of 25% of the possible crop,
while the beetles attacking oil-palms may cause losses of 70% or more
and, even after harvesting, some 20% of a country's maize crop may be
lost in storage from insect attack. Cowpea and other grain legumes may
sustain losses of up to 90% and bollworms can reduce cotton yields by
70–80%. Most of Africa between about 14° N and 29° S is rendered

seriously unproductive because of tsetse flies, and throughout the tropics malaria-carrying mosquitoes cause enormous mortality and suffering. Much still remains to be done in implementing known methods of control and in devising new strategies.

INSECT PESTS OF CULTIVATED PLANTS

Plants provide the diet of most insect species, and it is therefore not surprising that insects are often serious pests of cultivated plants and such plant products as timber, stored cereals, and other dried seeds or fruits. The number of such pests is enormous and, although some are local in their distribution, others occur world-wide or throughout temperate or tropical regions. Only a small selection of the economically more important or biologically more interesting species are discussed below. No attempt is made to indicate details of the best control measures, as these will vary greatly according to economic factors, climate, agricultural practice and legislative constraints. Some of the general principles underlying insect control are, however, discussed on pp. 326–42. Other biological factors that need to be taken into account when assessing the status of an injurious insect or devising methods for its control include the following: accurate identification and discrimination from closely allied species; full knowledge of the life-cycle and behaviour of adults and larvae; ecological relationships with other cultivated or wild host-plants; the importance of predators and parasites which may help in the natural control of the pest species; its

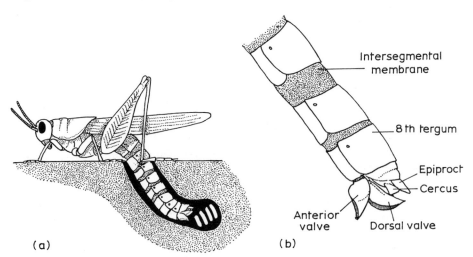

(a)   (b)

Fig. 143   Oviposition in the Desert Locust, *Schistocerca gregaria*
(a) Female during oviposition in soil; (b) terminal part of female abdomen with ovipositor.

291

possible role as a vector of plant-pathogenic fungi or viruses; the extent to which attack is primary or a secondary consequence of previous insect damage or weakness in the plant; and the variation in susceptibility shown by different cultivated crop varieties or resulting from different cultural techniques. It should also be remembered that as a result of changes in some of these factors from time to time, insects which once caused major injury in an area may decline in importance while other pest species may take their place.

Locusts and grasshoppers. The term 'locust' is correctly given to a few species of the Orthopteran family Acrididae, which also includes the short-horned grasshoppers. The distinctive feature of locusts, marking them off from grasshoppers, is their ability under special conditions to become gregarious, forming large swarms of adults or nymphs ('hoppers') consisting of millions of individuals capable of migrating during the daytime and feeding voraciously on a wide variety of crops and other plants when they settle. The best-known species are the Desert Locust, *Schistocerca gregaria*, whose distribution extends from N. Africa eastwards into the Indian subcontinent; the Red Locust, *Nomadacris septemfasciata*, which occurs in Africa from the equator to about 30° S; and the Migratory Locust (*Locusta migratoria*) with various subspecies from S. Europe, Africa, S. Russia, China, Australia and elsewhere. Other species, of more limited distribution or importance, include *Schistocerca americana* from C. and S. America, *Chortoicetes terminifera* from Australia, and *Dociostaurus maroccanus* from the Mediterranean countries and the Middle East. Female locusts lay their eggs in the soil, using the ovipositor to dig into the substrate and deposit the eggs within a tubular proteinaceous sac, the egg-pod, containing 60–100 eggs according to the species (Fig. 143). The nymphal instars, usually five in number, are broadly similar in structure to the adults and feed on similar plants. *Schistocerca* commonly attacks wheat, millet, rice, sorghum, pigeon-peas and citrus, whereas *Locusta* feeds mainly on graminaceous plants.

The characteristic gregarious swarms are only one manifestation of what is known as phase variation. Locust populations can, in fact, occur in two more or less distinct forms or phases connected by intermediate transitional states. In the solitary phase the insects behave rather as ordinary grasshoppers and do not aggregate into swarms or undertake migrations *en masse*. Such a solitary phase can be produced experimentally by rearing the locusts in isolation, whereas rearing them under crowded conditions gives rise to insects of the gregarious phase. The two phases differ not only in behaviour, but also, at least in some species, in colour, proportions of the body, fecundity and other physiological aspects. Under field conditions, environmental factors which are not fully understood may lead to solitary forms undergoing some degree of crowding. The hoppers developing in these conditions then tend to become gregarious and this process reinforces still further the effects of crowding. Such a process of 'gregarization' – which may extend over several generations before it is complete – tends to occur in more or less localized 'outbreak areas' (Fig. 144). In *Schistocerca* many such areas arise from time to time at various places within the geographical range of the species, but in other cases the outbreak area may be a much more permanently defined and restricted region. In *Locusta migratoria migratorioides* it is located in the flood-plains of the Middle Niger, and in *Nomadacris* outbreaks originate in the Rukwa Valley of Tanzania and around Lake Mweru in Zambia. From the outbreak areas swarms of the migratory phase move outwards to invade large areas of territory, breeding there but eventually giving rise to populations in the solitary phase as the locust plague subsides.

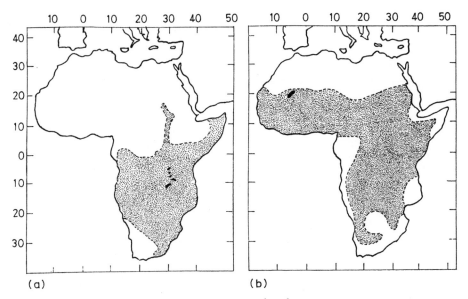

Fig. 144   Locust outbreak areas

(a) Red Locust, *Nomadacris septemfasciata* (1928–41); (b) Migratory Locust, *Locusta migratoria migratorioides* (1927–44). Outbreak areas black, invasion areas stippled.

Populations of grasshoppers, i.e. permanently solitary Acrididae, are less dense and much less spectacular than those of locusts, but they are sometimes quite serious pests locally. Over 25 species have been identified as injurious to the extensive grasslands of the western USA, and in Africa south of the Sahara *Zonocerus variegatus* and *Z. elegans* are pests of many crops, especially in the seedling stage.

Aphids and the transmission of virus diseases. The Aphidoidea are among the most serious insect pests of temperate regions, partly because of the direct injury caused by the feeding of the dense populations that build up during the summer, but also because many aphid species transmit virus diseases that weaken or destroy many cultivated crops. Good examples are provided by their effects on the production of potatoes. At least nine distinct types of potato virus disease are transmitted by aphids. Potato leaf-roll virus (PLRV) is among the most important and is a circulative virus, i.e. one requiring circulation through the body of the insect vector, with a latent period of 6–24 h before transmission can occur. *Myzus persicae* and, in Scotland, *Macrosiphum euphorbiae*, are its principal vectors. Potato virus Y (PY) is the most important non-circulative or 'stylet-borne' virus, transmitted mechanically without a latent period by many aphid vectors, including *Myzus persicae* and *Macrosiphum euphorbiae*. Both PLRV and PY are serious because potatoes are propagated vegetatively from tubers (the

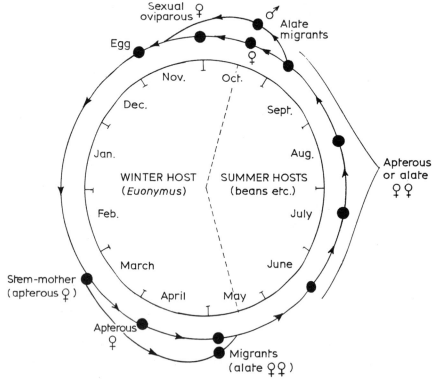

Fig. 145   Life-cycle of the Black Bean Aphid, *Aphis fabae*

Each small black circle represents a separate generation of insects. Males occur only during the sexual phase in the autumn; all other generations are composed exclusively of females, which may be alate or apterous, and except for the one sexual generation are parthenogenetic and viviparous.

so-called 'seed potatoes') and such tubers contain the virus when the plant on which they develop is infected. To prevent the degeneration of stocks of seed potatoes, virus-free plants are raised in cool, windy and rainy areas where aphid infestations are relatively low and where the crops are subject to inspection and certification schemes so that the few infected plants are 'rogued' out of the crop. Monitoring aphid populations and forecasting optimum dates for applying insecticides or harvesting form part of the more elaborate pest management systems operated in N. America.

Myzus persicae and *Aphis fabae* (Fig. 145) are vectors of sugar-beet viruses such as beet yellows, and it is interesting to note how annual variations in the incidence of this disease are related to environmental effects on its vector. It has been observed that yellows virus infection of sugar-beet is greatest after a mild winter and warm spring, and it is possible to predict the extent of the disease accurately from temperatures during the period from January to April. The reason for this relationship is that during mild winters many aphids overwinter on their summer hosts which contain the virus. They can therefore transmit the disease more effectively than those aphids which in hard winters have all had to overwinter as the egg stage on the primary woody hosts and which are therefore free of virus when they re-invade the beet crop in the spring.

Among other important aphid pests may be mentioned *Aphis fabae* on field beans, overwintering on the Spindle Tree (*Euonymus europaeus*) (Fig. 145), *Brevicoryne brassicae*, which is a pest of cabbages, Brussels sprouts and other brassica crops, and *Rhopalosiphum padi* which transmits barley yellow dwarf virus, occurring on cereals and other Gramineae in the summer and having *Prunus* as its winter host. *Chaetosiphon fragaefolii* is an important species on strawberries, transmitting 'yellow edge' and 'crinkle' viruses. This species is anholocyclic, with an incomplete life-cycle, living on strawberry throughout the year and having no sexual forms. *Acyrtosiphon pisum* is a widespread species on peas and other legumes, sometimes occurring in large colonies which cause serious direct injury as well as carrying virus diseases. *Viteus vitifolii* is the notorious vine phylloxera, which devastated European vineyards after being introduced from N. America in the latter part of the 19th century. However, it was found that European grape varieties could be grown successfully when grafted on to the resistant American root-stocks and the insect was therefore effectively controlled.

Leafhoppers and their allies. Leafhoppers (Fig. 146) are members of the Cicadellidae and again are important partly through the direct injury they cause and partly because they are vectors of diseases due to viruses and mycoplasmas. They are, for example, serious pests of potatoes, especially in N. America. A complex of species closely related to

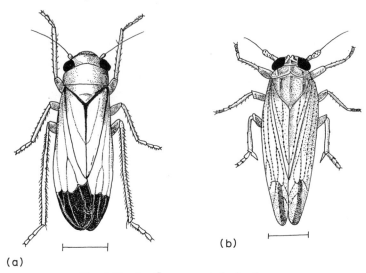

Fig. 146   Leafhoppers and planthoppers

(a) Green Rice Leafhopper, *Nephotettix nigropictus* (Cicadellidae), female (after Hill);
(b) Sugar-cane Planthopper, *Perkinsiella saccharicida* (Delphacidae). Scale lines = 1 mm.

Empoasca fabae causes 'hopperburn', a physiological condition due to their toxic saliva, while *Macrosteles fascifrons*, though it cannot reproduce on potato, will transmit a mycoplasma infection and *Circulifer tenellus* carries a virus disease. All three species undertake extensive northward migrations in N. America each summer, away from their more southerly overwintering areas. Another crop of world importance, rice, is also subject to serious injury by leafhoppers, in this case by species of *Nephotettix* (Green Leafhopper), which are more important as vectors than through their direct injury. *Nephotettix cincticeps* transmits the 'dwarf' virus in temperate areas, and *N. virescens* carries 'tungro' virus in the tropics. All *Nephotettix* species occur characteristically at low densities, are non-migratory, and are found also on graminaceous weeds. In contrast, another important pest of rice, the Brown Plant-hopper (*Nilaparvata lugens*) belonging to the related family Delphacidae, is mainly injurious through direct injury of the 'hopperburn' type (yellowing, followed by brown discoloration and death of the plant); it occurs at high population densities in outbreaks, is migratory but otherwise occurs only in tropical areas, and does not live on wild grasses. Another Delphacid, *Perkinsiella saccharicida*, the Sugar-cane Planthopper, was a pest of some importance in Hawaii, but has been successfully controlled there by a Mirid egg-predator *Tytthus mundulus*; it also occurs in S. Africa, Madagascar, S.E. Asia, Australia and S. America. Nymphs and adults feed on the leaves, sucking the sap and acting as vectors of the Fiji Disease virus. Eggs are embedded in the midrib and there may be five or six generations a year, with adults migrating from crop to crop. Members of the Cercopidae (froghoppers and cuckoo-spit insects) are not usually very injurious, but species of *Tomaspis* damage sugar-cane in S. America. The nymphs feed on the leaves or roots enclosed in a frothy spittle-mass and cause necrosis ('froghopper blight'), with wilting and death of the leaves leading to stunted plants.

Scale-insects and mealy bugs. These are members of the Coccoidea, a superfamily of Sternorrhynchan Homoptera with strongly defined sexual dimorphism (p. 146). Adult males are small, midge-like insects which do not feed and cause no injury to plants, but females are flattened, larva-like, sessile forms, degenerate in structure and often concealed beneath a scale-like waxy covering or provided with a powdery coat of wax particles. They and the rather similar juvenile stages may be present in large numbers, causing direct injury to the host-plant and, in some cases, carrying virus diseases such as swollen shoot of cocoa (carried by *Ferrisia virgata* and *Planococcus citri* or pineapple wilt (transmitted by *Dysmicoccus brevipes*). Female scale-insects lay their eggs protected by the covering scale or an ovisac of waxen threads, and the first-instar larvae are active 'crawlers' which colonize new hosts and are the main dispersive phase in the life-cycle. Among the economically important species may be mentioned the following: *Icerya purchasi*, the Cottony Cushion or Fluted Scale, a widespread pest of citrus and other plants; *Planococcus kenyae*, formerly an important pest of coffee in East Africa; and *Aspidiotus destructor*, an important pest of coconut palms wherever they occur. *Quadraspidiotus perniciosus*, the San José Scale, is a polyphagous species which causes major injury to deciduous fruit trees, mainly in subtropical areas, and the Mussel Scale *Lepidosaphes becki* and the Purple Scale *Chrysomphalus aonidum* are widespread pests of citrus fruits. *Aulacaspis tegalensis* occurs under the leaf-sheaths of sugar-cane, causing appreciable damage.

Coleopteran pests of orchard, plantation and field crops. The Coleoptera is the largest order of insects, containing about 370 000 species. A high proportion of these are phytophagous, so it is hardly surprising that they include many pests of cultivated plants. Most of the injurious species belong to three families – the Scarabaeidae (cockchafers, may-bugs and their allies), the Chrysomelidae (leaf-beetles) and the Curculionidae (weevils) – and it is mainly from these groups that the following examples are drawn. The Chrysomelid genera *Lema* and *Oulema* include species that attack wild grasses and cultivated cereals, the adults and slug-like larvae eating the leaf-tissues in longitudinal

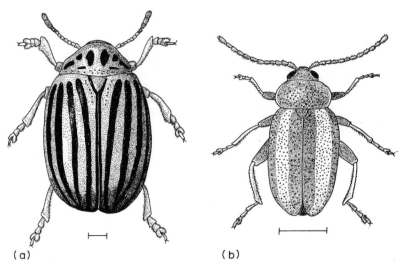

(a)   (b)

Fig. 147 Colorado Potato Beetle, *Leptinotarsa decemlineata* (Chrysomelidae)
(a) and Turnip Flea Beetle, *Phyllotreta nemorum* (Chrysomelidae) (b)
Scale lines = 1 mm.

strips between the veins. *Oulema melanopus* (Fig. 148) is sometimes a
serious pest of wheat and oats in Europe (and has spread rapidly in N.
America since its accidental introduction there about 1960), whereas
O. oryzae is a serious pest of rice in E. Asia. The Colorado Potato Beetle
(*Leptinotarsa decemlineata*, Fig. 147) is indigenous to the foothills of the
Rocky Mountains of N. America, where it feeds on wild Solanaceae,
especially *Solanum rostratum*. From about the 1850s it began to feed on
cultivated potatoes, spreading steadily eastwards and soon causing
devastation in the Midwestern States. Females lay up to 3000 eggs and
there are from one to four generations per year, depending on the
locality. Adults and larvae feed voraciously on potato foliage and
defoliate the crop. The beetle spread to Europe and had established itself
near Bordeaux by 1923, thereafter extending its range steadily eastwards
to reach the USSR by 1959 and Turkey by 1976, and is proving even
more injurious in Europe than in N. America. Quarantine regulations
and prompt eradication of accidental introductions have prevented its
establishment in the British Isles. Twenty or more genera of Chrysomelidae, including *Phyllotreta, Altica* (= *Haltica*), *Chaetocnema* and
Psylliodes, are the injurious flea-beetles, so-called because the adults
jump readily with their enlarged hind legs (Fig. 147). According to
species the larvae feed underground on the roots of their host-plants or
bore into its stems or mine the leaves. They attack various cultivated
plants including brassicas, cereals, potatoes and sugar-beet, as well as
cotton and other tropical crops, especially in the seedling stage.

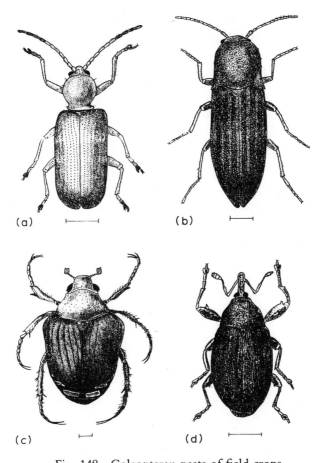

Fig. 148   Coleopteran pests of field crops

(a) Cereal Leaf Beetle, *Oulema melanopus*; (b) a click-beetle, *Agriotes lineatus*, the larvae of which are one species of wireworm; (c) Japanese Beetle, *Popillia japonica*; (d) Cotton Boll Weevil, *Anthonomus grandis*. ((a) and (b) after Balachowsky and Mesnil).
Scale lines = 1 mm.

The larvae of the click-beetles (family Elateridae) are long, tough-skinned, cylindrical 'wireworms', some species of which feed naturally in subterranean fashion in permanent grassland without doing serious harm (Figs 84 and 148). If the grassland is broken up for arable cultivation, however, the large, long-lived wireworm populations (which may reach several millions per hectare) cause serious injury to potatoes, spring wheat and oats, mangolds, swedes and other root-crops. Even long-standing arable land may harbour sufficiently large wireworm populations to affect sugar-beet and potato cultivation. *Agriotes lineatus*, *A. obscurus*, *A. sputator* and *Athous haemorrhoidalis* are

299

among the most injurious European species, but species of *Lacon* and *Heteroderes* are pests elsewhere.

Larvae of the very large family of weevils (Curculionidae) are phytophagous, the majority feeding internally on their hosts or beneath the ground on its roots. Some species are injurious to cultivated plants, and are among the most serious pests of agriculture. *Anthonomus grandis*, the Cotton Boll Weevil (Fig. 148), is a major pest of cotton in Mexico and the southern USA. It lays its eggs in the cotton squares or bolls, where the larvae feed and pupate, damaging the lint, which becomes discoloured and decays. There may be up to seven generations per year, the adults overwintering in soil litter and re-invading the crop in the spring. A closely related species, *Anthonomus pomorum*, is the Apple Blossom Weevil, whose larva feeds and pupates in the flower-buds of apple and sometimes of pear. The developing petals are cut through near their bases so that the flower-buds fail to open and turn brown, forming the characteristic 'capped blossoms'. The adults overwinter in leaf-litter and oviposit in the spring. *Rhynchophorus ferrugineus, R. phoenicis* and *R. palmarum* are large weevils injurious to date and oil-palms. Their larvae penetrate the crown and tunnel in the upper trunk of the palm, causing necrosis and decay that may lead to the crown breaking off. *Cylas formicarius* is a pantropical pest of sweet potatoes, with several generations per year; the larvae burrow into the stems and tubers, which they usually leave when mature, to pupate in the soil. Among other economically important weevils are *Ceutorrhynchus pleurostigmus* of brassicas, species of *Sitona* on peas and beans, and *Cosmopolitus sordidus* on bananas.

The injurious Scarabaeidae (*s.l.*) are moderate- or large-sized beetles whose fleshy C-shaped larvae ('white grubs') either feed in the soil, where they damage root-systems, or occur in rotting vegetation or plant tissue (Fig. 84). Species of *Schizonycha* damage the roots of many crop plants in E. Africa and Egypt, and are typical of many genera from other tropical areas and a wide range of crops. A West African species, *Prionoryctes caniculus*, is unusual in that its adults undertake seasonal migrations between swampy areas, where the larvae feed on the roots of many plant species, and yam fields, where they attack the tubers. *Oryctes rhinoceros* and a few other species of the genus are the large Rhinoceros Beetles, which attack coconuts and sometimes other palms in the Old World tropics and also have unusual habits. The adults may cause the death of the palm when they feed near its growing point; the females lay their eggs in decomposing vegetation, especially rotting palm trunks, where the larvae feed and pupate. In temperate areas the larve of Scarabaeid beetles are sometimes abundant in permanent grassland, and species such as *Melolontha melolontha* may occur occasionally as plagues of adults which feed on the leaves of deciduous trees.

However, in general they are not major pests, though the Japanese Beetle *Popillia japonica* (Fig. 148c), which was introduced accidentally into the USA about 1916, caused serious injury to many crops before its control by a bacterial disease.

Lepidopteran pests of field crops. Many families of this large order contain injurious species, some among the most serious pests of agriculture and horticulture. The damage is done by the larvae, which feed almost exclusively on living plants or plant products, and which may attack the leaves, stem, roots, fruits and other parts, depending on the species. Damage is direct, through consumption of the plant tissues, sometimes amounting to defoliation or destruction of the whole plant or

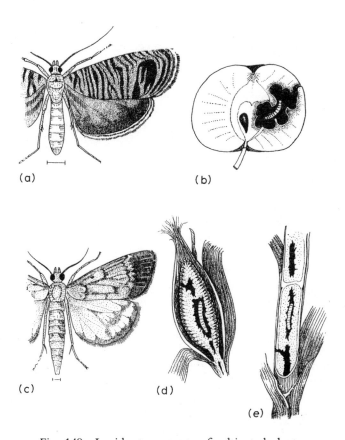

Fig. 149   Lepidopteran pests of cultivated plants

(a) Codling Moth, *Cydia pomonella* (Tortricidae), adult, dorsal view; (b) larva of *Cydia pomonella* in apple fruit; (c) European Corn Borer Moth, *Ostrinia nubilalis* (Pyralidae), adult, dorsal view; (d), (e) larva of *Ostrinia nubilalis* in cob and stalk of maize. (After Hill.) Scale lines = 1 mm.

301

serious injury to its economically important organs such as seeds, fruits or tubers. Adult Lepidoptera feed on plant secretions such as nectar, and do not injure plants. Only a selection of the more important species are referred to below.

Phthorimaea operculella is a Gelechiid moth, probably of S. American origin but now widely distributed in tropical and subtropical regions, where its larvae are very injurious to potatoes, mining the leaves and stems and invading the tubers, which they continue to damage after lifting and storage. Another Gelechiid, *Platyedra* (= *Pectinophora*) *gossypiella*, is the Pink Bollworm of cotton, found in both Old and New World countries. Young larvae enter the green bolls, in which they feed and develop, eating the seeds and often allowing secondary rotting of the boll. When fully fed the caterpillar pupates in the boll or, more usually, in soil litter after escaping through a circular emergence hole. By enforcing a close season between one cotton crop and the next, populations can be reduced considerably. *Plutella xylostella*, the Diamond-back Moth, is a cosmopolitan pest of brassicas and other Cruciferae. It lays its eggs on the leaves, which are then mined by the first-instar larva and subsequently eaten from the lower surface by older larvae; pupation occurs beneath the leaf in a silken cocoon. *Cydia* (= *Carpocapsa*) *pomonella* (Tortricidae) is the Codling Moth of apples, a serious pest in temperate and subtropical areas (Fig. 149). Newly hatched larvae burrow into the developing fruit, tunnelling in them and damaging the core and flesh. Mature larvae escape through a conspicuous exit-hole, from which brown frass exudes, and seek crevices in the bark of the tree. In warmer regions these larvae then pupate to give a second generation of adults, but in the cooler countries, they hibernate over the winter and pupate in the spring. A related species, *Cydia molesta*, the Oriental Fruit Moth, with rather similar habits but four or five generations per year, is a pest of peaches and other fruit in many warmer countries. Yet a third member of the genus, *Cydia nigricana*, the Pea Moth, is a serious pest of peas in Europe and, since its introduction there about 1900, in N. America. Eggs laid in early summer on exposed parts of the plant produce young larvae which bore into the developing pods and feed there on the seeds (one or two larvae per pod). When fully grown the larva emerges, falls to the ground and overwinters in the soil; pupation takes place in the following spring.

The family Pyralidae includes several species with stem-boring larvae attacking rice in Asia, of which *Chilo suppressalis*, *Tryporyza incertulas* and *Sesamia inferens* are widely distributed. Their economic importance has declined somewhat since the 1960s, but this situation will probably continue to require an integration of cultural practices, insecticidal and biological control, and the planting of resistant varieties. Another Pyralid, the European Corn-borer, *Ostrinia nubilalis* (Fig. 149), is an important pest of maize, especially since its accidental introduction into N. America about 1917, and is closely related to *O. furnacalis*, an Asian species which also attacks millet, sorghum and other grains. Young larvae feed on the leaves and inflorescences then bore into the leaf-ribs and stem, where they tunnel downwards, causing infested plants to break off or not to mature their cobs properly. Pupation occurs in the soil and there may be more than one generation per year, with larvae overwintering low down in the stems.

The family Noctuidae includes some of the most injurious Lepidopteran pests. The larvae of *Busseola fusca* is the Maize Stalk-borer, found on maize and sorghum in much of Africa south of the Sahara. Younger larvae feed among the apical leaves or on the cobs before boring into the centre of the stalk, where they feed until fully grown and where they pupate. Mature larvae of the second generation may enter diapause until the onset of the rainy season. *Heliothis armigera* of the Old World and *H. zea*, a closely related New World species, are the bollworms of cotton, but maize, beans, tomatoes and other crops are also attacked; the larvae bore into the cotton bolls or attack the flower buds and fruits. *Agrotis segetum* and other species of *Agrotis, Euxoa, Noctua*, etc., are widely distributed pests, attacking seedlings and many different vegetables and root-crops. The brownish larvae are 'cutworms', living in the soil; they either feed on the roots or come to the surface at night and cut through the stems, especially of seedlings, at ground level. The genus *Spodoptera* includes some serious pests known as armyworms or leafworms. *Spodoptera exempta*, from parts of Africa, southern Asia and Australia, and *S. exigua*, with a wider distribution, are armyworms, whose larvae occur periodically in gregarious swarms, moving together and causing great damage to the foliage and stems of graminaceous and other crops. *Spodoptera litura* and *S. littoralis*, closely related but with distinct geographical ranges, have larvae which are foliage feeders on a variety of crop plants, but which can also sometimes behave like cutworms. Finally, two genera of Noctuidae that are mainly injurious to cotton may be noted: *Earias*, the Spiny Bollworms, damage the terminal shoots, flower-buds and bolls in various parts of the Old World and Australasia, and *Diparopsis* includes the Red Bollworms from Africa.

Dipteran pests of field crops. In general the medical and veterinary importance of the Diptera is of much greater significance than their role as pests of cultivated plants, but the larvae of some Diptera are injurious to crops, especially those of the families Cecidomyiidae (gall-midges) and Tephritidae (fruit-flies). Among the gall-midges *Contarinia sorghicola* can be a serious pest of sorghum in parts of Africa, the USA and elsewhere, the larvae feeding on the developing seeds, as do also those of

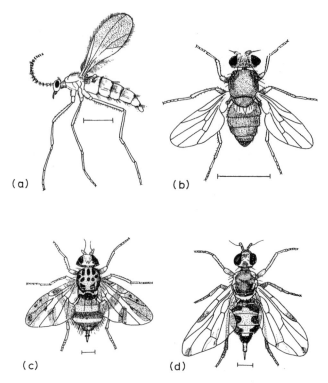

(a)   (b)   (c)   (d)

Fig. 150   Dipteran pests of field crops

(a) *Contarinia tritici*, female (Cecidomyiidae); (b) *Oscinella frit* female (Chloropidae); (c) *Ceratitis capitata* (Tephritidae); (d) *Dacus oleae* (Tephritidae). Scale lines = 1 mm. (After Balachowsky and Mesnil.)

C. tritici, one of several species of wheat midges (Fig. 150a). *Pachydiplosis oryzae* is a serious pest of rice in parts of Africa and S.E. Asia; its larvae gall the terminal bud, where they pupate. An important pest of wheat, the Hessian Fly *Mayetiola destructor* is also a Cecidomyiid. It was introduced from Europe into N. America, probably by mercenaries from Hessen in N. Germany during the War of American Independence, and is also a pest in parts of Africa and New Zealand. Its larva attacks the straw, and the plant becomes stunted and forms fewer tillers. There are two or more generations, with the diapausing larvae overwintering to pupate in the following spring. As the adult flies live for only a few days it is possible to arrange for wheat to be sown when the young plants are least likely to be attacked; varieties resistant to the pest have also been developed (but see p. 285). Among the Tephritidae (= Trypetidae) the genus *Dacus* includes two species with injurious larvae: those of *D. cucurbitae*, the Melon Fly, tunnel in the fruit of melons and other cucurbits in Africa and Hawaii, whereas larvae of *D.*

oleae live in the fruits of olive, greatly reducing the yield of this crop in the Mediterranean region and parts of Africa and Pakistan (Fig. 150). *Ceratitis capitata*, another Tephritid, is a serious pest of many subtropical and deciduous fruits (especially citrus and peaches) in the Mediterranean area and parts of Africa and C. and S. America. Eggs are laid beneath the skin of the fruit, in which the larvae develop. Badly damaged fruits fall to the ground and the larvae pupate in the soil.

The larvae of several other groups of Cyclorrhaphan Diptera are sometimes pests of cultivated plants. One of these is *Oscinella frit*, the Frit Fly, a Chloropid whose larvae are primarily associated with wild grasses, but which can attack cereal crops, especially spring oats (Fig. 150). Eggs laid on young plants in April or May produce larvae which burrow in the central shoot, and the larvae of second and subsequent generations invade the florets and feed on the seeds. Larvae overwinter in grass stems and pupate in the spring. A related family, the Psilidae, includes *Psila rosae*, whose larvae mine the fleshy tap-roots of carrots and sometimes also attack celery and parsnips. Among the Muscidae, *Delia radicum*, the Cabbage Root Fly, has larvae which feed on the roots of brassicas in many areas of the northern hemisphere, stunting or killing the plants. They pupate in the soil and have two or three generations per year, overwintering as the diapausing pupae. *Delia antiqua*, the Onion Fly, has a somewhat similar life-cycle, the larvae tunnelling in the onion bulbs and causing them to rot.

INSECT PESTS OF FORESTRY, TIMBER AND STORED PRODUCTS

Insects injurious to forestry and woodlands. Growing trees, whether in commercially managed forests, plantations and nurseries or in woodlands, parks and gardens, are subject to attack by a large number of insect species, which may be grouped broadly according to their feeding habits as defoliators, wood-borers, gall-makers, bark-feeders, root-feeders, and those boring into buds, leaves, shoots or seeds. Most are pests because of the direct injury they cause by primary or secondary attack, but some transmit pathogenic fungi or promote subsequent fungal decay. Only a selection of the more serious pests are mentioned below, and it should be remembered that many trees are able to withstand a substantial degree of periodic insect infestation without suffering major long-term damage. In many cases chemical control of forest and woodland pests is impracticable or too expensive, and there is an emphasis on cultural and similar forest management techniques in maintaining an appropriately low level of attack.

Among the bark-feeding and wood-boring pests of forestry the

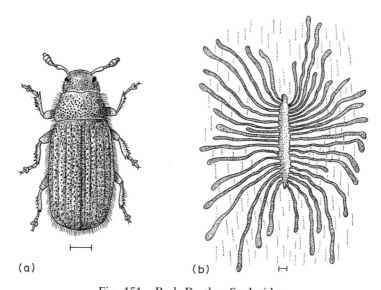

(a)   (b)

Fig. 151   Bark Beetles: Scolytidae

(a) *Dendroctonus micans*, dorsal view; (b) galleries of *Scolytus scolytus*, the Large Elm Bark Beetle, with central brood gallery and radiating larval galleries. Scale lines = 1 mm.

Coleopteran family Scolytidae (Fig. 151) is of considerable importance and includes the true bark-beetles and the pin-hole borers and ambrosia beetles. Apart from the dispersal flight of the adult beetles, all stages of the Scolytidae are present beneath the bark or within the wood. The true bark-beetles construct a complicated gallery system between the bark and the wood. A short entrance tunnel cut by the female leads to a pairing chamber from which radiate a more or less stellate pattern of mother-tunnels, in the walls of which small niches are cut to accommodate the eggs. The larvae which hatch from these then cut galleries for themselves, branching off from the mother-tunnel and impressed more or less deeply in the wood, depending on whether the bark of the tree is thin or thick. Additional feeding tunnels are also cut by the adults. An elaborate pattern of galleries, easily revealed when the bark is stripped, is therefore characteristic of a bark-beetle infestation and may help to identify the species concerned. Full-grown larvae undergo metamorphosis in pupation chambers lying in the bark or wood at the end of the larval galleries.

A wide variety of trees is attacked by different groups of bark-beetles. Those injurious to conifers are among the most important and include *Tomicus* (= *Myelophilus*) *piniperda*, the Pine-shoot Beetle, and species of *Ips* in Europe together with *Dendroctonus* species in N. America. Hardwood trees are generally injured less seriously, but *Hylurgopinus rufipes* and a few species of *Scolytus* (especially *S. scolytus* and *S.*

306

multistriatus) are vectors of Dutch Elm Disease. This is caused by a fungus, *Ceratocystis ulmi*, whose spores are introduced into the tree by the invading beetles. The fungus, which eventually kills the tree, grows saprophytically in the brood galleries, its spores contaminating the new generation of beetles, which then transmit it to healthy trees. Some bark-beetles are associated with other fungi that cause blue staining of softwoods and damage or kill the tree. Though bark-beetles may injure healthy trees, they tend generally to attack those which are already weakened by unfavourable growing conditions or damaged by storms, fire, defoliating insects or pathogenic fungi. The invasion of a tree by the beetles and the development of an attack are controlled by a complex of pheromones released from the beetles' hind gut into the frass and which differ from one species to another; an example is discussed on p. 55.

The ambrosia beetles and pin-hole borers are also Scolytids but with somewhat different habits from the bark-borers. The beetles tunnel deeply into the wood, often in a characteristic fashion, and the larvae either develop in special niches, where they pupate, or live together with adults and pupae in a common gallery. The walls of the tunnels are coated with dark-coloured ambrosia fungi, of various species, on the fruiting bodies of which the larvae and adults feed and which the adults carry with them when they invade other trees. Ambrosia beetles are more widespread in tropical forests, where some species are pests of newly-felled logs, producing wormy timber of reduced value. Species of *Xyleborus, Platypus* and *Doliopygus* are included among the injurious ambrosia beetles and pin-hole or shot-hole borers.

The Curculionidae (weevils) include a few serious pests of forest trees. The larvae of the Large Pine Weevil *Hylobius abietis* live in the roots of dying conifers, especially in root-stumps, on which the eggs are also laid. They do relatively little damage, but the adults that emerge are able to live for up to 3 years and feed on the bark and needles of conifers; they may cause serious injury to pine and spruce in young plantations (especially among 3–4-year-old trees). Members of the genus *Pissodes* are also injurious, the different species attacking different coniferous hosts; their larvae live beneath the bark, where they eat meandering tunnels in the sapwood, later penetrating more deeply to pupate.

One of the best-known defoliators of oaks is the larva of the Green Oak Tortrix Moth, *Tortrix viridana*, which is widespread in N.W. Europe and the Mediterranean area, feeding on the developing buds, flowers and leaves, the edges of which it first rolls and ties down with silk. Pupation occurs on the leaf or on herbage beneath the tree, and the adult female lays eggs which then overwinter on the tree. Bad attacks may cause virtually complete defoliation, though the tree will produce a second flush of leaves. Another Tortricid, the Spruce Budworm

Choristoneura (= Archips) fumiferana is a pest of conifer forests in N. America, where the larvae defoliate and sometimes kill not only spruce (*Picea*), but also fir (*Abies*), pine (*Pinus*), larch (*Larix*) and hemlock (*Tsuga*). Larvae first mine and then feed externally on the foliage of the terminal shoots, which are webbed together to form nests in which the young larvae overwinter, feeding and pupating there in the following year to provide a summer generation of moths. The larvae of the Pine-shoot Moth *Rhyacionia buoliana*, also a Tortricid, bore into the buds of leading or side shoots of pine trees soon after hatching, causing death of the bud with resulting deformation of the tree or a proliferation of small shoots. The half-grown larva overwinters in a silken shelter, moving from bud to bud when it resumes activity in the spring, and burrowing into the stem to pupate in a silk-lined chamber. The damage is most serious to young trees between 3 and 15 years old, and this and related species are pests in Europe and parts of N. America.

The Lepidopteran family Lymantriidae includes several species which are or were of considerable economic importance in forestry. The Nun Moth, *Lymantria monacha*, has caused enormous devastation in the forests of C. Europe when feeding on spruce and pine, but it will also attack some deciduous trees and has a wide distribution in the Old World temperate zone, where it is often not a pest. Overwintering eggs are laid on the trunk of the tree late in the summer and larvae start feeding on the leaves in the following spring; pupation occurs in a silken cocoon in crevices of the bark. The closely related Gypsy Moth, *Lymantria dispar*, is injurious in some parts of the Palaearctic Region and in 1869 it was accidentally introduced into eastern N. America, where it has caused much greater damage. The eggs, laid in compact batches in July, hatch in the following spring and the larvae feed on a wide range of deciduous and evergreen trees, where they pupate in silken cocoons to produce a new generation of moths late in the summer. Defoliation and even the death of the tree can follow a serious attack. Another Lymantriid, the Brown-tail Moth *Euproctis chrysorrhoea*, has had a similar history as a pest after its introduction from Europe into N. America, but it has a rather different life-cycle and is now largely under control. Young larvae overwinter in communal silken nests and complete their development in the spring and summer to produce the next generation of adults.

Insect pests of timber. The most serious injury to timber in tropical and some subtropical areas is due to species of Isoptera or termites (pp. 138–9), many of which bore into timber and burrow extensively in it, causing major structural damage and even the collapse of wooden buildings if unchecked. The damage is done almost entirely by members of the worker caste, and the injurious species differ in the various parts of the world. The mode of attack differs from one instance to another, but in general the workers remove most of the wood except for a surface layer which is left to protect them. Dry-wood termites (members of the family Kalotermitidae) eat out galleries which later merge to form large cavities occupied by the whole colony. Though the individual colonies are small, there may be many present in a building. Other species with larger colonies have subterranean nests or occupy old tree-stumps. These may be some distance from the building attacked, the termites entering it from tunnels in the soil, along cavities in walls or by covered ways that they construct on the surface to circumvent otherwise impassable barriers. Cavities eaten out of the wood may be filled with soil, and woodwork below soil level or encased in masonry may disappear completely. In many subtropical areas of the northern hemisphere species of *Reticulitermes* (damp-wood termites of the family Rhinotermitidae) are the major pests. Further south the dry-wood termites become serious, especially some species of *Cryptotermes*, and the most injurious damp-wood forms are now species of *Coptotermes*. In the family Termitidae, *Macrotermes* and *Odontotermes* are subterranean mound-building forms active in Africa, India and S.E. Asia, and species of *Nasutitermes* are also important locally. Termite damage to buildings is best prevented by appropriate constructional methods and by the use of timbers which have been impregnated with insecticide or are naturally resistant to attack. Among the latter may be mentioned teak (*Tectona grandis*), American mahogany (*Swietenia mahagonia*), iroko (*Chlorophora tinctoria*) and some cedars such as *Cedrela toona*.

A number of beetles have larvae which burrow into domestic timber, furniture and other wooden articles, riddling the wood with their tunnels and causing its eventual destruction. Among these may be mentioned members of the families Lyctidae, Anobiidae and Cerambycidae. The Lyctidae or Powder-post beetles have females with a long oviscapt which enables them to deposit their eggs in cracks or pores in such timbers as oak, ash, walnut, elm and many exotic hardwoods. The larva then enters dry sapwood, rich in starch, on which it feeds; *Lyctus brunneus*, the commonest of the Powder-post beetles, is cosmopolitan and a serious pest of seasoned timber in houses and wood-yards (Fig. 152). The Anobiidae include the notorious Death-watch Beetle, *Xestobium rufovillosum*, whose larvae occur naturally in oak and willow trees, but can also cause serious damage to the structural hardwood timbers of old buildings such as churches. The larvae can bore into the heartwood and are most likely to occur wherever timber has already been affected by fungal decay. *Anobium punctatum* (Fig. 152) is the well-known Woodworm or Furniture Beetle, whose larvae can be very injurious to floorboards, plywood, furniture, wickerwork and other domestic articles; both softwoods and some hardwoods are attacked,

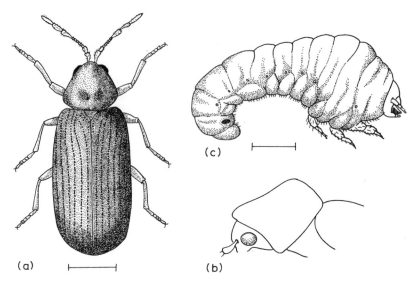

Fig. 152   Insect pests of timber

(a) Furniture Beetle, *Anobium punctatum* (Anobiidae), dorsal view; (b) lateral view of *Anobium*, showing hood-like pronotum; (c) larva of a powder-post beetle, *Lyctus brunneus* (Lyctidae), lateral view. ((a) and (b) after Hinton and Corbet, (c) after Britton.) Scale lines = 1 mm.

especially the sapwood, and injury is favoured by damp conditions. Another Anobiid, *Ptilinus pecticornis*, whose males have characteristic comb-like antennae, occurs outdoors on beech, but can also attack woodwork and furniture indoors. The family Cerambycidae includes very many species whose larvae burrow in the wood of living and dead trees, and in some cases, where the larvae are particularly long-lived, they may survive the felling of the tree and beetles emerge later from the damaged timber, often after it has been transported far from its country of origin. A Cerambycid pest more characteristic of structural timber over much of Europe and many other parts of the world is the House Longhorn, *Hylotrupes bajulus*, which lays its eggs in cracks in softwood timbers such as roof-joists and rafters, into which the larvae burrow. There they feed on the sapwood, leaving a thin surface layer intact and, depending on the protein content of the wood, their larval life lasts for 3–15 years. As in the other timber-dwelling beetles mentioned above, pupation occurs in the wood and the adult bites its way out through an exit-hole. Another Cerambycid, the Wharfborer *Nacerda melanura*, has a predilection for wet, rotten wood and is best known from harbours, docks and boats. It will attack softwoods and hardwoods equally, and the adults sometimes occur in large numbers, occasionally even appearing in houses and office buildings after emerging from infested wood.

310

Insect pests of stored products. Many Coleoptera attack stored foodstuffs such as cereals, cereal products and other seeds or fruits, as well as materials of animal or plant origin such as furs or cured tobacco. Weevils (Curculionidae) of the genus *Sitophilus* (= *Calandra*) are important cosmopolitan primary pests of cereal grains: *S. zeamais* and *S. oryzae* are closely related species which feed especially on maize and rice, whereas *S. granarius* is a temperate pest of wheat and other stored grains. The eggs are laid in the grains and the larva feeds there, consuming the contents and then pupating. The adult eventually bites its way out through a small circular emergence hole. The seeds of peas, beans and other legumes are attacked by members of the family Bruchidae, of which three important representatives are *Acanthoscelides obtectus, Callosobruchus chinensis* and *C. maculatus*. Eggs are laid on the surface of the seeds or pod – sometimes before the crop is harvested – and the larva bores into the seed, the contents of which it consumes. Pupation occurs within the seed and the adult emerges by pushing open a small circular 'window' of superficial tissue. Secondary grain pests are those which do not damage intact grains, but attack those already broken or feed on materials such as flour or meal produced by milling or crushing the grains. *Tribolium castaneum* and *T. confusum* are two species of Tenebrionid beetles which attack stored grains and foodstuffs in this way, the larvae living among the material and pupating there. The adults may live for up to a year and lay a total of 400–500 eggs over most of this period. *Oryzaephilus* (= *Silvanus*) *surinamensis* and *O. mercator* (Silvanidae) are cosmopolitan beetles with similar habits, feeding on a rather wide range of stored foodstuffs of plant or animal origin. *Lasioderma serricorne* (Anobiidae) is another widespread pest attacking a variety of stored products including tobacco, cocoa beans, groundnuts and legumes. All kinds of dried animal materials, such as skins, furs and woollen products, are the main foods of the family Dermestidae. Species of *Dermestes* attack bacon, smoked meat and fish, furs, skins and other keratin-containing material; *Attagenus pellio* is a carpet beetle, and species of *Anthrenus* can damage woollen materials and collections of dried insects. The Khapra Beetle, *Trogoderma granarium*, is also a Dermestid but lives in stored grain and legume seeds, flourishing in such places as maltings. Finally, the Anobiid beetle *Stegobium paniceum*, which breeds in bakery products and a wide variety of other foodstuffs, is a widespread pest in kitchens and food-stores.

The Lepidoptera include a few major pests of stored foodstuffs, such as the Angoumois Grain Moth, *Sitotroga cerealella* (Gelechiidae) and three species of *Ephestia* (*E. elutella, E. cautella* and *E. kuehniella*) belonging to the Pyralidae. In *Sitotroga* the eggs are laid on the surface of maize, wheat, sorghum and other grains (often before they are harvested); the larva enters a grain, consuming its contents and pupating

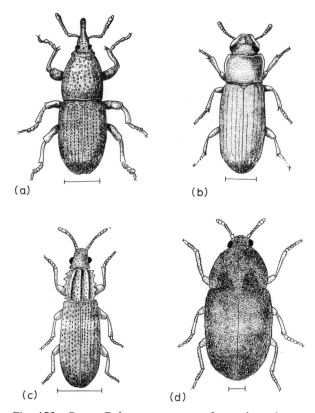

Fig. 153   Some Coleopteran pests of stored products
(a) Grain Weevil, *Sitophilus granarius* (Curculionidae) (after Balachowsky and Mesnil); (b) Confused Flour Beetle, *Tribolium confusum* (Tenebrionidae) (after Hinton and Corbet); (c) Saw-toothed Grain Beetle, *Oryzaephilus surinamensis* (Silvanidae) (after Borror and White); (d) *Dermestes ater* (Dermestidae) (after Hinton and Corbet). Scale lines = 1 mm.

there beneath a small circular 'window', through which the adult later escapes. *Ephestia cautella* attacks grain, dried fruits, beans and nuts. Eggs are laid on the food, producing larvae which feed among a silken web that they spin, and which later pupate in crevices. Woollen carpets, upholstery, blankets, garments and similar articles are seriously injured by larvae of the clothes moths, a few species of the family Tineidae, which are also able to attack furs, feathers and other keratinous materials, and have even been recorded from some stored foodstuffs. *Tineola bisselliella*, the Common Clothes Moth, has larvae which spin a long silken gallery, while *Tinea pellionella* and related species are the Case-bearing Clothes Moths, whose larva lives in a compact, tubular case of silk, to which fragments of its food adhere. Serious damage is most likely to occur if garments and other articles are soiled with sweat or proteinaceous material and are left undisturbed for long periods.

INSECTS OF MEDICAL AND VETERINARY IMPORTANCE

Several different families include insects injurious to the health and well-being of man and domesticated animals, partly because they cause direct injury or irritation, but more often because they act as carriers (vectors) of pathogenic micro-organisms such as nematodes, Protozoa, bacteria and viruses. Table 3 lists some of the more important groups and indicates the reasons for their medical or veterinary significance. They are considered in greater detail below, but it is first worth emphasizing

Table 3 Some insects of medical and veterinary importance

Order	Family	Genera	Disease
Phthiraptera	Pediculidae	*Pediculus*	Louse-borne typhus
Hemiptera	Reduviidae	*Triatoma, Panstrongylus, Rhodnius*	Chagas' disease
Diptera	Psychodidae	*Phlebotomus Lutzomyia*	Leishmaniasis, Sandfly fever (virus)
	Culicidae (mosquitoes)	*Anopheles*	Malaria
		Aedes, Anopheles, Culex	Filariasis, various virus diseases
		Aedes, Haemagogus	Yellow fever
		Mansonia, Psorophora	Virus diseases
	Simuliidae	*Simulium*	Onchocerciasis
	Tabanidae (horse-flies)	*Chrysops*	Transmits *Loa* (Nematoda)
	Muscidae	*Musca*	Plays a part in transmitting dysentery, typhoid, anthrax, cholera, yaws, etc., in tropics
	Glossinidae (tsetse flies)	*Glossina*	Trypanosomiasis (sleeping sickness and nagana)
	Gasterophilidae	*Gasterophilus*	Horse bot-fly
	Calliphoridae	*Cochliomyia*	Screw-worm of cattle
		Lucilia, Protophormia	'Strike' of sheep
	Oestridae	*Hypoderma*	Warble-fly of cattle
		Dermatobia	Human warble-fly
		Oestrus	Sheep nostril-fly
Siphonaptera	Pulicidae	*Xenopsylla*	Plague, murine typhus
	Ceratophyllidae	*Nosopsyllus*	Plague

313

some common features of vector species and the pathogens that they transmit. The majority of vectors belong to the order Diptera (two-winged flies), a group in which specialized blood-sucking habits have evolved several times and which are thus well adapted to transmit micro-organisms via the skin and bloodstream. In most cases it is the female alone which takes blood in the Diptera, the males feeding only on sugary plant secretions. It has also been shown that among the pathogens and their vectors there may be groups of closely allied strains or very similar species, often difficult to distinguish by traditional taxonomic methods, but differing in their biology and epidemiological role. There are also, in many cases, complex ecological relationships between populations of man, domestic animals and wild vertebrates, so that transmission of pathogens may occur both within each of these and from one population to another. A human disease may therefore in some cases be perpetuated through the persistence of the infection in wild or domesticated reservoir hosts and vector relations between these and human populations need special attention. Persistence of viruses may also occur in the vector population through transovarial transmission to successive generations. In many cases a given species of pathogen is transmitted by different vector species or with different degrees of effectiveness in the different parts of its geographical range, depending on local environmental conditions, social practices, and variations in the behaviour of vector and pathogen. Finally, it is necessary to remember that effective action against these diseases may be achieved not only by vector control, but also by chemotherapeutic or immunological measures against the pathogens. Total eradication of vector-borne diseases is not generally an immediate prospect, and it needs to be emphasized that vector control usually requires a greater reduction in the size of the vector population than is the case for the control of agricultural pests. Insecticidal control of the vector is usually necessary, alone or in combination with other methods.

Lice, typhus and relapsing fever. Three forms of sucking lice (Phthiraptera: Siphunculata) can occur on man under unhygienic conditions. The crab-louse (*Pthirus pubis*) is usually found among the pubic hair, the head-louse (a form of *Pediculus humanus*) lives on the scalp and head hairs, mainly of children, while the body-louse (another form of *P. humanus*) lives on the body between the skin and the clothing, on which its eggs are laid. Like all other members of the Siphunculata, these insects live on their hosts throughout all developmental stages and have highly specialized mouthparts (Fig. 154) with which they pierce the skin and feed on the blood. Under experimental conditions all three can transmit the causal organism of epidemic typhus (*Rickettsia prowazeki*), but only the body form of *Pediculus humanus* is a vector of

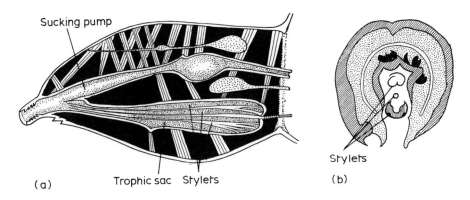

Fig. 154   Head and mouthparts of a sucking louse (Phthiraptera: Siphunculata)
(a) Longitudinal section of head, including trophic sac (after Snodgrass); (b) transverse
section of head of *Pediculus* (after Vogel).

the disease under natural circumstances, mainly those in which hygiene
has deteriorated as a result of poverty, war or natural disasters. Lice
become infected with the rickettsiae when they feed on someone
suffering from the disease, and the micro-organisms multiply in the
insect's gut and pass out with its faeces, which are infective on contact
with skin abrasions or delicate membranes such as the conjunctiva.
Insecticidal lotions and dusts are effective against lice, and the control of
a typhus epidemic in Naples in 1943 was one of the earliest successes of
the then recently introduced DDT. *Pediculus humanus* also transmits a
form of relapsing fever due to *Borellia recurrentis*; the spirochaetes are
taken up by the louse when it feeds on an infected person and
transmitted to another host when the louse is crushed and the micro-
organisms in its haemocoel enter through abrasions of the skin.

Reduviid bugs and Chagas' disease. Chagas' disease, caused by the
Protozoan *Trypanosoma cruzi*, is a chronic endemic condition affecting
millions of people in C. and S. America. It is usually transmitted by
Reduviid bugs of the subfamily Triatominae. The hundred or more
species feed by piercing the skin and sucking the blood of a variety of
mammals or birds, but a few of them (notably *Panstrongylus megistus*,
Triatoma infestans and *Rhodnius prolixus*) invade or live in human
dwellings. Here they form persistent colonies in cracks and crevices,
coming out at night to feed on the sleeping occupants. These habits,
combined with the fact that the insects can survive for months between
blood-meals and that once infected they can transmit the trypanosome
for the rest of their long life, make them effective vectors, carrying the
disease to man from other people or from the reservoir population of
wild and domesticated animals. The bug takes up the trypanosomes

315

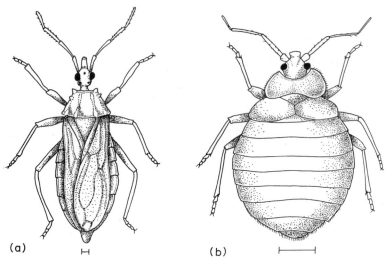

(a)   ⊢   (b)   ⊢────┥

Fig. 155   Hemiptera of medical importance
(a) *Panstrongylus megistus* (Reduviidae) (after Castellani and Chambers); (b) Bed Bug, *Cimex lectularius* (Cimicidae) (after McKenny Hughes and Johnson). Scale lines = 1 mm.

when it feeds and they undergo development in the insect's gut. After a week or two infective (metacyclic) forms of the trypanosome pass out with the insect's semi-liquid faeces (which are usually produced when it is feeding). From the faeces the infective stages of the trypanosome enter the vertebrate host's bloodstream through abrasions in the skin, or through delicate mucous membranes or the conjunctiva. Further development of the disease is usually slow, but the trypanosomes often invade heart muscle and other tissues, where they multiply and eventually produce serious effects. Regular house-spraying with persistent insecticides have provided some control of the disease, but only improved buildings and hygiene offer hope of more effective eradication.

Mosquitoes and human disease. Mosquitoes (Fig. 156) are members of the Dipteran family Culicidae (subfamily Culicinae) and many different species are involved in the transmission of malaria, some filarial nematodes, and many virus diseases. Human malaria is due to infection with one or more of four species of the parasitic Protozoan *Plasmodium*, which spends much of its life-cycle in the red blood-cells. Largely as a result of the pioneering work of Ross and Grassi at the end of the 19th century, it was shown that these parasites are transmitted by species of the mosquito genus *Anopheles* (though other genera of mosquitoes and other malarial parasites may be involved in the malarial infections of reptiles, birds and wild mammals). Male mosquitoes feed on naturally occurring sugary plant secretions, but the females usually also require a blood-meal in order to obtain the protein needed to

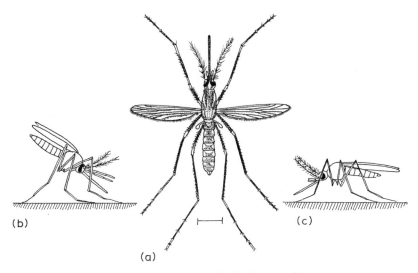

Fig. 156   Mosquitoes (Culicidae, Culicinae)
(a) Yellow Fever Mosquito, *Aedes aegypti* female, dorsal view (scale line = 1 mm); (b), (c)
respective resting postures of Anopheline and Culicine mosquitoes.

mature their eggs. When a female mosquito feeds on a vertebrate host, she penetrates its skin with a rigid bundle of structures consisting of the labrum, hypopharynx and four very long, delicate stylets (representing the greatly modified mandibles and maxillary laciniae; cf. Fig. 91). This bundle probes the tissues of the host and soon enters a blood capillary, the insect's saliva is pumped into the wound (preventing coagulation of the blood) and blood is sucked up along a channel between the labrum and stylets to enter the mosquito's alimentary canal. If the mosquito has fed on an infected person, the blood will contain gametocytes of the malarial parasite. These give rise in the mosquito's gut to male and female gametes, and the zygotes resulting from fertilization form motile ookinetes which migrate through the wall of the gut, eventually giving rise on its outer surface to spherical oocysts, each containing large numbers of sporozoites. These in turn invade the salivary glands of the mosquito and represent the infective stages which are injected into a new human host with the mosquito's saliva when it feeds again. The developmental cycle of the parasite in the mosquito takes 8–10 days at 28° C and cannot be completed below 15° C, so natural transmission of malaria does not occur in the cooler parts of the world or at high altitudes.

The epidemiology and control of malaria entail a detailed knowledge of the mosquito vectors at all stages of their life-cycle. Of the 400 or so known species of *Anopheles*, about 60 can transmit malaria naturally and about 30 are important vectors in various parts of the world. Some of these are members of complexes of 'sibling species' which are difficult to separate by the usual structural criteria that taxonomists employ, though they may differ appreciably in their behaviour, ecology, efficiency as vectors, and in more obscure characters such as the banding patterns of their larval salivary gland chromosomes. Included among such species complexes are *Anopheles gambiae* and *A. arabiensis*, which are important vectors in Africa, *Anopheles leucosphyrus* from S.E. Asia, *Anopheles punctulatus* and its close allies in parts of Australasia, and the *Anopheles maculipennis* complex, some of whose seven members were formerly vectors in parts of Europe where malaria has now been eradicated, and which still retain their potential for transmission. Other important vector species include *Anopheles funestus* (Africa south of the Sahara), *A. claviger* (Middle East), *A. stephensi* (Middle East across to India, S.E. Asia and China), *A. culifacies* (India, S.E. Asia) and *A. albimanus* (southern USA to C. and parts of S. America). Among the various factors which determine how important a species of mosquito will be as a vector are such characteristics as the general habitats it occupies, the extent to which it prefers to feed on man as compared with other animals, the times of day at which it feeds, its longevity, flight-range, reactions to light, whether it is active indoors or outside, and whether it tends to rest indoors after feeding.

Anopheles mosquitoes lay batches of 100–200 eggs in or near water, from which the aquatic larvae hatch. These have a characteristic appearance with a relatively large thoracic region and a longer, cylindrical abdomen which ends in a short respiratory siphon (Fig.

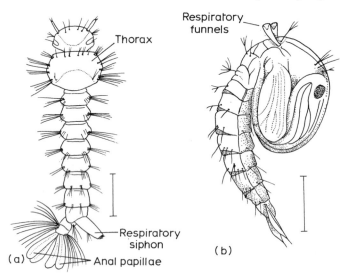

Fig. 157   Immature stages of *Aedes aegypti* (Culicidae)
(a) Larva, dorsal view; (b) pupa, lateral view. Scale lines = 1 mm. (After Séguy.)

157a). The larva normally floats horizontally beneath the surface film, obtaining its oxygen from the atmosphere and feeding on bacteria and other small particles in the water, sweeping them towards its mouth by a pair of secondary, articulated mouth-brushes (Fig. 118b). There are four larval instars, after which the larva moults into a characteristically comma-shaped pupa (Fig. 157), also aquatic, whose swollen thoracic region bears a pair of respiratory horns through which it obtains atmospheric oxygen. The aquatic habitats of mosquito larvae are very varied, and include permanent and temporary bodies of water, which may be natural or artificial, different species of mosquito having characteristic preferences. Most species are found in freshwater pools or marshes, often in association with floating vegetation, some preferring sunlit areas while others like shade. The larvae of some species, such as *Anopheles plumbeus*, live in rain-filled tree-holes and others are found in the water that accumulates in the leaf-axils of Bromeliads. Wells, cisterns, tin-cans and other artificial receptacles are utilized by some species such as *Anopheles stephensi* (an important urban vector), and the larvae of others live in small temporary puddles in cart-tracks, hoofprints and so on. A few species prefer brackish water or tidal swamps. Large bodies of open water do not usually provide breeding places, though larvae may live in pools or pockets of still water near the margins of such habitats. The sites available for the larvae of vector species help to determine control measures in particular areas and it needs to be remembered that engineering works connected with irrigation, drainage and other forms of water control may, by their effects on aquatic habitats, encourage or discourage the growth of mosquito populations.

Mosquitoes are also involved in the transmission of filarial nematodes. Adults of the nematodes *Wuchereria bancrofti* and *Brugia malayi* occur in human lymphatic systems and connective tissues, where they obstruct the lymph nodes and cause gross distension of the legs and other organs (elephantiasis). Fertilized females produce numerous microfilarial larvae which enter the bloodstream and appear more or less periodically in the peripheral blood vessels. From these they are taken up by a feeding mosquito, pass through its gut wall into the haemocoel and reach the thoracic muscles. Here, over a period of a few weeks, they undergo developmental changes and then migrate to the proboscis of the mosquito. When the insect feeds again the mature infective larvae escape from the tip of the proboscis and enter the skin of the victim, so completing the cycle of transmission. Human filariasis is transmitted by various species of mosquitoes, including members of the *Aedes scutellaris* complex, *Anopheles* species and, in urban areas, by *Culex fatigans* which breeds in polluted water. There is an interesting relationship between the time of day when the vector is active and the occurrence of

319

microfilariae in the peripheral blood of the human host. So-called 'periodic' strains of the parasite show a peak of peripherally circulating microfilariae at night and are transmitted by night-feeding species of mosquito, whereas in 'sub-periodic' strains the maximum peripheral occurrence is less clearly defined and may occur in the daytime when diurnally active species of vector are available.

Mosquitoes are implicated in the transmission of most of the arthropod-borne viruses (arboviruses) which affect man, as well as those that circulate in wild and domestic animal populations. They include the viruses responsible for many forms of encephalitis, those causing haemorrhagic and other forms of dengue fever, and that responsible for yellow fever. These have several features in common: the viruses circulate in the blood of the vertebrate host as well as invading other tissues; they multiply there and in the mid-gut cells of the mosquito, from where they can spread in due course to its salivary glands. From these the virus can be injected into whatever vertebrate host it next feeds upon. Yellow fever is found in South and Central America and in tropical Africa, where serious epidemics occurred in the past through transmission by *Aedes aegypti*. These have been reduced through effective immunization and vector control programmes, but the virus also occurs in wild reservoir populations of forest monkeys, among which it is transmitted by other mosquito species and from which human infections can occur and spread into towns. The disease has not reached Asia, though the occurrence there of suitable vectors constitutes a potential danger.

Control of mosquito-borne diseases by attacking the vectors needs a detailed knowledge of the species responsible for transmission in each particular area, including accurate identification and taking full account of the larval and adult biology – behaviour, habitat preferences, biting activity and relationships with man and reservoir hosts when these exist. Large-scale environmental management schemes, such as drainage or filling of breeding places, may be required, and personal protection by screening and repellents is obviously desirable. Insecticidal treatment of larval habitats and the resting places of adults are otherwise the main methods of control. More recently the evolution of mosquito strains resistant to insecticides, combined with concern for environmental pollution by pesticides, has led to considerable experimental interest in genetic and other biological methods of control (p. 338).

Tsetse flies and trypanosomiasis. Tsetse flies (Fig. 158) are members of the genus *Glossina*, now usually placed in a family of its own, the Glossinidae, close to the houseflies and their allies (Muscidae), which they resemble in a general way but from which they are clearly distinguished by the feathery hairs on the arista of the antenna and the

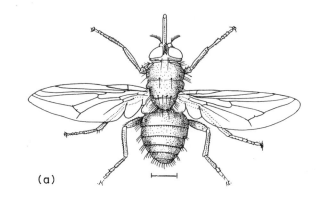

(a)

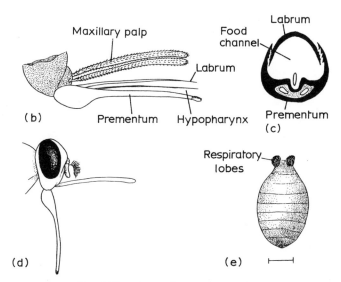

Maxillary palp

Labrum

Food channel

Labrum

(b) Prementum Hypopharynx

Prementum
(c)

Respiratory lobes

(d) (e)

Fig. 158   Tsetse flies (Glossinidae)

(a) *Glossina tabaniformis*, dorsal view (after Séguy); (b) mouthparts of *Glossina*, lateral view in resting position with parts separated; (c) transverse section of proboscis to show feeding channel, up which blood is sucked; (d) position of mouthparts in feeding posture; (e) puparium, showing posterior spiracular processes. Scale lines = 2 mm.

characteristically hatchet-shaped discal cell of the wing. They are present over extensive areas ('fly-belts') of tropical Africa, where their role as vectors of various species of *Trypanosoma* has serious effects on human health in rural areas and on the rearing of cattle. The mouthparts of both sexes are highly modified for sucking the blood of mammalian hosts (Fig. 158), though the various species show fairly well-defined preferences among man, domestic animals and wild game. Tsetse flies seek their hosts by sight and take blood-meals every few days, after

321

which they rest among vegetation. The females are viviparous, nourishing the larvae one at a time in an uterus-like expansion of the genital tract and depositing it when fully grown. The larva burrows into the soil, where it pupates almost immediately and eventually gives rise to an adult of the next generation. The various species differ in their ecological requirements and habitat preferences, some occurring among vegetation along the banks of rivers and lakes, others breeding in more open woodland or savannah. The species of *Trypanosoma* involved are *T. gambiense* and *rhodesiense*, respectively causing Gambian and Rhodesian forms of sleeping sickness in man, and members of the *T. vivax, congolense* and *brucei* groups causing 'nagana' of cattle. The 22 or so species of *Glossina* fall into three groups. Members of the *fusca* group of species are high-forest forms that do not transmit human trypano-somiasis, though they may contribute to the spread of the cattle disease. The *palpalis* group includes *G. palpalis* itself and *G. tachinoides*, which are important vectors of Gambian sleeping sickness in man and to a lesser extent of nagana in cattle; they are generally riverine or lacustrine forms associated with the vegetation along streams, rivers, lakes or mangrove swamps. The *morsitans* species group includes species from open woodland and savannah; *G. morsitans* and *G. pallidipes* are major vectors of Rhodesian sleeping sickness and nagana. Tsetse fly control depends on selective clearing of the characteristic associated vegetation, selective destruction of the wild game animals on which vectors may feed in some areas, and selective insecticidal treatment and trapping in preferred habitats. More recently, sterile-male techniques (p. 339) are being studied on an experimental scale.

Other Dipteran vectors of disease. Several other families of Diptera besides the mosquitoes and tsetse flies are vectors of pathogenic micro-organisms. The Simuliidae are the rather small, stoutly built 'black-flies' whose females normally possess rasping mouthparts (Fig. 117). The larvae and pupae (Fig. 159) occur in running water, often where there is a rapidly flowing current. They are normally attached to submerged vegetation or stones, but a few species have the unusual habit of attaching themselves to the cuticle of mayfly larvae or Crustacea, which then carry them about (phoresy). Simuliids bite viciously, causing pain and inflammation, and several species are capable of transmitting filarial nematodes, Protozoa and viruses among various vertebrate hosts (man, cattle, other mammals and birds). The most serious human disease for which they act as vectors is onchocerciasis, occurring in tropical Africa and C. America and caused by the nematode *Onchocerca volvulus*. The skin of the sufferer becomes coarsened and fissured, nodules develop and in some areas the condition leads to blindness. Microfilariae are taken up from the skin of infected persons when the fly feeds; they

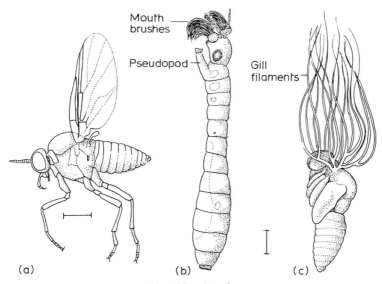

Fig. 159   *Simulium*
(a) Adult; (b) larva; (c) pupa, with spiracular gills. (After Smart.) Scale lines = 1 mm.

undergo development in its thoracic muscles and are passed on by another bite. The chief vectors are some members of the *Simulium damnosum* complex and *S. neavei* in Africa, and *S. metallicum* and *S. ochraceum* in C. America. *Simulium damnosum* can be controlled by larvicides applied to the streams where it breeds, but it it is difficult to deal with species whose larvae occur in many small streams and trickles.

Species of *Phlebotomus, Sergentomyia* and *Lutzomyia* are 'sandflies' belonging to the family Psychodidae, and are involved in the transmission of various species of *Leishmania* (Protozoa) among wild animal populations and man (Fig. 117a–c). The human leishmaniases appear in two main forms: dermal leishmaniases are due to forms of the parasite which occur in wild rodents in the Old and New Worlds, while visceral leishmaniasis has an Old World distribution, with dogs and wild Canids as the reservoir hosts. There are several epidemiological forms of each main disease, and the vector species differ from one area to another. As in most of the other haematophagous Diptera, only the female Phlebotomines suck blood. They feed at night, when they may take up the *Leishmania* from its vertebrate host. The Protozoa acquire flagella and multiply in the insect's gut, passing forward and accumulating in the pharynx, from which they enter the mouthparts and infect a new host when the insect feeds. Adult sandflies rest during the day in rodent burrows, among foliage, rock crevices and other sites, and some species are more or less domestic. The larvae develop in moist soil, leaf litter, rock crevices and similar habitats, and are difficult to control, as are also the wild adults, though those species which enter buildings can be dealt with by residual insecticides.

Some pathogenic micro-organisms are transmitted by Diptera which do not suck blood, but whose habits are such that they convey infection mechanically after feeding or resting on contaminated materials. Because of their close association with human populations and the readiness with which they feed on all sorts of moist substances (including foodstuffs, faeces and decomposing organic materials), the houseflies *Musca domestica, M. sorbens* and their close allies are able to transmit many bacterial and virus diseases. The most important of these are various forms of diarrhoea and dysentery due to *Salmonella* and *Shigella* and, in the Old World tropics, a serious form of corneal ulceration (trachoma) that leads to blindness. Normal domestic hygiene is effective in controlling houseflies in temperate regions, but more intensive measures may be needed in hotter countries.

Dipteran larvae parasitic in mammals. In some species of Diptera the larval stages are parasites in the internal or superficial tissues or in the internal body cavities of mammals, including some domesticated animals and, more rarely, in man. The condition is known as myiasis, and it may occur occasionally or facultatively, or as an obligate mode of life in members of several families of higher Diptera. Such species include the cattle warble-flies, *Hypoderma bovis* and *H. lineatum*, the horse bots *Gasterophilus intestinalis* and its allies, and the sheep nostril-fly *Oestrus ovis*, as well as many others with comparable habits from wild hosts.

Adult females of *Hypoderma* attach their eggs to hairs on the flanks and legs of cattle. After hatching, the young larvae enter the host's skin and migrate through its body, eventually forming a swelling (the 'warble') beneath the skin of the back when they are fully grown. Here they perforate the skin to form a breathing hole from which they later escape to pupate in the soil. As well as injuring the cattle, warble larvae reduce the commercial value of the hides. A related species, *Dermatobia hominis*, from C. and S. America, has a somewhat similar life-cycle in man, where the mature larvae cause pain and ulceration when they appear beneath the skin. *Gasterophilus intestinalis* lays its eggs on the front legs of horses and other Equidae. The eggs hatch after being licked by the host, and the larvae migrate along the alimentary canal, becoming attached by their mouth-hooks to the mucosae of the stomach, on which they feed and where they may occur in large numbers (though their effects seem less serious than might be expected). When mature the larvae detach themselves and pass out with the faeces to pupate in the soil. Other species of *Gasterophilus* with similar general habits become attached to different parts of the alimentary canal. The sheep nostril-fly *Oestrus ovis* is viviparous, depositing its larvae in the nostrils of sheep, from where the young larvae migrate to the frontal sinuses, causing irritation and sometimes obstructing the nasal passages. When mature they are sneezed out and pupate in the soil.

Infestation of more superficial tissues of mammalian and other vertebrate hosts occurs in several members of the blue-bottle family Calliphoridae and the related flesh-flies (Sarcophagidae). Among those species attacking man and domesticated animals may be mentioned the following: *Cordylobia anthropophaga*, the African tumbu-fly, causes cutaneous myiasis; *Cochliomyia* (= *Callitroga*) *hominivorax*, the screw-worm fly, has larvae which are obligate parasites feeding on the tissues of cattle after entering through wounds or unbroken skin; *Lucilia sericata, L. cuprina* and *Protophormia terraenovae* are responsible for 'strike' of sheep, the larvae feeding on and causing serious injury to the superficial tissues.

Fleas and disease. Many species of fleas (Siphonaptera) are able naturally or experimentally to transmit bacteria, rickettsiae and viruses among wild and domesticated animal populations, especially those of rodents. Some of these micro-organisms also cause human disease when transmitted by fleas or other means from animal to man or from person to person. The most important of such diseases are bubonic plague, caused by the bacterium *Yersinia* (= *Pasteurella*) *pestis*, and murine typhus, due to *Rickettsia typhi* and *R. prowazeki*. Plague bacteria are acquired by a flea when it feeds on the blood of an infected host, and these then multiply in the insect's gut, eventually blocking the proventriculus. When such a blocked flea tries to feed on a new host it regurgitates bacteria into the wound, so passing on the infection. Historically, epidemic plague, such as occurred in the Black Death during the 14th century, the 'Great Plague' of 1664–6 and the Indian epidemic of 1898–1918, is associated with the spread of the bacterial infection among urban rat populations followed by transmission to man and further spread among the human population. The rat-fleas *Xenopsylla cheopis* and, to a lesser extent, *Nosopsyllus fasciatus* are important vectors. It must be remembered that although epidemic plague has now declined greatly, reservoir infections, transmitted by many species of fleas, occur among wild rodent populations in many parts of the world and constitute foci of potential human disease. Of some veterinary interest is the fact that the tapeworm *Dipylidium caninum* of dogs and cats has the fleas *Ctenocephalides canis* and *C. felis* as its intermediate hosts. The mature proglottides of the tapeworm pass out with the dog's faeces and are eaten by the flea larvae, in whose gut the eggs hatch. The embryos migrate to the haemocoel of the flea larva, where they survive its metamorphosis and transform into cysticercoids which infect dogs that eat their fleas.

INSECTICIDAL CONTROL

Before about 1940 the insecticides in common use were: (a) simple inorganic materials like hydrogen cyanide or lead arsenate; (b) more complicated organic compounds of plant origin such as nicotine or extracts of derris root (containing rotenoids) or pyrethrum flowers (containing a mixture of pyrethrins); (c) petroleum or tar-oil distillates containing a mixture of hydrocarbons or derived organic compounds; or (d) a few synthetic organic chemicals such as the ovicide 4,6–dinitro-o-cresol (DNOC) or the fumigants chlorpicrin and methyl bromide. A considerable change occurred over the next decade, with the introduction of synthetic organic substances of very high toxicity to insects, of which the best known was DDT. These made possible some highly effective methods for the chemical control of many pests, but their indiscriminate use also led in many cases to such undesirable consequences as the development of resistant strains of the pest species, the reduction of populations of predators and parasitoids responsible for some degree of natural control, toxicity hazards to man and long–term toxic effects on wildlife, especially on some species of birds. A more balanced approach to the use of insecticides has therefore become necessary and some of the problems involved are discussed later in this section (pp. 332–5).

The modern insecticides now in more or less widespread use fall into the following four categories:

1. chlorinated hydrocarbons such as DDT, γ-HCH and Dieldrin
2. organophosphates, such as Malathion, Phorate and Dimethoate
3. carbamate insecticides, such as Carbaryl and Carbofuran
4. synthetic pyrethroids such as resmethrin and permethrin

The structural formulae of a selection of these compounds are given in Fig. 160, while Table 4 summarizes some of their important properties. A number of other substances, broadly classed as insect growth regulators, have also been regarded in recent years as potentially useful insecticides. They include compounds like diflubenzuron and other benzoylphenylurea derivatives, which inhibit the synthesis of chitin, as well as juvenile hormone antagonists such as Precocene 1 and 2. Among the advantages claimed for them is their rapid environmental degradation and the inability of insects to develop resistance to their action. They have not yet attained importance in large-scale practical field control.

The desirable properties of an insecticide are that it should be highly toxic to the insects being controlled, but selective in the sense that it causes the least possible harm to predators and parasitoids of the pest, and to beneficial species such as honey-bees and other pollinators of crop

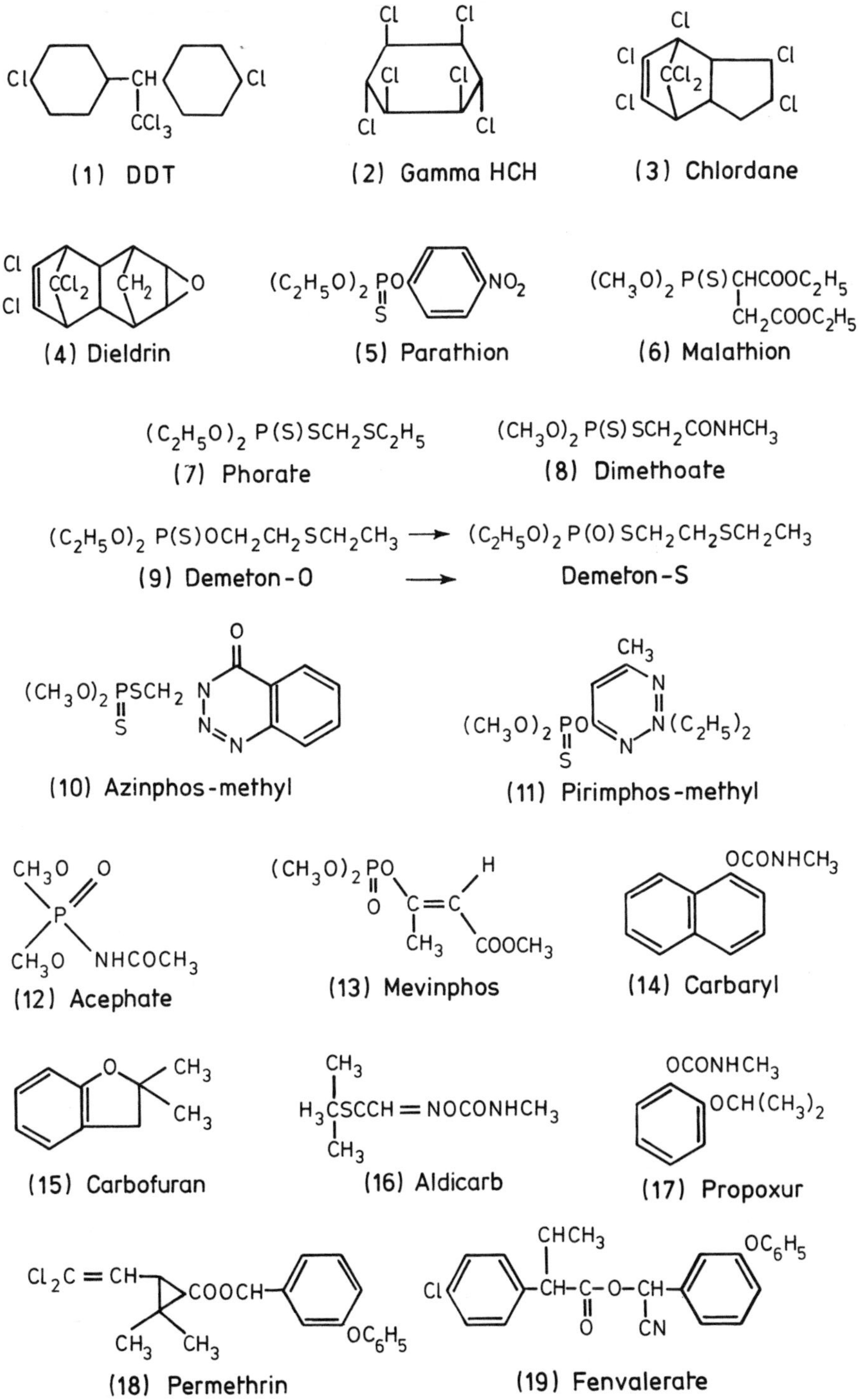

(1) DDT

(2) Gamma HCH

(3) Chlordane

(4) Dieldrin

(5) Parathion

$(CH_3O)_2 P(S) CHCOOC_2H_5$
                $CH_2COOC_2H_5$

(6) Malathion

$(C_2H_5O)_2 P(S) SCH_2SC_2H_5$

(7) Phorate

$(CH_3O)_2 P(S) SCH_2CONHCH_3$

(8) Dimethoate

$(C_2H_5O)_2 P(S)OCH_2CH_2SCH_2CH_3 \longrightarrow (C_2H_5O)_2 P(O) SCH_2CH_2SCH_2CH_3$

(9) Demeton-O $\longrightarrow$ Demeton-S

$(CH_3O)_2 PSCH_2$ ...
(10) Azinphos-methyl

(11) Pirimphos-methyl

(12) Acephate

(13) Mevinphos

(14) Carbaryl

(15) Carbofuran

$H_3CSCCH = NOCONHCH_3$
(16) Aldicarb

(17) Propoxur

(18) Permethrin

(19) Fenvalerate

Fig. 160   Structural formulae of some insecticides

Table 4 Some properties of selected insecticides

Compound	Date	Persistence	Systemic effects	LD$_{50}$ (mg/kg)	Alkali compatability	Remarks
DDT	1944	Long	No	113–118	Yes	Use now limited
γ–HCH	1945	Moderate to long	Slight pseudosystemic	88–91	Yes	Toxic to a few plants
Chlordane	1945	Long	No	457–490	Yes	Use now limited
Dieldrin	1948	Long	No	46	Yes	Mainly for soil treatment
Parathion	1947	Moderate	Slight pseudosystemic	3.6–13.0	No	Note high acute toxicity
Malathion	1950	Short to moderate	No	2800	No	
Phorate	1954	Moderate	Yes	1.6–3.7	Yes	Used as granules due to toxicity
Dimethoate	1956	Moderate	Yes	320–380	No	
Demeton	1951	Moderate	Yes	2.5–12.0	No	Aphicide, note high toxicity
Azinphos–methyl	1953	Moderate to long	No	1850	No	
Pirimphos–methyl	1970	Moderate	Slight pseudosystemic	2050	No	
Acephate	1971	Moderate	Slight	866–945	No	
Mevinphos	1953	Short	Yes	3–12	No	Note high acute toxicity
Carbaryl	1956	Moderate	Slight	850	Yes	Toxic to fish
Carbofuran	1967	Moderate	Yes	8–14	Yes	
Aldicarb	1965	Moderate	Yes	0.93	Yes	For soil treatment as granules due to high acute toxicity
Propoxur	1959	Moderate	No	90–128	Yes	
Permethrin	1973	Moderate to long	No	430–4000	Yes	
Fenvalerate	1972	Moderate to long	No	300–630	Yes	

NOTES: The lines separate the four main categories of insecticides: organochlorines, organophosphates, carbamates and pyrethroids, respectively.
The LD$_{50}$ refers to oral dosages for rats.
The dates refer to the year of commercial introduction.

plants. It should also not be toxic to the plants or domesticated animals on which it may be used, nor should it be dangerous to man and other vertebrates. Finally, it should be cheap to produce, easy and safe to formulate in high concentrations and stable when stored under various climatic conditions. No substance possesses all of these attributes to an equally high degree and in practice the choice of an insecticide usually involves some compromise among them, also taking into account whatever non-insecticidal control measures are available. Some of the topics indicated above are discussed in more detail below.

Mode of action of insecticides. The use of insecticides needs to be considered in terms of their varied modes of action. Broadly speaking, an insecticide may act in one or more of four ways: as a stomach poison, as a contact insecticide, through systemic effects or as a fumigant.

Stomach poisons are those which act after being eaten by the insect when it feeds on material bearing a deposit of the insecticide. They are therefore likely to be particularly effective in the control of external leaf-feeding insects such as many beetles and the larvae of Lepidoptera, whose biting mouthparts are used to chew up foliage, buds, stems, and so on. Timber-boring insects may also ingest stomach poisons which have been used to impregnate the wood after a tree has been felled. The classical example of a stomach poison was lead arsenate, which is only effective in this way, but many insecticides developed more recently, such as DDT and γ-HCH, behave as stomach poisons as well as having a contact effect.

Contact insecticides are those which enter the insect by penetrating the cuticle, often in some restricted and more permeable region of the body. The insect may therefore acquire a lethal dose either by contact with an emulsion or suspension of the insecticide in the form of spray droplets, or by walking over a superficial film of the insecticide as a solid deposit or in some non-volatile carrier liquid. Insects which occur externally on plants in easily accessible places or those which rest on easily treated surfaces in the open or inside buildings are particularly susceptible and the majority of insecticides act by a contact effect.

Systemic insecticides are those which are absorbed by plants and then translocated so that they or their toxic derivatives are available in those parts of the plant on which the pest feeds. They are therefore particularly appropriate in the control of insects that feed with piercing, suctorial mouthparts, such as aphids and scale-insects, or those that live within the plant, such as stem-borers or leaf-miners. Some substances which are not truly systemic in action may nevertheless penetrate for short distances into plant tissue and thus exert what may be called a pseudosystemic effect on insects that live superficially within the plant, as do leaf-mining larvae.

Fumigants are gases or materials of high vapour pressure which yield toxic concentrations in the atmosphere and are absorbed by the insect, mainly through its spiracles and tracheal system. They include substances such as hydrogen cyanide, ethylene dibromide and epoxy-ethane (ethylene oxide) and are used, with appropriate precautions, in closed fumigation chambers, beneath tarpaulins, or in leak-proof buildings such as greenhouses and warehouses, often for the control of insects living within compact materials such as stored grains or soil, and which cannot easily be reached by other forms of insecticide.

A full understanding of the physiological and biochemical mechanisms through which insecticides exert their lethal effects is desirable, but not yet attained for all the materials in common use. The organophosphates and carbamates act by their inhibitory effect on the enzyme cholinesterase which is normally found in the nervous system where it is responsible for the breakdown of acetylcholine after the latter has accomplished its role in synaptic transmission of nerve-impulses. On the other hand, DDT and the pyrethroids seem to act by inhibiting calcium-dependent enzymes responsible for the breakdown of ATP (adenosine triphosphate), thus interfering with the transport of Na^+ and K^+ ions across the nerve axon membrane, and so disrupting the normal course of axonal transmission of nerve-impulses. In addition to these effects on peripheral nerves, the very rapid paralytic action of the pyrethroids ('knock-down') appears to be due to an effect on the central nervous system of the insect.

Methods of insecticide formulation. Insecticides are usually supplied to the user as concentrated preparations that have to be diluted with water, or as powders in which the insecticide has been mixed with an inert solid carrier. The kinds of formulation available vary considerably, depending on the circumstances in which it is to be used, but solid synthetic insecticides are commonly dissolved in an organic solvent with an added surface-active ingredient to produce an 'emulsifiable concentrate' to which water is added before use at an appropriate concentration of the active material. In other cases the toxicant may be absorbed on or mixed with an inert wettable powder, which forms a very fine suspension when water is added. When the insecticide forms one component in a mixture of pesticides it is important that both they and any added surface-active ingredients should be compatible. Some insecticides, for example, are decomposed by alkaline fungicides and the two cannot therefore be used together. Other solid formulations include dusts, in which the toxicant is mixed with a light inert filler, or baits, where it is incorporated into edible materials like bran. Insecticides to be used in confined spaces, such as domestic fly-sprays, may be formulated in aerosol containers, while those used for glasshouse crops may, if heat-stable, be mixed with pyrotechnic substances and used as 'smokes'. Gaseous fumigants may be generated *in situ* from reagents that are more convenient to handle. Another method of formulation, used especially when treating seedling crops with systemic insecticides such as Phorate or Aldicarb, involves the adsorption of the toxicant on granules of a mineral or synthetic material. Such granular formulations are less hazardous to the operator and may be required by safety regulations when the insecticide has a high mammalian toxicity.

Insecticide application. Many different methods are used to apply insecticides, depending on the crop, the site where control is being carried out, and the formulation available. Liquid preparations are normally applied by some kind of spraying equipment, which may vary from simple, readily portable, hand-operated sprayers to large motorized vehicles or aerial spraying machinery attached to light aircraft. The essential components in all cases are a pump, from which liquid is forced under pressure into a lance, or boom, bearing one or more nozzles, out of which the liquid emerges as a more or less fine spray or mist. An important feature of such application is the total volume of liquid distributed over a given area. High-volume application of an agricultural insecticide might amount to the delivery of 1000 l of liquid per ha of bushes and trees or 700 l/ha of ground crops. Machinery delivering a lower volume, at correspondingly higher concentrations of toxicant in the spray-liquid, would provide 200 l/ha or more, while low or ultra-low volume spraying might deliver 50–100 l/ha. Ultra-low volume spraying requires special equipment and formulations of the insecticide at high concentrations in a non-volatile solvent or as micronized wettable powders. The design of the nozzles and the pressures used will influence the performance of spraying equipment. Some nozzles produce a flat fan of spray, commonly used in ground spraying, whereas others provide a cone of droplets. These may vary in diameter from about 50–100 μm in fine mist to over 400 μm in coarse sprays and the mean diameter and spectrum of droplet sizes both depend on nozzle design. Flying insects may be most effectively controlled by aerosols or fine mists composed of droplets below 50 μm in diameter which float in the air, but stationary or crawling insects are best controlled by coarser sprays. Air-blast sprayers operate in a manner different from the hydraulic sprayers described above; the nozzles here are simple apertures from which the jet of liquid is sheared off into droplets when air is blown across it by a fan. More recently other devices have been developed for the atomization of insecticidal liquids, replacing the conventional nozzle by a spinning disk (as in certain ultra-low volume sprayers) or by the use of an electrostatic mechanism.

Evolution of resistance to insecticides. Repeated use of insecticides has led on many occasions to the evolution of strains of the pest species that are resistant to the toxicants employed. This is because the continual application of insecticides creates strong selective pressures leading to the death of the genetically more susceptible individuals and the survival of the genetically more resistant ones, with a consequent increase in the frequency of genes conferring resistance. Early indications of this occurred when hydrogen cyanide fumigation was first practised against scale-insects on citrus trees, but the problem became much more acute when intensive and widespread application of highly toxic synthetic insecticides became common after about 1945. By 1983 some 400 species of injurious insects and mites had become resistant to one or more pesticides and some species had developed strains resistant to all four major categories of insecticides (organophosphates, organochlorines, carbamates and pyrethroids). Over the same period the financial costs and time needed to develop new insecticides increased steadily, with the result that insecticide resistance is becoming a major hindrance to the control of crop pests and disease vectors, as, for example, in mosquito control.

As a rule insects resistant to a member of one of the major groups of insecticides are also resistant to other compounds of the same group. This phenomenon is known as cross-resistance and should be distinguished from multiple resistance, in which a species has evolved a genotype conferring resistance to two or more insecticides with different modes of action. Resistance mechanisms are of several different kinds: some are behavioural, involving the avoidance of microhabitats contaminated with insecticides; many result from decreased rates of cuticular penetration; others involve increased rates of detoxication via different enzymatically controlled pathways; while still others depend on decreased sensitivity at target sites (e.g. decreased susceptibility of cholinesterases to organophosphates or carbamates). In general it appears that changed resistance is due to the selection of major autosomal genes and a variety of modifiers; many loci showing mutations that confer resistance have been identified in some insects such as the housefly *Musca domestica*. The speed with which resistance develops in a population seems to depend on a number of factors, including the frequency and spatial extent of insecticidal treatment and the pest species involved; it appears to develop more rapidly at the lower trophic levels in a food-web, and perhaps less rapidly among parasitoids than it does in their hosts. Typically some 10–15 generations may be required for a population to evolve effective resistance; a population of the Colorado Potato Beetle *Leptinotarsa decemlineata* in Long Island, New York, evolved resistance to DDT in seven years and then successively to azinphos-methyl, carbofuran and pyrethroids in five, two and two years, respectively. There does not seem at present to be any simple way in which the development of resistance can be overcome, though one might expect it to be less of a problem in well-organized pest management systems, where insecticide use is reduced to a minimum, immigration of non-resistant forms occurs and alternative control methods are also in operation.

Toxicity of insecticides to other organisms. An important factor helping to decide the choice and usage of insecticides is the toxicity which they may show to organisms other than the insect pest one wishes to control. Broadly, these other organisms include: (a) man; (b) the natural enemies (predators and parasites) of the pest species, which will generally include insects and perhaps some other invertebrates as well as fish and birds; (c) beneficial insects such as honey-bees and other pollinators; (d) domestic animals and cultivated plants; (e) other species which need to be conserved on environmental, moral or aesthetic grounds. Few if any insecticidal treatments are likely to leave all these varied organisms unaffected; some compromise is needed and one has to balance the relative advantages of pest control (which may be unattainable in any other way) against the disadvantages of injury to other organisms. In reaching such a decision much will depend on the extent to which, in a given region, much-needed crops are being ravaged or insect-borne diseases are causing serious debilitation and death.

Toxicity to man and other vertebrates may be considered in terms of acute toxicity, resulting from exposure to high concentrations, usually over a short period, and chronic toxicity, due to lower concentrations exerting long-term cumulative effects. Acute toxicity is mainly of concern to those engaged in the manufacture and application of insecticides, and some indication of the compounds more or less toxic to mammals is available from Table 4 which gives the oral median lethal dose (LD_{50}) for rats in milligrams per kilogram of body weight. This is the dose required to kill 50% of the experimental animals in a given time. The LD_{50} is a measure which will vary from one species to another and also depends on the mode of administration, whether oral, applied to the skin or inhaled. It is clear from the table that substances like DDT show very low toxicity (i.e. have a high LD_{50}), whereas others, such as phorate, exhibit high acute toxicity. Statutory regulation of the conditions of work with poisonous substances usually operates well in advanced countries, and entails safety precautions such as adequate labelling and the use of protective clothing, including gloves, boots and respirators if need be; voluntary codes of practice may also be operated. In general, granular formulations are safer than sprays, and gaseous or atomized materials are the most dangerous, but variations in toxicity from one substance to another may be decisive. Hydrogen cyanide and methyl bromide are particularly dangerous fumigants.

Chronic toxicity is in many respects more difficult to deal with. This is partly because adverse effects take much longer to be recognized and are sometimes difficult to establish with certainty. Contamination of the environment may also occur over wide areas and toxic residues may accumulate in the tissues of those far from the sites of insecticide application. The persistence of the insecticide will depend on the rate at which it is decomposed into harmless end-products under the influence of light and oxidation or through contact with the soil (including soil micro-organisms), and also on the rate at which absorbed insecticide is degraded by biochemical detoxication mechanisms within the plants or animals involved. Legal or voluntary restraints on the amounts of insecticidal residues that can be tolerated on edible crops will also affect the amounts likely to be absorbed. In general, repeated application of insecticides which retain their toxicity for long periods, such as organochlorine compounds like DDT and Dieldrin, lead to high levels of accumulation in the fatty tissues of animals at high trophic levels in the food-web, such as fish-eating fish and predatory birds, where chronic toxicity effects have been demonstrated clearly. Insecticides of much higher acute toxicity but lower stability and persistence may therefore cause fewer long-term environmental hazards.

The effects of insecticides on the natural enemies of pest species is most important. Many potential pests of cultivated plants may be controlled quite well by their predators and parasitoids under natural conditions. However, if these controlling agents are readily killed by insecticides, then the species on which they prey may increase rapidly and assume the status of a pest. Early examples of this followed the injudicious use of highly toxic broad-spectrum organochlorine insect-icides such as DDT in the later 1940s. In English apple orchards the previously unimportant Fruit-tree Red Spider Mite *Panonychus ulmi* quickly became a serious pest when its most important predator, the Mirid *Blepharidopterus angulatus*, was killed by DDT. In California populations of the Cottony Cushion Scale *Icerya purchasi*, which had been effectively controlled on citrus by the predatory Coccinellid beetle *Rodolia cardinalis*, increased for the same reason when *Rodolia* popula-tions were drastically reduced through insecticide application. Such insecticide-induced pest outbreaks and the emergence of new pests have been recorded repeatedly and there are many examples of the toxicity of broad-spectrum insecticides to such generalized insect predators as the Coccinellidae, Anthocoridae, Nabidae and some Miridae. It is not easy to forecast such developments in detail, since the interactions between potential or actual pests and their predators and parasitoids are usually very complex and inadequately understood, even for major

334

crops, while their relative susceptibilities to insecticides are even less well known.

BIOLOGICAL CONTROL METHODS

The term 'biological control' is sometimes applied only to control through the use of the insect predators and parasitoids of pest species. This is certainly an important method of combating insect pests, but it is only one of a number of methods in which biological principles can be applied and which are now increasing in number and scientific interest, even if some of them are still experimental or of limited applicability at present.

Insect pest control by predators and parasitoids. The general biology of insect predators and parasitoids and the role they play in regulating natural populations of insects is discussed on pp. 218ff. and 272ff. Here we are concerned with ways in which the relationships between a pest species and its predators and parasites can be manipulated in order to reduce the population density of the pest and maintain it at relatively low levels, such as are acceptable in the light of social or economic considerations. Two aspects of the problem may be considered: first, the effects of introducing into an area predators or parasitoids which were not previously present there and, secondly, the conservation and augmentation of established predators and parasitoids which thereby become more effective in controlling the pest.

The deliberate introduction of predators and parasitoids from elsewhere has achieved many striking successes. During the 1880s citrus growing in California was seriously threatened by attacks of the Cottony Cushion Scale *Icerya purchasi*, which was thought to have been introduced there from Australia, where it was apparently subject to effective natural control by a parasitoidal fly *Cryptochaetum iceryae* and a predatory Coccinellid beetle *Rodolia* (= *Vedalia*) *cardinalis*. These natural enemies had not accompanied the scale-insect when it was originally transported accidentally to the USA. They were therefore introduced artificially into California, and within a few years *Rodolia* had brought the *Icerya* populations under control. Following this very striking achievement, other equally effective introductions of predators and parasitoids were made in many parts of the world. In Hawaii the Sugar-cane Planthopper *Perkinsiella saccharicida* was found to be causing serious damage around 1900. Several Chalcidoid egg-parasitoids were introduced artificially from Australia with partial success, and the pest was finally brought under effective control by a Heteropteran predator *Tytthus mundulus* (Miridae) from Fiji, which sucks out the contents of the *Perkinsiella* eggs. Yet a third well-known example concerns the

Coconut Moth *Levuana iridescens*, the larva of which had become seriously injurious in Fiji by the 1920s. In this case there were no records of the pest occurring outside Fiji, but another moth of the same family, *Artona catoxantha*, was known to be heavily parasitized in Java and Malaysia by a Tachinid fly, *Ptychomyia remota*. This was introduced to Fiji and rapidly established itself as a parasite of *Levuana*, bringing the pest completely under control. Since these early examples, control by the introduction of predators and parasitoids has been widely practised against a variety of agricultural pests. An analysis made by DeBach in 1971 showed that natural enemies had been imported against 223 species of injurious insects and that a measurable degree of control had been obtained with 120 of these introductions, 90 of which had been substantially or completely successful.

The advantages of control by predatory and parasitoidal insects are very clear. The method is usually highly specific, since the natural enemies usually restrict their attacks to one or a few related species. Once introduced successfully, the predators or parasitoids provide virtually permanent control, requiring no more than periodic monitoring, and the method therefore has high economic benefits in relation to the costs incurred. It is also quite free of the toxicity hazards and other undesirable environmental effects of chemical insecticides. However, some attempts at control by the introduction of natural enemies have not been successful, nor is it easy to forecast the extent to which control is likely to be achieved in any particular instance. Suggestions that the method is more successful in controlling pests inhabiting islands or comparable ecologically isolated regions such as California, or that it is more effective against pests of perennial crops than annual ones, are not well supported by the available evidence.

Conservation and augmentation of existing predators and parasitoids is an important aspect of integrated pest management (p. 341), though it requires a more detailed knowledge of the life-cycles and ecology of both the pests and their enemies than is often available. Careful use of insecticides so as to minimize their adverse effects on the predators and parasitoids is obviously desirable, and in some cases a supply of honeydew or nectar for the parasitoids or the provision of shelter or alternative host species has helped to maintain them at higher population densities. Modified cultivation and harvesting procedures and the introduction of additional crops among the main one may also have a beneficial effect, though it is necessary to consider each situation on its own merits, and this may require careful research. Augmentation of the natural parasitoidal fauna by repeated mass releases of specially reared insects has also been practised. These may usually be regarded as 'inundative' releases, which must be undertaken on a regular basis, unlike the so-called 'inoculative' releases, after which the predator or parasitoid is expected to establish itself. Notable examples of augmentation occur in the case of *Trichogramma* spp., Chalcidoid egg-parasites of many Lepidoptera, which have been used against *Heliothis, Platyedra, Agrotis* and other species. The green lacewing *Chrysopa carnea*, a Neuropteran predator with a wide range of prey, has also been used in the same way against a wide variety of field and orchard pests. Augmentation methods are particularly suitable under the very closely controlled conditions of cultivation used for glasshouse crops. One of the earliest successes of this kind was the use of the Chalcidoid *Encarsia formosa* to control the whitefly *Trialeurodes vaporariorum* on tomatoes and cucumbers, though the method is not effective at temperatures below 24° C. Despite some successes it is not always easy to assess the commercial value of control by augmentation of natural enemies, nor can the results which may be obtained be readily forecast in particular cases; such methods are likely to be most successful when combined with other techniques of control.

Predators and parasitoids have played little part in control strategies for insects of medical and veterinary importance. Mosquito larvae are actively preyed upon by the fish *Gambusia affinis*, which has been introduced widely in tropical areas as part of antimalarial measures since about 1920. Other species of fish, a parasitic nematode, *Reesimermis nielseni*, and the predacious larvae of another species of mosquito, *Toxirhynchites brevipalpis*, have also been used experimentally in mosquito control, but have not yet been shown to have much practical value.

Pest control by micro-organisms. Although there is no doubt that some viruses, bacteria, Protozoa, fungi and nematodes are pathogenic to various insect species, the practical use of these micro-organisms for pest control under field conditions has not realized the potentialities that they seem to offer and only a few examples will be cited. It is to be hoped that the great advantages of these agents – their high specificity, natural modes of dissemination and absence of pollution and toxicity hazards – will eventually be exploited more effectively.

Over 300 pathogenic viruses have been isolated from insect pests of agricultural importance, and it has been known for many years that some viruses have played an important role in the natural control of some insects, as in the well-known case of the Diprionid sawfly *Gilpinia hercyniae* which caused such damage in Canadian spruce forests after it had been accidentally introduced there from Europe. The most promising viruses for practical pest control are those known as nuclear polyhedrosis viruses and granulosis viruses, sometimes referred to as inclusion viruses and treated as members of the viral genus *Baculovirus*.

These are not pathogenic to man and higher animals, and show considerable specificity in their virulence towards insects. Nuclear polyhedrosis viruses infect Lepidopteran larvae, multiplying in the nuclei of cells in the epidermis, fat-body, blood, tracheae and sometimes other tissues; they also occur in the midgut cells of Diprionid sawfly larvae. Granulosis viruses occur primarily in the fat-body of Lepidopteran larvae, multiplying in both the nuclei and cytoplasm. There is particular interest in the potentialities that viruses may have in integrated control programmes directed against the Gypsy Moth, *Lymantria dispar*, and species of *Spodoptera* and *Heliothis*.

Two species of spore-forming bacteria, *Bacillus popilliae* and *B. thuringiensis*, have been used successfully in pest control. *Bacillus popilliae* infects the larvae of Scarabaeid beetles and has been employed against the Japanese Beetle *Popillia japonica* in N. America. Ingested spores germinate in the gut and the bacteria invade the haemocoel, where they multiply and sporulate, causing the haemolymph to take on a milky appearance, and killing the larvae after a few days. The bacteria cannot be cultivated in artificial media, but infected larvae are used to produce spores that are dried, mixed with talc and the resulting 'spore dust' applied to grassland harbouring the subterranean *Popillia* larvae. These ingest spores and the soil also becomes inoculated with the pathogen. Infection of *Popillia japonica* with this bacterium is thought to have been a major factor in the control of the beetle. *Bacillus thuringiensis* was first studied after its isolation from larvae of *Ephestia kuehniella* and has been used as a microbial control agent against a number of pests from the order Lepidoptera, to members of which it is specific. The bacteria, which can be grown commercially by a mass-culture fermentation technique, produce a high-molecular weight glycoprotein crystal when they sporulate. Dormant spores and crystals are harvested, dried and formulated as wettable powders or liquid concentrates as though they were chemical insecticides. When ingested by susceptible feeding larvae the glycoprotein breaks down in the gut, attacks its epithelium and prevents further feeding; in some species the spores also germinate and cause a form of septicaemia. The relatively high specificity of *B. thuringiensis* and its lack of toxicity to man and higher animals make it a desirable control agent, but the number of pest species against which it has been used successfully is not very great, and it is usually supplemented by other methods.

Genetic control of insect pests. The essential feature of these methods is the introduction into pest populations through the natural mating processes of genetic factors which reduce fecundity or diminish other undesirable features such as the ability to transmit pathogenic micro-organisms. The best-known of such methods are the so-called sterile-male techniques, first devised to control the screw-worm fly of cattle, *Cochliomyia hominovorax*, on the island of Curaçao around 1954. The sterile-male technique involves the mass rearing of large numbers of male insects which are then sterilized artificially by ionizing radiation or the application of synthetic chemosterilants. The sterile males are then released into the pest population and will seek out the normal, naturally occurring females, with which they will mate. Matings with sterile males will however, produce no offspring, so the population will decline and continued release of sterile males may be expected to reduce it to levels of little economic importance. The technique is a genetic method of control, since it consists essentially of artificially inducing dominant lethal mutations in the spermatozoa of irradiated males. These are effective in fertilizing the eggs, but the resulting zygote dies at an early stage of embryonic development. The original screw-worm control programme eliminated the pest from Curaçao and has subsequently been extended to Mexico and the USA. Despite some setbacks it continues to provide practical control, though it has required the maintenance of a barrier zone in Mexico to reduce continual northward migration of flies into the area from C. America.

Because the sterile-male technique is highly specific, controlling only the pest species, with no adverse effects on beneficial insects or other wildlife, it is a highly desirable method of control, and experimental programmes for applying it to other pests have been actively pursued. However, the method does require several conditions for its success. Sterilized males need to be released in sufficiently large numbers and they must be able to compete successfully for mates with the normal males. The sterilized males must distribute themselves well throughout the area in which control is being attempted, and the pest species must not be divided into populations between which there are barriers to mating. The method may also have to contend with continuous migration of normal males into the area where sterile releases are being conducted, and it may therefore be more successful on islands or other isolated areas than over large continental regions. Finally, of course, the technology needed to conduct factory-scale rearing, sterilization and release requires considerable organization and expertise. Nevertheless, sterile-insect control programmes have been developed against the Mediterranean Fruit-fly or Medfly, *Ceratitis capitata*, in Mexico and the Nile Valley, and against the Oriental Fruit-fly *Dacus dorsalis* in Taiwan; it is also being tested for its effectiveness against tsetse fly, *Glossina* spp. Control methods involving other rather different genetic techniques for inducing hybrid sterility or to modify the capacity of insects to act as vectors of pathogenic micro-organisms are also being studied, though in a more limited or experimental way and not always with practically successful results.

Cultural practices and insect pest control. The injurious effects of insects on crop plants can often be reduced by modifying the methods of cultivation in use. The details of such methods will clearly depend on the biology of the crop, and on the life-cycles and ecological relationships of its whole complex of pest species, but among those that have been found useful in particular cases are: (a) choice of suitable dates for sowing or harvesting; (b) destruction of crop residues, volunteer plants and alternative hosts for the pest; (c) rotation of crops to avoid continuous build-up of pest populations; (d) use of mixed cropping systems which may encourage natural enemies, create barriers to infestation, or divert the pest species from crops most at risk; and (e) attention to the general principles of good agriculture, including weed-control, pruning and the encouragement of strong, healthy growth. One of the better-known examples of cultural control is the delayed sowing of winter wheat in parts of N. America to avoid oviposition by the autumn brood of the Hessian Fly, *Mayetiola destructor*. Another is the reduction of populations of the Cotton-boll Weevil *Anthonomus grandis* and the Pink Bollworm *Platyedra gossypiella* by prompt destruction of the plants after harvesting. A third example is the reduction of injury to coconuts by the Coreid bug *Pseudotheraptus wayi* when they are interplanted with citrus or cashew, which harbour an ant, *Oecophylla longinoda*, that preys on the *Pseudotheraptus*. Cultural practices may often be modified at little cost and can be accompanied by other methods of control.

The use of insect–resistant plant varieties. As indicated on pp. 197-8, many plants have evolved genetically determined resistance mechanisms against attack by insects, either in the form of physical barriers such as pubescence and unusually hard tissues, or through the production of chemical substances that deter the feeding or ovipositing insect. Crop plants which are susceptible to a pest species because they lack these defensive features can, in some cases, be replaced by other varieties which incorporate them and are therefore more resistant to attack. In principle this can provide a very advantageous method of pest control, with a very favourable cost–benefit ratio, and some empirical observations on plant resistance have long been known: the resistance of the wheat variety 'Underhill' to the Hessian Fly *Mayetiola destructor* was noted as far back as 1782! Modern techniques of plant-breeding have led to new resistant cultivars of a number of crops. Varieties of wheat resistant to *Mayetiola* or to the Wheat-stem Sawfly *Cephus cinctus*, of maize resistant to *Ostrinia nubilalis* and of alfalfa (clover) resistant to the Spotted Alfalfa Aphid *Therioaphis maculata* have been planted widely in N. America. Varieties of cotton that, because of their hairiness, are resistant to the leafhopper *Empoasca fascialis* have been developed successfully in Africa, and the introduction of resistant American rootstocks saved European vineyards from destruction by the Vine Phylloxera *Viteus vitifolii*.

In some cases the genetic and physiological bases of resistance have been established, though they may be quite complicated. Wheat varieties resistant to *Cephus* have solid stems, within which oviposition and larval development do not readily take place. Solid stems may, however, depend upon one or more dominant, recessive or complementary genes, according to the parental varieties used in the crosses. Also, whereas resistance to *Mayetiola* may be determined by a single dominant or partially dominant allele in some varieties, it may involve alleles at up to eight loci in others. Again, resistance to different pest species, or even to a single species, may depend on a number of different mechanisms, each with its own system of genetic control. A further complication may arise from the fact that a pest species may also show considerable genetic diversity, and include several strains or 'biotypes', some of which can overcome the resistance that the plant shows to others. As many as eight different biotypes have been recognized in *Mayetiola destructor*, and it appears that to each of the dominant alleles conferring resistance on the host-plant (wheat) there correspond in the insect a recessive allele which can overcome the resistance. Perhaps because of their parthenogenetic mode of reproduction, aphids appear readily to develop biotypes able to overcome plant resistance. Circumstances like these, coupled with the fact that a plant's resistance to insect attack needs to be combined with other agriculturally desirable features such as high yield and resistance to fungal pathogens, help to explain why the production of resistant cultivars may call for long and difficult research.

Integrated pest management. The history of insect pest control may be divided very broadly into three periods. Before the advent of synthetic insecticides in the 1940s most pests were controlled, with greater or lesser success, partly by their natural enemies and partly by the relatively selective and rather infrequently or inefficiently applied insecticides then available. Control was often unsatisfactory, and many pests caused considerable damage. It was succeeded by the period from about 1945 to 1965, during which modern synthetic insecticides were used intensively, especially in N. America, resulting at first in very efficient control of many major pests, but later giving rise to concern as the limitations of largely insecticidal control and the actual or potential dangers of injudicious use became apparent. The third (and present) phase is one which recognizes the advantages and the drawbacks of all methods of insect control, chemical and biological (in the widest sense of that term), and which seeks to integrate them in a single coherent strategy that ensures their best possible use. These strategies form what is now sometimes known as integrated pest management (IPM), and though most of its guiding axioms follow naturally from sound biological principles, it is worth summarizing them briefly.

The concept of integrated pest management involves the following ideas:

1. Attention should be directed towards the crop or other environmental area as a whole rather than at any one feature of it.

2. Control methods should relate to the complex of actually or potentially important insect pests rather than to individual species.

3. The objective should be to reduce injury to acceptably low levels rather than to attempt total eradication of a pest, which is usually impracticable.

4. Attention should be paid to the array of predators and parasitoids which may be exerting some degree of natural control over the pests. These natural enemies should be conserved or supplemented.

5. Environmental or cultural methods of control should be encouraged and made as efficient as possible.

6. The use of insect-resistant cultivars should be encouraged and developed.

7. Insecticides should, wherever possible, be chosen with regard to their selective action and used so as to minimize adverse effects on natural enemies of the pest and on human and other animal populations (e.g. by choosing optimal times and modes of application).

8. Control methods should be compatible with one another and should take into account whatever other biological and social constraints exist.

9. It should be remembered that conditions vary from place to place and from time to time, and that integrated pest management programmes therefore need to be implemented in a flexible manner.

Elaborate systems of pest management involving intensive agricultural practices, large-scale collaborative organization, mathematical modelling and forecasting, and advanced technological methods of disseminating information have been developed, especially in N. America. These need not or cannot be applied everywhere; the main features embodied in integrated pest management can often be implemented more simply, and merely represent the application of biological principles outlined in this chapter. Pressed to extremes, they encounter the difficulty that the ecological and other information needed may be too great to be ascertainable by any realistic programme of observation and experiment.

9

Select classified bibliography

The following is a small selection from the very extensive literature on insects; some emphasis has been placed on recent books and reviews, most of which contain further, more comprehensive bibliographic information.

1. GENERAL

Bibliographies, abstracts and reviews

Derksen, W. and Göllner-Scheiding, U. (1963–75) *Index Litteraturae Entomologicae; Ser. 2, Die Welt-Literatur über die gesamte Entomologie von 1864 bis 1900*, Akademie der Landwirtschaftswissenschaften der DDR, Berlin, 5 Vols.

Gilbert, P. and Hamilton, C.J. (1983) *Entomology. A Guide to Information Sources*, Mansell, London, 237 pp.

Horn, W. and Schenkling, S. (1928–9) *Index Litteraturae Entomologicae; Ser. 1, Die Welt-Literatur über die gesamte Entomologie bis inklusive 1863*, Horn, Berlin, 4 Vols, 1426 pp.

Rohlfien, K. (1977) Bibliographie entomologischer Bibliographien (1920–1970). *Beitr. Entomol.*, **27**, 313–79.

The most complete cumulative bibliography is the *Zoological Record, Insecta* (1864→), published in annual parts by BIOSIS, Philadelphia. The major entomological abstracting journals are *Abstracts of Entomology* (BIOSIS, Philadelphia, 1970→), *Entomology Abstracts* (Information Retrieval, New York, 1969→) and the *Review of Applied Entomology* (*Series A: Agricultural; Series B: Medical and Veterinary*) (CAB International Institute of Entomology, 1913→). On-line computerized versions of the more recent parts of *Abstracts of Entomology*, the *Review of Applied Entomology*, and the *Zoological Record* are available. The following serials, appearing annually, publish authoritative reviews of special topics: *Advances in Insect Physiology* (Academic Press, London, 1968→) and *Annual Review of Entomology* (Annual Reviews, Palo Alto, 1956→).

General works

Beier, M. (ed.) (1968→) Arthropoda: Insecta, in *Handbuch der Zoologie* (eds J.-G. Helmcke, D. Starck and H. Wermuth), De Gruyter, Berlin, 2. Auflage, Bd 4, 2. Hälfte.

Borror, D.J., Delong, D.M. and Triplehorn, C.A. (1981) *An Introduction to the Study of Insects*, Saunders, Philadelphia, 5th edn, 847 pp.

Chapman, R.F. (1982) *The Insects: Structure and Function*, Hodder and Stoughton, London, 3rd edn, 919 pp.

Daly, H.V., Doyen, J.T. and Ehrlich, P.R. (1978) *An Introduction to Insect Biology and Diversity*, McGraw-Hill, New York, 664 pp.

Eidmann, H. (1970) *Lehrbuch der Entomologie*, Parey, Hamburg, 2nd edn, 633 pp.

Essig, E.O. (1942) *College Entomology*, Macmillan, New York, 900 pp.

Evans, H.E. (1984) *Insect Biology*, Addison-Wesley, Reading, Massachusetts, 436 pp.

Frost, S.W. (1959) *Insect Life and Natural History*, Dover, New York, 526 pp.

Gillott, C. (1980) *Entomology*, Plenum Press, New York, 746 pp.

Grassé, P.P. (ed.) *Traité de Zoologie. Insectes*, Masson, Paris, Vol. 8, 797 pp. (1974); 910 pp. (1975); Vol. 9, 1117 pp. (1949); Vol. 10, 1948 pp. (1951).

Mackerras, I.M. (ed.) (1970, 1974) *The Insects of Australia,* CSIRO, Melbourne, 1029 pp., Suppl., 146 pp.

Richards, O.W. and Davies, R.G. (1977) *Imms' General Textbook of Entomology*, Chapman and Hall, London, 10th edn, 2 Vols, 1300 pp.

Romoser, W.S. (1981) *The Science of Entomology*, Macmillan, New York, 2nd edn, 575 pp.

Ross, H.H., Ross, C.A. and Ross, J.R.P. (1982) *A Textbook of Entomology*, Wiley, New York, 4th edn, 696 pp.

Singh, P. and Moore, R.F. (eds) (1985) *Handbook of Insect Rearing*, Elsevier, Amsterdam, Vol. 1, 474 pp.; Vol. 2, 500 pp.

Smith, R.F., Mittler, T.E. and Smith, C.N. (eds) (1973) *History of Entomology*, Annual Reviews, Palo Alto, 517 pp.

Torre-Bueno, J.R. de la (1962) *A Glossary of Entomology*, Brooklyn Entomological Society, New York, 336 pp.

Weber, H. (1933) *Lehrbuch der Entomologie*, Fischer, Jena, 726 pp. (Reprinted Koeltz Antiquariat, Koenigstein, 1966.)

Weber, H. (1974) *Grundriss der Insektenkunde*, Fischer, Stuttgart, 5th edn, 640 pp. (Revised by H. Weidner.)

2. INSECT STRUCTURE AND FUNCTION

General morphology, histology and ultrastructure

Blackman, R.L., Hewitt, G. and Ashburner, M. (1981) Insect cytogenetics. *Symp. R. Entomol. Soc. Lond.,* **10**, 1–278.

Hamilton, K.G.A. (1971–2) The insect wing. I–IV. *J. Kansas Entomol. Soc.,* **44**, 421–33; **45**: 54–8, 145–62, 295–308.

King, R.C. and Akai, H. (eds) (1982, 1984) *Insect Ultrastructure*, Plenum Press, New York, Vol. 1, 508 pp.; Vol. 2, 650 pp.

Matsuda, R. (1965) Morphology and evolution of the insect head. *Mem. Am. Entomol. Inst.,* **4**, 1–334.

Matsuda, R. (1970) Morphology and evolution of the insect thorax. *Mem. Entomol. Soc. Canada,* **76**, 1–431.

Matsuda, R. (1975) *Morphology and Evolution of the Insect Abdomen*, Pergamon Press, Oxford, 568 pp.

Smith, D.S. (1968) *Insect Cells: Their Structure and Function*, Oliver and Boyd, Edinburgh, 372 pp.

Snodgrass, R.E. (1935) *Principles of Insect Morphology*, McGraw-Hill, New York, 667 pp.

Weidner, H. (1982) Morphologie, Anatomie und Histologie, in *Handbuch der Zoologie* (eds J.-G. Helmcke, D. Starck and H. Wermuth), **4**(2), Lfg. 27, 1–531.

White, M.J.D. (1973) *Animal Cytology and Evolution*, Cambridge University Press, Cambridge, 3rd edn, 961 pp.

General physiology and biochemistry

Birch, M.C. and Haynes, K.F. (1982) *Insect Pheromones*, Edward Arnold, London, 60 pp.

Blum, M.S. (1981) *Chemical Defenses of Arthropods*, Academic Press, London, 562 pp.

Blum, M.S. (ed.) (1985) *Fundamentals of Insect Physiology*, Wiley, Chichester, 598 pp.

Bradley, T.J. and Miller, T.A. (eds) (1984) *Measurement of Ion Transport and Metabolic Rate in Insects*. Springer, New York, 236 pp.

Hummel, H.E. and Miller, T.A. (eds) (1984) *Techniques in Pheromone Research*, Springer, New York, 464 pp.

Kerkut, G.A. and Gilbert, L.J. (eds) (1984) *Comprehensive Insect Physiology and Pharmacology*, Pergamon Press, Oxford, 13 Vols.

Locke, M. and Smith, D.S. (eds) (1980) *Insect Biology in the Future*, Academic Press, New York, 977 pp.

Mordue, W., Goldsworthy, G.J., Brady, J. and Blaney, W.M. (1981) *Insect Physiology*, Blackwell, Oxford, 116 pp.

Rockstein, M. (ed.) (1973–4) *The Physiology of Insecta*, Academic Press, New York, 6 Vols.

Rockstein, M. (ed.) (1978) *Biochemistry of Insects*, Academic Press, New York, 656 pp.

Wigglesworth, V.B. (1972) *Principles of Insect Physiology*, Chapman and Hall, London, 7th edn, 827 pp.

Skeletomuscular system

Andersen, S.O. (1980) Biochemistry of insect cuticle. *A. Rev. Entomol.* **24**, 29–61.

Hepburn, H.R. (ed.) (1976) *The Insect Integument*, Elsevier, Amsterdam, 571 pp.

Lipke, H., Sugumaran, M. and Henzel, W. (1983) Mechanisms of sclerotization in Dipterans. *Adv. Insect Physiol.*, **17**, 1–84.

Neville, A.C. (1975) *Biology of the Arthropod Cuticle*, Springer, Berlin, 448 pp.

Richards, A.G. (1951) *The Integument of Arthropods*, University of Minnesota Press, Minneapolis, 411 pp.

Tregear, A.T. (ed.) (1977) *Insect Flight Muscle*, Elsevier, Amsterdam, 367 pp.

Usherwood, P.N.R. (ed.) (1975) *Insect Muscle*, Academic Press, London, 621 pp.

Locomotion

Delcomyn, F. (1985) Factors regulating insect walking, *A. Rev. Entomol.*, **30**, 239–56.

Gewecke, M. and Wendler, G. (eds) (1985) *Insect Locomotion*, Parey, New York, 260 pp.

Graham, D. (1985) Pattern and control of walking in insects. *Adv. Insect Physiol.*, **18**, 31–140.

Herreld, C.F. and Fourtner, C.R. (eds) (1981) *Locomotion and Energetics in Arthropods*, Plenum Press, New York, 554 pp.

Johnson, C.G. (1969) *Migration and Dispersal of Insects by Flight*, Chapman and Hall, London, 763 pp.

Kammer, A.E. and Heinrich, B. (1978) Insect flight metabolism. *Adv. Insect Physiol.*, **13**, 133–228.

Nachtigall, W. (1974) *Insects in Flight*, Allen and Unwin, London, 153 pp.

Pringle, J.W.S. (1957) *Insect Flight*, Cambridge University Press, Cambridge, 133 pp.

Rainey, R.C. (ed.) (1975) Insect flight. *Symp. R. Entomol. Soc. Lond.* **7**, 1–287.

Nervous system and neurobiology

Borkovec, A.B. and Kelly, T.J. (eds) (1984) *Insect Neurochemistry and Neurophysiology*, Plenum Press, New York, 523 pp.

Breer, H. and Miller, T.A. (eds) (1985) *Neurochemical Techniques in Insect Research*, Springer, Berlin, 324 pp.

Huber, F. and Markl, H. (eds) (1983) *Neuroethology and Behavioural Physiology*, Springer, Berlin, 412 pp.

Miller, T.A. (1979) *Insect Neurophysiological Techniques*, Springer, New York, 308 pp.

Miller, T.A. (ed.) (1980) *Neurohormonal Techniques in Insects*, Springer, New York, 282 pp.

Strausfeld, N.J. (1976) *Atlas of an Insect Brain*, Springer, Berlin, 230 pp.

Strausfeld, N. (ed.) (1983) *Functional Neuroanatomy*, Springer, Berlin, 426 pp.

Treherne, J.E. (ed.) (1974) *Insect Neurobiology*, North-Holland, Amsterdam, 450 pp.

Young, D.A. (1973) *Developmental Neurobiology of Arthropods*, Cambridge University Press, Cambridge, 263 pp.

Sense organs and sensory physiology

Altner, H. and Loftus, R. (1985) Ultrastructure and function of insect thermo- and hygroreceptors. *A. Rev. Entomol.*, **30**, 273–95.

Carlson, S.D. and Chi, C. (1979) The functional morphology of the insect photoreceptor. *A. Rev. Entomol.*, **24**, 379–416.

Chapman, R.F. (1982) Chemoreception: the significance of receptor numbers. *Adv. Insect Physiol.*, **16**, 247–346.

Dethier, V.G. (1963) *The Physiology of Insect Senses*, Methuen, London, 266 pp.

Goodman, L.J. (1970) The structure and function of the dorsal ocellus of insects. *Adv. Insect Physiol.*, **7**, 97–195.

Horridge, G.A. (ed.) (1974) *The Compound Eye and Vision of Insects*, Clarendon Press, Oxford, 595 pp.

Kalmring, K. and Eisner, N. (eds) (1985) *Acoustic and Vibrational Communication in Insects*, Parey, New York, 230 pp.

Lewis, T. (ed.) (1984) *Insect Communication*, Academic Press, London, 414 pp.

Payne, T.L., Birch, M.C. and Kennedy, C.E.J. (1986) *Mechanisms in Insect Olfaction*, Clarendon Press, Oxford, 384 pp.

Wehner, R. (ed.) (1972) *Information Processing in the Visual System of Arthropods*, Springer, Berlin, 334 pp.

Zacharuk, R.Y. (1980) Ultrastructure and functions of insect chemosensilla. *A. Rev. Entomol.*, **25**, 27–48.

Insect behaviour

Baker, R.R. (1983) Insect territoriality. *A. Rev. Entomol.*, **28**, 65–89.

Barton-Browne, L. (1974) *Experimental Analysis of Insect Behaviour*, Springer, Berlin, 366 pp.

Bell, W.J. (ed.) (1985) Insect search behaviour. *J. Insect Physiol.*, **31**(11), 837–97.

Claridge, M.F. (1985) Acoustic signals in the Homoptera, behaviour, taxonomy and evolution. *A. Rev. Entomol.*, **30**, 297–317.

Fraenkel, G.S. and Gunn, D.L. (1961) *The Orientation of Animals. Kineses, Taxes and Compass Reactions*, Dover, New York, 2nd edn, 376 pp.

Howse, P.E. and Miller, P.L. (1984) *Mechanisms of Insect Behaviour*, Blackwell, Oxford, 272 pp.

Lloyd, J.E. (1983) Bioluminescence and communication in insects. *A. Rev. Entomol.*, **28**, 131–60.

Matthews, R.W. and Matthews, J.R. (1978) *Insect Behaviour*, Wiley–Interscience, New York, 507 pp.

Prestwich, G.D. and Blomquist, G.J. (eds) (1987) *Pheromone Biochemistry*, Academic Press, New York, 546 pp.

Shorey, H.H. and McKelvey, J.J. (1977) *Chemical Control of Insect Behaviour*, Wiley–Interscience, New York, 414 pp.

Tinbergen, N. (1951) *The Study of Instinct*, Clarendon Press, Oxford, 228 pp.

Wehner, R. (1984) Astronavigation in insects. *A. Rev. Entomol.*, **29**, 277–98.

Wood, D.L. (1982) The role of pheromones, kairomones and allomones in the host selection and colonization behaviour of bark beetles. *A. Rev. Entomol.*, **27**, 411–46.

Alimentary canal, digestion and nutrition

Brues, C.T. (1946) *Insect Dietary*, Harvard University Press, Cambridge, Massachusetts, 466 pp.

Dadd, R.H. (1973) Insect nutrition: current developments and metabolic implications. *A. Rev. Entomol.*, **18**, 381–420.

Dow, J.A.T. (1986) Insect midgut function. *Adv. Insect Physiol.*, **19**, 187–328.

Phillips, J.E., Manrahan, J., Chamberlin, M. and Thomson, B. (1986) Mechanisms and control of reabsorption in insect hindgut. *Adv. Insect Physiol.* **19**, 329–422.

Richards, A.G. and Richards, P.A. (1977) The peritrophic membranes of insects. *A. Rev. Entomol.*, **22**, 219–40.

Rodriguez, J.G. (ed.) (1973) *Insect and Mite Nutrition*, North-Holland, Amsterdam, 717 pp.

Singh, P. (1977) *Artificial Diets for Insects, Mites and Spiders*, Plenum Press, New York, 606 pp.

Slansky, F. and Rodriguez, J.G. (eds) (1987) *Nutritional Ecology of Insects, Mites, Spiders and Related Invertebrates*, Wiley, New York, 1032 pp.

Vanderzant, E.S. (1974) Development, significance and application of artificial diets for insects. *A. Rev. Entomol.*, **19**, 139–60.

Respiratory system and respiration

Hinton, H.E. (1947) On the reduction of functional spiracles in the aquatic larvae of the Holometabola, with notes on the moulting process of spiracles. *Trans. R. Entomol. Soc. Lond.*, **98**, 449–73.

Hinton, H.E. (1969) Respiratory systems of insect egg shells. *A. Rev. Entomol.*, **14**, 343–68.

Keilin, D. (1944) Respiratory systems and respiratory adaptations in larvae and pupae of Diptera. *Parasitology*, **36**, 1–66.

Miller, P.L. (1966) The regulation of breathing in insects. *Adv. Insect Physiol.*, **3**, 279–354.

Thorpe, W.H. (1950) Plastron respiration in aquatic insects. *Biol. Rev.*, **25**, 344–90.

Whitten M.J. (1972) Comparative anatomy of the tracheal system. *A. Rev. Entomol.*, **17**, 373–402.

Wigglesworth, V.B. (1983) The physiology of insect tracheoles. *Adv. Insect Physiol.*, **17**, 85–148.

Circulatory system and haemolymph

Crossley, A.C. (1975) The cytophysiology of insect blood. *Adv. Insect Physiol.*, **11**, 117–221.

Gupta, A.P. (ed.) (1979) *Insect Haemocytes: Development, Forms, Functions and Techniques*, Cambridge University Press, Cambridge, 614 pp.

Gupta, A.P. (ed.) (1987) *Haemocytic and Humeral Immunity in Arthropods*, Wiley, New York, 550 pp.

Jones, J.C. (1977) *The Circulatory System of Insects*, Thomas, Springfield, Illinois, 255 pp.

McCann, F.V. (1970) Physiology of insect hearts. *A. Rev. Entomol.*, **15**, 173–200.

Richards, A.G. (1963) The ventral diaphragm of insects. *J. Morphol.*, **113**, 17–34.

Salt, G. (1970) *The Cellular Defence Reactions of Insects*, Cambridge University Press, Cambridge, 117 pp.

Excretory system, excretion and osmoregulation

Bradley, T.J. (1987) Physiology of osmoregulation in mosquitoes. *A. Rev. Entomol.*, **32**, 439–62.

Craig, R. (1960) The physiology of excretion in the insect. *A. Rev. Entomol.*, **5**, 53–68.

Gupta, B.L., Moreton, R.B., Oschman, J.L. and Wall, B.J. (eds) (1977) *Transport of Ions and Water in Animals*, Academic Press, London, 817 pp.

Madrell, S.H.P. (1971) The mechanism of insect excretory systems. *Adv. Insect Physiol.*, **8**, 200–331.

Shaw, J. and Stobbart, R.H. (1963) Osmotic and ionic regulation in insects. *Adv. Insect Physiol.*, **1**, 315–99.

Endocrine and other glands

Beckage, N.E. (1985) Endocrine interactions between endoparasitic insects and their hosts. *A. Rev. Entomol.*, **30**, 371–413.

Bhaskaran, G., Friedman, S. and Rodriguez, J.G. (eds) (1983) *Current Topics in Insect Endocrinology and Nutrition*, Plenum Press, New York, 362 pp.

Chippendale, A.M. (1977) Hormonal regulation of insect diapause. *A. Rev. Entomol.*, **22**, 121–38.

Downer, R.G.H. and Laufer, H. (eds) (1983) *Endocrinology of Insects*, Liss, New York, 707 pp.

Forsyth, D.J. (1972) The structure of the pygidial defence glands of Carabidae (Coleoptera). *Trans. Zool. Soc. Lond.*, **32**, 249–309.

Gilbert, L.I. (ed.) (1976) *The Juvenile Hormones*, Plenum Press, New York, 572 pp.

Gupta, A.P. (ed.) (1983) *Neurohaemal Organs of Arthropoda. Their Development, Evolution, Structures and Functions*, Thomas, Springfield, Illinois, 629 pp.

Keeley, L.L. (1978) Endocrine regulation of fat-body development and function. *A. Rev. Entomol.*, **23**, 329–52.

Miles, P.W. (1972) The saliva of Hemiptera. *Adv. Insect Physiol.*, **9**, 153–255.

Miller, T.A. (ed.) (1980) *Neurohormonal Techniques in Insects*, Springer, New York, 340 pp.

Mordue, W. (ed.) (1984) *Photoperiodic Regulation of Insect and Molluscan Hormones*, Pitman, London, 304 pp.

Morgan, E.D. and Poole, C.F. (1976) The extraction and determination of ecdysones in arthropods. *Adv. Insect Physiol.*, **12**, 17–62.

Novak, J.A. (1975) *Insect Hormones*, Chapman and Hall, London, 2nd edn, 624 pp.

Pratt, G.E. and Brooks, G.T. (eds) (1981) *Juvenile Hormone Biochemistry – Action, Agonism and Antagonism*, Elsever/North-Holland, Amsterdam, 455 pp.

Raabe, M. (1982) *Insect Neurohormones*, Plenum Press, New York, 368 pp.

Raabe, M. (1983) The neurosecretory–neurohaemal system of insects; anatomical, structural and physiological data. *Adv. Insect Physiol.*, **17**, 205–304.

Riddiford, L.M. and Willis, J.H. (eds) (1981) Insect systems: milestones and new horizons in endocrinology, physiology and development. *Am. Zool.*, **21**, 623–791.

Staal, G.B. (1986) Antijuvenile hormone agents. *A. Rev. Entomol.*, **31**, 391–429.

Staddon, B.W. (1979) The scent glands of Heteroptera. *Adv. Insect Physiol.*, **14**, 351–418.

Wigglesworth, V.B. (1970) *Insect Hormones*, Oliver and Boyd, Edinburgh, 159 pp.

Environmental physiology

Beck, S.D. (1980) *Insect Photoperiodism*, Academic Press, New York, 2nd edn, 387 pp.

Beck, S.D. (1983) Insect thermoperiodism. *A. Rev. Entomol.*, **28**, 91–108.

Brady, J. (1974) The physiology of insect circadian rhythms. *Adv. Insect Physiol.*, **10**, 1–115.

Danilevskii, A.S. (1965) *Photoperiodism and Seasonal Development of Insects*, Oliver and Boyd, Edinburgh, 282 pp.

Edney, E.B. (1977) *Water Balance in Land Arthropods*, Springer, Berlin, 282 pp.

Heinrich, B. (ed.) (1981) *Insect Thermoregulation*, Wiley, New York, 328 pp.

Hoffman, K.H. (ed.) (1984) *Environmental Physiology and Biochemistry of Insects*, Springer, Heidelberg, 396 pp.

Lees, A.D. (1955) *The Physiology of Diapause in Arthropods*, Cambridge University Press, Cambridge, 150 pp.

Machin, J. (1979) Atmospheric water absorption in arthropods. *Adv. Insect Physiol.*, **14**, 1–48.

May, M.L. (1979) Insect thermoregulation. *A. Rev. Entomol.*, **24**, 313–50.

Saunders, D.S. (1982) *Insect Clocks*, Pergamon Press, Oxford, 2nd edn, 420 pp.

Tauber, M.J., Tauber, C.A. and Masaki, S. (1986) *Seasonal Adaptations of Insects*, Oxford University Press, New York, 432 pp.

Wharton, G.W. and Richards, A.G. (1978) Water vapour exchange kinetics in insects and acarines. *A. Rev. Entomol.*, **23**, 309–28.

Reproductive system and reproduction

Berry, S.J. (1982) Maternal direction of oogenesis and early embryogenesis in insects. *A. Rev. Entomol.*, **27**, 205–27.

Blum, M.S. and Blum, N.A. (eds) (1979) *Sexual Selection and Reproductive Competition in Insects*, Academic Press, London, 463 pp.

Bownes, M. (1986) Expression of the genes coding for vitellogenin. *A. Rev. Entomol.*, **31**, 507–31.

Chen, P.S. (1984) The functional morphology and biochemistry of insect male accessory glands and their secretions. *A. Rev. Entomol.*, **29**, 233–55.

Dumser, J.B. (1981) The regulation of spermatogenesis in insects. *A. Rev. Entomol.*, **25**, 341–69.

Engelmann, F. (1970) *The Physiology of Insect Reproduction*, Pergamon Press, Oxford, 307 pp.

Engelmann, F. (1979) Insect vitellogenin: identification, biosynthesis and role in vitellogenesis. *Adv. Insect Physiol.*, **14**, 49–108.

Hagedorn, H.H. and Kunkel, J.G. (1979) Vitellogenin and vitellin in insects. *A. Rev. Entomol.*, **24**, 475–506.

Hinton, H.E. (1981) *Biology of Insect Eggs*, Pergamon Press, Oxford, 3 Vols.

Jacobson, M. (1972) *Insect Sex Pheromones*, Academic Press, New York, 382 pp.

Raabe, M. (1986) Insect reproduction: regulation of successive steps. *Adv. Insect Physiol.*, **19**, 29–154.

Schaller, F. (1971) Indirect sperm transfer by soil arthropods. *A. Rev. Entomol.*, **16**, 407–46.

Scudder, G.G.E. (1971) Comparative morphology of insect genitalia. *A. Rev. Entomol.*, **16**, 379–406.

Smith, E.L. (1969) Evolutionary morphology of external insect genitalia. I. *Ann. Entomol. Soc. Am.*, **62**, 1051–79.

Snodgrass, R.E. (1957) A revised interpretation of the external reproductive organs of male insects. *Smithsonian Misc. Collns*, **135**(6), 1–60.

Telfer, W.H. (1982) Development and physiology of the oocyte-nurse cell syncitium. *Adv. Insect Physiol.*, **11**, 223–320.

Thornhill, R. and Alcock, J. (1983) *The Evolution of Insect Mating Systems*, Harvard University Press, Cambridge, Massachusetts, 537 pp.

Tuxen, S. (ed.) (1970) *Taxonomist's Glossary of Genitalia in Insects*, Munksgaard, Copenhagen, 2nd edn, 359 pp.

3. DEVELOPMENT AND METAMORPHOSIS

Anderson, D.T. (1973) *Embryology and Phylogeny in Annelids and Arthropods*. Pergamon Press, London, 495 pp.

Ashburner, M.C. (1970) Function and structure of polytene chromosomes during insect development. *Adv. Insect Physiol.*, **7**, 2–96.

Beck, S.D. (1980) *Insect Photoperiodism*, Academic Press, New York, 2nd edn, 387 pp.

Beck, S.D. (1983) Insect thermoperiodism. *A. Rev. Entomol.*, **28**, 91–108.

Brown, V.K. and Hodek, I. (eds) (1983) *Diapause and Life Cycle Strategies in Insects*, Junk, The Hague, 283 pp.

Chen, P.S. (1971) *Biochemical Aspects of Insect Development*, Karger, New York, 230 pp.

Counce, S.J. and Waddington, C.H. (eds) (1972) *Developmental Systems: Insects*, Academic Press, London, 2 Vols.

Danilevskii, A.S. (1965) *Photoperiodism and Seasonal Development in Insects*, Oliver and Boyd, Edinburgh, 283 pp.

Edwards, J.S. (1969) Postembryonic development and regeneration of the insect nervous system. *Adv. Insect Physiol.*, **6**, 98–139.

Hagen, H.R. (1951) *Embryology of the Viviparous Insects*, Ronald Press, New York, 472 pp.

Hinton, H.E. (1963) The origin and function of the pupal stage. *Proc. R. Entomol. Soc. Lond.*, **38A**, 77–85.

Hinton, H.E. (1973) Some neglected phases in metamorphosis. *Proc. R. Entomol. Soc. Lond.*, **35C**, 55–64.

Hinton, H.E. (1980) *The Biology of Insect Eggs*, Pergamon Press, Oxford, 3 Vols, 1125 pp.

Johannsen, O.A. and Butt, F.H. (1941) *Embryology of Insects and Myriapods*, McGraw-Hill, New York, 462 pp.

Jungreis, A.M. (1979) Physiology of moulting in insects. *Adv. Insect Physiol.*, **14**, 109–83.

Larsen-Rapport, E.W. (1986) Imaginal disc determination: molecular and cellular correlates. *A. Rev. Entomol.*, **31**, 145–75.

Lawrence, P.A. (ed.) (1976) Insect development. *Symp. R. Entomol. Soc. Lond.*, **8**, 240 pp.

Lees, A.D. (1955) *The Physiology of Diapause in Arthropods*, Cambridge University Press, Cambridge, 150 pp.

Peterson, A. (1960) *Larvae of Insects. An Introduction to Nearctic Species*, The Author, Columbus, Ohio, 4th edn, 416 pp.

Ransom, R. (ed.) (1982) *Handbook of* Drosophila *Development*, Elsevier, Amsterdam, 289 pp.

Reynolds, S.E. (1980) Integration of behaviour and physiology in ecdysis. *Adv. Insect Physiol.*, **15**, 475–595.

Sander, K. (1976) Specification of the basic body pattern in insect embryogenesis. *Adv. Insect Physiol.*, **12**, 125–238.

Sehnal, F. (1985) Morphology of insect development. *A. Rev. Entomol.*, **30**, 89–109.

Snodgrass, R.E. (1954) Insect metamorphosis. *Smithsonian Misc. Collns*, **122**(9), 1–124.

Thomson, J.A. (1975) Major patterns of gene activity during development in holometabolous insects. *Adv. Insect Physiol.*, **11**, 321–98.

Ursprung, H. and Nöthiger, R. (eds) (1972) *The Biology of Imaginal Disks*, Springer, Berlin, 172 pp.

Wigglesworth, V.B. (1959) *The Control of Growth and Form*, Cornell University Press, Ithaca, New York, 140 pp.

4. CLASSIFICATION AND BIOLOGY

Taxonomic principles

Anon (1984) *International Code of Zoological Nomenclature*, British Museum (Natural History), London, 3rd edn, 320 pp.

Berlocher, S.H. (1984) Insect molecular systematics. *A. Rev. Entomol.*, **29**, 403–33.

Blackwelder, R.E. (1967) *Taxonomy: A Text and Reference Book*, Wiley, New York, 698 pp.

Daly, H.V. (1985) Insect morphometrics. *A. Rev. Entomol.*, **30**, 415–38.

Diehl, S.R. and Bush, G.L. (1984) An evolutionary and applied perspective of biotypes. *A. Rev. Entomol.*, **29**, 471–504.

Farber, P. (1978) A historical perspective on the impact of the type concept on insect systematics. *A. Rev. Entomol.*, **23**, 91–9.

Hennig, W. (1979) *Phylogenetic Systematics*, University of Illinois Press, Urbana, 263 pp.

Mayr, E. (1969) *Principles of Systematic Zoology*, McGraw-Hill, New York, 428 pp.

Sneath, P.H. and Sokal, R.R. (1973) *Numerical Taxonomy*, Freeman, San Francisco, 573 pp.

Systematics and identification

Detailed bibliographies on a world basis are provided by Brues *et al.* (1956) and Hollis (1980). Bibliographies for the European fauna include those of Gaedicke (1981), Göllner-Scheiding (1967–71) and Sims *et al.* (1988). The major regional faunas, issued in parts, usually dealing with separate families in the case of the large insect orders, are as follows: *Danmarks Fauna* (1907→), *Fauna d'Italia* (1965→), *Fauna Entomologica Scandinavica* (1973→), *Fauna Japonica* (1960→), *Fauna of British India, Fauna of New Zealand* (1982→), *Fauna of Saudi Arabia, Fauna SSSR* (1935→), *Faune de France* (1922–64), *Insects of Hawaii* (1948→), *Insects of Micronesia* (1954→), *Royal Entomological Society Handbooks for the Identification of British Insects* (1954→), *Tierwelt Mitteleuropas* (1926→), and *Tierwelt Deutschlands* (1925→). A selection of more general systematic works is listed below and others are arranged under the different orders of insects on pp. 354–69.

Bland, R.G. and Jaques, H.E. (1978) *How to Know the Insects*, Brown, Dubuque, Iowa, 409 pp.

Borror, D.J. and White, R.E. (1970) *A Field Guide to the Insects of North America north of Mexico*, Houghton Mifflin, Boston, 404 pp.

Brues, C.T., Melander, A.L. and Carpenter, F.M. (1956) *Classification of Insects*, Harvard University Press, Cambridge, Massachusetts, 2nd edn, 917 pp.

Chinery, M. (1973) *A Field Guide to the Insects of Britain and Northern Europe*, Collins, London, 352 pp.

Chinery, M. (1986) *Collins' Guide to the Insects of Britain and Western Europe*, Collins, London, 320 pp.

Chu, H.F., (1949) *How to Know the Immature Insects*, Brown, Dubuque, Iowa, 243 pp.

Costa Lima, A. de (ed.) (1938–62) *Insetos do Brasil*. Escuola Nacional de Agronomia, Rio de Janeiro, 12 Vols.

Danks, H.V. (ed.) (1979) Canada and its insect fauna. *Mem. Entomol. Soc. Canada*, **108**, 1–573.

Essig, E.O. (1958) *Insects and Mites of Western North America*, Macmillan, New York, 1056 pp.

Gaedicke, R. (1981) Bibliographie der Bestimmungstabellen europäischer Insekten (1974–78). *Beitr. Entomol.*, **31**, 235–304.

Göllner-Scheiding, U. (1967–71) Bibliographie der Bestimmungstabellen europäischer Insekten (1880–1963). *Beitr. Entomol.*, **17**, 697–958; *Mitteilungen* *zool. Museum Berlin,* **45**, 1–156; *Dt. entomol. Zeitschr.,* **17**, 33–118, 433–76; **18**, 1–84, 287–360.

Hollis, D. (ed.) (1980) *Animal Identification. A Reference Guide,* Vol. 3, *Insecta,* British Museum (Natural History), London, 160 pp.

Holm, E. and Scholtz, C.H. (eds) (1985) *Insects of Southern Africa,* Butterworth, London, 564 pp.

Mackerras, I.M. (ed.) (1970, 1974) *The Insects of Australia,* CSIRO, Melbourne, 1029 pp.; Suppl., 146 pp.

Sims, R.W., Freeman, P. and Hawksworth, D.L. (1988) *Key Works to the Fauna and Flora of the British Isles and Northwestern Europe,* 5th edition. Oxford University Press, Oxford, 328pp.

Skaife, S.H. (1979) *African Insect Life,* Country Life, London, 279 pp. (Revised edn by J. Ledger.)

Swann, L.A. and Papp, C.S. (1972) *The Common Insects of North America,* Harper and Row, New York, 750 pp.

1. Diplura

Condé, B. (1956) Matériaux pour une monographie des Diploures Campodéides. *Mém. Muséum Nat. d'Hist. Nat.,* **12** (1955), 1–201.

Gyger, H. (1960) Untersuchungen zur postembryonalen Entwicklung von *Dipljapyx humberti* (Grassi). *Verh. naturforsch. Gesellschaft Basel,* **71**, 29–95.

Marten, W. (1939) Zur Kenntnis von *Campodea. Zeitschr. Morphol. Ökol. Tiere,* **36**, 40–88.

Paclt, J. (1957) Diplura. *Genera Insectorum,* Fasc. **212**, 1–123.

Smith, L.M. (1961) Japygidae of North America. 8. *Ann. Entomol. Soc. Am.,* **54**, 437–41.

Tuxen, S.L. (1959) The phylogenetic significance of ontogeny in entognathous apterygotes. *Smithsonian Misc. Collns,* **157**, 379–416.

2. Protura

Janetschek, H. (1970) Ordnung Protura (Beintastler), in *Handbuch der Zoologie,* Bd 4, 2. Halfte, Lfg. 14, Beitr. 3, pp. 1–58.

Nosek, J. (1973) *The European Protura, their Taxonomy, Ecology and Distribution with Keys for Determination,* Muséum d'Histoire Naturelle, Geneva, 345 pp.

Nosek, J. (1978) Key and diagnoses of Proturan genera of the world. *Annotat. Zool. Bot.,* **122**, 1–59.

Raw, F. (1956) The abundance and distribution of Protura in grassland. *J. Animal Ecol.,* **25**, 15–21.

Tuxen, S.L. (1949) Über den Lebenszyklus und die postembryonale Entwicklung zweier dänischer Proturengattungen. *Kongelige Danske Videnskab. Selsk. Skr.,* **6**, 49 pp.

Tuxen, S.L. (1964) *The Protura,* Hermann, Paris, 360 pp.

Yin, W. (1968) Studies on Chinese Protura. *Acta Entomol. Sinica,* **2**, 26–34.

3. Collembola

Agrell, I. (1949) Studies on the postembryonic development of Collemboles. *Arkiv Zool.,* **41A**(12), 1–35.

Butcher, J.W., Snider, R. and Snider, R.J. (1971) Bioecology of edaphic Collembola and Acarina. *A. Rev. Entomol.*, **16**, 249–89.

Christiansen, K.A. (1964) Bionomics of Collembola. *A. Rev. Entomol.*, **9**, 147–78.

Gisin, H. (1960) *Collembolenfauna Europas*, Natural History Museum, Geneva, 312 pp.

Paclt, J. (1956) *Biologie der primär flügellosen Insekten*, Fischer, Jena, 258 pp.

Richards, W.R. (1968) Generic classification, evolution and biogeography of the Sminthuridae of the World (Collembola). *Mem. Entomol. Soc. Canada*, **53**, 1–54.

Salmon, J.T. (1964) An index to the Collembola. *Bull. R. Soc. N.Z.*, **7**, 644 pp.

Scott, H.G. (1961) Collembola. Pictorial keys to the Nearctic genera. *Ann. Entomol. Soc. Am.*, **54**, 104–13.

Stach, J. (1947–63) The Apterygotan fauna of Poland in relation to the world-fauna of this group of insects. *Acta monogr. Inst. zool., Krakow*, **1947**, 488 pp.; **1949**, 341 pp.; **1949**, 122 pp.; **1951**, 100 pp.; **1954**, 219 pp.; **1956**, 287 pp.; **1957**, 113 pp.; **1960**, 151 pp.; **1963**, 126 pp.

4,5. Archaeognatha and Zygentoma

Birket-Smith, S.J.P. (1974) On the abdominal morphology of the Thysanura (Archaeognatha and Thysanura *s. str.*). *Entomol. Scand., Suppl.*, **6**, 1–67.

Delany, M.J. (1954) Thysanura and Diplura. *R. Entomol. Soc. Lond. Handbooks for the Identification of British Insects*, **1**(2), 7 pp.

Janetschek, H. (1954) Ueber Felsenspringer der Mittelmeerländer. *Eos*, **30**, 163–314.

Lindsay, E. (1940) The biology of the silverfish *Ctenolepisma longicaudata* Esch., with particular reference to its feeding habits. *Proc. R. Soc. Victoria (N.S.)*, **52**, 35–83.

Palissa, A. (1964) Apterygota – Urinsekten. *Tierwelt Mitteleuropas*, **4**(1), 407 pp.

Remington, C.L. (1954) The suprageneric classification of the order Thysanura (Insecta). *Ann. Entomol. Soc. Am.*, **47**, 277–86.

Sahrhage, D. (1953) Oekologische Untersuchungen an *Thermobia domestica* (Packard) und *Lepisma saccharina* L. *Zeitschr. wissenschaftliche Zool.*, **157**, 77–168.

Wygodzinsky, P. (1972) A review of the silverfish (Lepismatidae, Thysanura) of the United States and Caribbean area. *Am. Museum Novitates*, **2481**, 1–86.

6. Ephemeroptera

Berner, L. (1959) Tabular summary of the biology of North American mayfly nymphs. *Bull. Florida St. Museum*, **4**, 1–58.

Brittain, J.E. (1982) Biology of mayflies. *A. Rev. Entomol.*, **27**, 119–47.

Demoulin, G. (1958) Nouveau schéma de classification des Archodonates et des Ephéméroptères. *Bull. Inst. R. Sci. Nat. Belg.*, **34**(27), 1–10.

Edmunds, G.F. (1972) Biogeography and evolution of Ephemeroptera. *A. Rev. Entomol.*, **17**, 21–42.

Edmunds, G.F., Jensen, S.L. and Berner, L. (1976) *The Mayflies of North and Central America*, University of Minnesota Press, Minneapolis, 330 pp.

Flannagan, J.F. and Marshall, K.E. (eds) (1980) *Advances in Ephemeropteran Biology*, Plenum Press, New York, 566 pp.

Ide, F.P. (1935) Post-embryological development of Ephemeroptera (mayflies), external charactera only. *Can. J. Res.*, **12**, 433–78.

Illies, J. (1968) Ephemeroptera (Eintagsfliegen), in *Handbuch der Zoologie* (eds J.-G. Helmcke, D. Starck and H. Wermuth), **4**(2), 63 pp.

Kimmins, D.E. (1972) A revised key to the adults of the British species of Ephemeroptera with notes on their ecology. *Scient. Publns Freshwat. Biol. Assoc.*, **15**, 2nd edn, 75 pp.

Koss, R.W. and Edmunds, G.F. (1974) Ephemeropteran eggs and their contribution to phylogenetic studies of the order. *Zool. J. Linn. Soc.*, **55**, 267–349.

Macan, T.T. (1979) A key to the nymphs of the British species of Ephemeroptera with notes on their ecology. *Scient. Publns Freshwat. Biol. Assoc.*, **20**, 3rd edn, pp. 1–79.

Needham, J.G., Traver, J.R. and Hsu, Y. (1935) *The Biology of Mayflies*, Comstock, Ithaca, New York, 759 pp.

Peters, W.L. and Peters, J.G. (1973) *Proceedings of the 1st International Conference on Ephemeroptera*, Brill, Leiden, 312 pp.

Tshernova, O.A. (1970) On the classification of fossil and Recent Ephemeroptera. *Entomol. Obozrenie*, **49**, 124–45 (In Russian). (English transl. in *Entomol. Rev. Washington*, **49**, 71–81.)

7. Odonata

Allen, D., Davies, L. and Tobin, P. (1985) *The Dragonflies of the World: a Systematic List of the Extant Species of Odonata*, Societas Internationales Odonatologica, Utrecht, 2 Vols.

Corbet, P.S. (1962) *A Biology of Dragonflies*, Witherby, London, 247 pp.

Corbet, P.S. (1980) Biology of Odonata. *A. Rev. Entomol.*, **25**, 189–218.

D'Aguilar, J., Dommanger, J.L. and Préchac, R. (1986) *A Field Guide to the Dragonflies of Britain, Europe and North Africa*, Collins, London, 336 pp.

Fraser, F.C. (1957) *A Reclassification of the Order Odonata*, Royal Zoological Society of New South Wales, Sydney, 133 pp.

Gambles, R.M. (ed.) (1981) *Advances in Odonatology*, Netherlands Entomological Society, Amsterdam, Vol. 1, 308 pp.

Gardner, A.E. (1954) A key to the larvae of the British Odonata. *Entomol. Gazette*, **5**, 157–71, 193–213.

Hammond, C.O. (1983) *The Dragonflies of Great Britain and Ireland*, Harley Books, Colchester, 2nd edn (revised R. Merritt), 116 pp.

Kormondy, E.J. (1961) Territoriality and dispersal in dragonflies (Odonata). *J. N.Y. Entomol. Soc.*, **69**, 42–53.

Needham, J.G. and Westfall, M.J. (1954) *A Manual of Dragonflies of North America* (Anisoptera), University of California Press, Berkeley, 615 pp.

Paulson, D.R. (1974) Reproductive isolation in damselflies. *System. Zool.*, **23**, 40–9.

Pritchard, G. (ed.) (1984) *Advances in Odonatology*, University Press, Calgary, Vol. II, 207 pp.

St Quentin, D. and Beier, M. (1968) Odonata (Libellen), in *Handbuch der Zoologie* (eds J.-G. Helmcke, D. Starck and H. Wermuth), Vol. 4(2); Lfg. 3, 39 pp.

Snodgrass, R.E. (1954) The dragonfly larva. *Smithsonian Misc. Collns*, **123**(2), 38 pp.

Walker, E.M. and Corbet, P.S. (1953, 1975) *The Odonata of Canada and Alaska*, University Press, Toronto, 3 Vols.

8. Plecoptera

Baumann, R.W., Gaufin, A.F. and Surdick, R.F. (1977) The stoneflies (Plecoptera) of the Rocky Mountains. *Mem. Am. Entomol. Soc.* **31**, 1–208.

Brinck, P. (1949) Studies on Swedish stoneflies. *Opuscula Entomol., Suppl.,* **11**, 250 pp.

Claassen, P.W. (1931) *Plecoptera Nymphs of North America*, Thomas Say Foundation, Springfield, 199 pp.

Hynes, H.B.N. (1976) Biology of the Plecoptera. *A. Rev. Entomol.,* **21**, 135–53.

Hynes, H.B.N. (1977) A key to the adults and nymphs of British stoneflies (Plecoptera). *Scient. Publns. Freshwat. Biol. Assoc.,* **17**, 3rd edn, 92 pp.

Illies, J. (1965) Phylogeny and zoogeography of the Plecoptera. *A. Rev. Entomol.,* **10**, 117–40.

Illies, J. (1966) Katalog der rezenten Plecoptera. *Bronn's Klassen und Ordnungen des Tierreichs,* **82**, 632 pp.

Stark, B.P. and Gaufin, A.R. (1979) The stoneflies (Plecoptera) of Florida. *Trans. Am. Entomol. Soc.,* **104**, 391–433.

Zwick, P. (1973) Insecta: Plecoptera. Phylogenetisches System und Katalog. *Bronn's Klassen und Ordnungen des Tierreichs,* **94**, 465 pp.

Zwick, P. (1980) Plecoptera (Steinfliegen), in *Handbuch der Zoologie* (eds J.-G. Helmcke, D. Starck and H. Wermuth), **4**(2), 2/7, 1–115.

9. Grylloblattodea

Gurney, A.B. (1961) Further advances in the taxonomy and distribution of the Grylloblattidae. *Proc. Biol. Soc. Washington,* **74**, 67–76.

Kamp, J.W. (1970) The cavernicolous Grylloblattodea of the western United States. *Ann. Spéléol.,* **25**, 223–30.

Kamp, J.W. (1979) Taxonomy, distribution and zoogeographic evolution of Grylloblatta in Canada (Insecta: Notoptera). *Canadian Entomol.,* **105**, 1235–49.

Walker, E.M. (1937) *Grylloblatta*, a living fossil. *Trans. R. Soc. Canada,* **31**, 1–10.

10. Orthoptera

Beier, M. (1972) Saltatoria (Grillen und Heuschrecken), in *Handbuch der Zoologie* (eds J.-G. Helmcke, D. Starck and H. Wermuth), **4**(2), Lfg. 17, 1–217.

Blatchley, W.S. (1920) *The Orthoptera of Eastern North America*, Nature Publishing, Indianapolis, 784 pp.

Chopard, L. (1938) La biologie des Orthoptères. *Encyclopédie entomol.*, **20**, 1–541.

Chopard, L. (1951) Orthopteroides. *Faune Fr.*, **56**, 359 pp.

Dirsh, V.M. (1975) *Classification of the Acridomorphoid Insects*, Classey, Farringdon, 184 pp.

Harz, K. and Kaltenbach, A. (1969, 1975, 1976) *Die Orthopteren Europas*, Junk, The Hague, 3 Vols.

Helfer, J.R. (1963) *How to Know the Grasshoppers, Cockroaches and their Allies*, Brown, Dubuque, Iowa, 353 pp.

Otte, D. (1981, 1984) *The North American Grasshoppers*, Harvard University Press, Cambridge, Massachusetts, 2 Vols.

Pierce, G.W. (1948) *The Songs of Insects*, Harvard University Press, Cambridge, Massachusetts, 329 pp.

Ragge, D.R. (1965) *Grasshoppers, Crickets and Cockroaches of the British Isles*, Warne, London, 299 pp. (Suppl. in *Entomol. Gazette*, **24**, 227–246, 1973.)

Richards, O.W. and Waloff, N. (1954) Studies on the biology and population dynamics of British grasshoppers. *Anti-Locust Bull.*, **17**, 182 pp.

Uvarov, B.P. (1966, 1977) *Grasshoppers and Locusts. A Handbook of General Acridology*, Cambridge University Press, Cambridge, 2 Vols.

11. Phasmida

Bedford, G.O. (1978) Biology and ecology of the Phasmatodea. *A. Rev. Entomol.*, **23**, 125–50.

Beier, M. (1957) Arthropoda. Insecta. Orthopteroidea: Ordnung Cheleutoptera Crampton 1915 (Phasmida Leach 1815), in *Bronn's Klassen und Ordnungen des Tierreichs*, **5**, Abt. iii (6, 9), pp. 305–454.

Beier, M. (1968) Phasmida (Stab- oder Gespenstheuschrecken), in *Handbuch der Zoologie* (eds J.-G. Helmcke, D. Starck and H. Wermuth), **4**(2), Lfg. 6, 56 pp.

Clark, J.T. (1976) The eggs of stick insects (Phasmida): a review with descriptions of the eggs of eleven species. *Syst. Entomol.*, **1**, 95–105.

Key, K.H.L. (1957) Kentromorphic phases in three species of Phasmatodea. *Austral. J. Zool.*, **5**, 247–84.

12. Dermaptera

Beier, M. (1958) Dermaptera, in: *Bronn's Klassen und Ordnungen des Tierreichs*, **5**, Buch 6, Lfg. 3, pp. 455–585.

Giles, E.T. (1963) The comparative external morphology and affinities of the Dermaptera. *Trans. R. Entomol. Soc. Lond.*, **115**, 95–164.

Günther, K. and Herter, K. (1974) Ordnung Dermaptera (Ohrwürmer), in *Handbuch der Zoologie* (eds J.-G. Helmcke, D. Starck and H. Wermuth), **4**(2), Lfg. 23, 1–158.

Nakata, S. and Maa, T.C. (1974) A review of the parasitic earwigs (Dermaptera: Arixenina, Hemimerina). *Pacific Insects*, **16**, 307–74.

Popham, E.J. (1985) The mutual affinities of the major earwig taxa (Insecta, Dermaptera). *Zeitschr. zool. System. Evolutionsforsch.*, **23**, 199–214.

Popham, E.J. and Brindle, A. (1966–9) Genera and species of the Dermaptera. Parts 1–10. *Entomologist,* **99**, 132–5, 241–6, 269–78; **100**, 35–8, 105–8, 255–62; **101**, 133–6, 196–201, 276–80; **102**, 61–6.

Sakai, S. (1970–6) Dermapterorum Catalogus Praeliminaris. *Spec. Bull. Daito Bunka Univ.*, 9 Parts.

Steinmann, H. (1973) A zoogeographical checklist of World Dermaptera. *Folia Entomol. Hung. (N.S.)*, **26**, 145–54.

Steinmann, H. (1975) Suprageneric classification of Dermaptera. *Acta zool. Acad. Scient. Hung.*, **21**, 195–220.

13. Embioptera

Davis, C. (1940) Family classification of the order Embioptera. *Ann. Entomol. Soc. Am.*, **33**, 677–82.

Kaltenbach, A. (1968) Embiodea (Spinnfüsser), in *Handbuch der Zoologie* (eds J.-G. Helmcke, D. Starck and H. Wermuth), **4**(2), 2/8, 29 pp.

Ross, E.S. (1944) A revision of the Embioptera or web-spinners of the New World. *Proc. US Natn. Museum*, **94**, 401–504.

Ross, E.S. (1966) The Embioptera of Europe and the Mediterranean region. *Bull. Br. Museum (Nat. Hist.), Entomol.*, **17**(7), 273–326.

Ross, E.S. (1970) Biosystematics of the Embioptera. *A. Rev. Entomol.*, **15**, 157–72.

14. Dictyoptera

Beier, M. (1968) Mantodea (Fangheuschrecken), in *Handbuch der Zoologie* (eds J.-G. Helmcke, D. Starck and H. Wermuth), **4**(2), Lfg. 4, 47 pp.

Beier, M. (1974) 13. Ordnung Blattariae (Schaben), in *Handbuch der Zoologie* (eds J.-G. Helmcke, D. Starck and H. Wermuth), **4**(2), Lfg. 23, 127 pp.

Bell, W.J. and Adiyodi, K.G. (eds) (1981) *The American Cockroach*, Chapman and Hall, London, 530 pp.

Guthrie, D.M. and Tindall, A.R. (1968) *The Biology of the Cockroach*, Edward Arnold, London, 416 pp.

Kumar, R. (1975) A review of the cockroaches of West Africa and the Congo Basin (Dictyoptera: Blattaria). *Bull. Inst. Fr. d'Afrique Noire (Sci. Nat.)*, **37**, 27–121.

McKittrick, F.A. (1964) Evolutionary studies of cockroaches. *Mem. Cornell Univ. Agric. Exp. Stn.*, **389**, 197 pp.

Princis, K. (1966) Zur Systematik der Blattaria. *Eos*, **36**, 427–49.

Roth, L.M. (1970) Evolution and taxonomic significance of reproduction in Blattaria. *A. Rev. Entomol.*, **15**, 75–96.

Roth, L.M. and Willis, E.R. (1960) The biotic associations of cockroaches. *Smithsonian Misc. Collns*, **141**, 470 pp.

See also works by Chopard (1938, 1951) and Ragge (1965) under Orthoptera.

15. Isoptera

Ernst E. and Arago, R.L. (1986). *A Bibliography of Termite Literature, 1966–78*, Wiley, New York, 912 pp.

Harris, W.V. (1971) *Termites, their Recognition and Control*, Longman, London, 2nd edn, 187 pp.

Howse, P.E. (1970) *Termites: a Study in Social Behaviour*, Hutchinson, London, 150 pp.

Krishna, K. and Weesner, F.M. (eds) (1969–70) *Biology of Termites*, Academic Press, New York, 2 Vols.

Lee, K.E. and Wood, T.G. (1971) *Termites and Soils*, Academic Press, New York, 252 pp.

Prestwich, G. (1984) Defense mechanisms of termites. *A. Rev. Entomol.*, **29**, 201–32.

Sands, W.A. (1972) The soldierless termites of Africa (Isoptera: Termitidae). *Bull. Br. Museum (Nat. Hist.), Entomol.*, **18**, 1–244.

Snyder, T.E. (1949) Catalog of the termites (Isoptera) of the world. *Smithsonian Misc. Collns*, **112**, 1–490.

Snyder, T.E. (1949, 1961, 1968) Annotated subject-heading bibliography of termites 1350 BC to AD 1954. *Smithsonian Misc. Collns*, **130**, 1–305; **143**(3), 1–137; **152**(3), 1–188.

Weidner, H. (1970) Isoptera (Termiten), in *Handbuch der Zoologie* (eds J.-G. Helmcke, D. Starck and H. Wermuth), **4**(2), Lfg. 13, 147 pp.

Yin, C.M. and Gillott, C. (1975) Endocrine control of caste differentiation in *Zootermopsis angusticollis* Hagen (Isoptera). *Canadian J. Zool.*, **53**, 1701–8.

16. Zoraptera

New, T.R. (1978) Notes on Neotropical Zoraptera with descriptions of two new species. *System. Entomol.*, **3**, 361–70.

Weidner, H. (1969) Die Ordnung Zoraptera oder Bodenläuse. *Entomol. Zeitschr.*, **79**, 39–51.

Weidner, H. (1970) Zoraptera (Bodenläuse), in *Handbuch der Zoologie* (eds J.-G. Helmcke, D. Starck and H. Wermuth), **4**(2), Lfg. 13, 1–12.

17. Psocoptera

Badonnel, A. (1934) Recherches sur l'anatomie des Psoques. *Bull. Biol. Fr. Belg., Suppl.*, **18**, 1–241.

Günther, K.K. (1974) Staubläuse. Psocoptera. *Tierwelt Deutschlands*, **61**, 314 pp.

New, T.R. (1974) Psocoptera. *R. Entomol. Soc. Lond. Handbooks for the Identification of British Insects*, **1**(7), 102 pp.

Smithers, C.N. (1972) The classification and phylogeny of the Psocoptera. *Mem. Austral. Museum*, **14**, 351 pp.

Thornton, I.W.B. (1985) The geographical and ecological distribution of arboreal Psocoptera. *A. Rev. Entomol.*, **30**, 175–96.

Weidner, H. (1972) 16. Ordnung Copeognatha (Staubläuse), in *Handbuch der Zoologie* (eds J.-G. Helmcke, D. Starck and H. Wermuth), **4**(2), Lfg. 18, 1–94.

18. Phthiraptera

Buxton, P.A. (1947) *The Louse. An Account of the Lice which infest Man, their Medical Importance and Control*, Edward Arnold, London, 2nd edn, 164 pp.

Clay, T. (1951) An introduction to the classification of the avian Ischnocera (Mallophaga), Part 1. *Trans. R. Entomol. Soc. Lond.*, **102**, 171–94.

Clay, T. (1970) The Amblycera (Phthiraptera: Insecta). *Bull. Br. Museum (Nat. Hist.), Entomol.*, **25**, 73–98.

Eichler, W. (1963) Mallophaga, in *Bronn's Klassen und Ordnungen des Tierreichs*, **5**(3), 7(b), 1–290.

Emerson, K.C. (1972) *Checklist of the Mallophaga of North America*, Parts I–IV, Desert Test Centre, Utah, 200 pp.; 118 pp.; 28 pp.; 216 pp.

Ferris, G.F. (1951) The sucking lice. *Mem. Pacific Coast Entomol. Soc.*, **1**, 1–320.

Hopkins, G.H.E. (1949) The host-associations of the lice of mammals. *Proc. Zool. Soc. Lond.*, **119**, 387–604.

Hopkins, G.H.E. and Clay, T. (1952) *A Check List of the Genera and Species of Mallophaga*, British Museum (Natural History), London, 362 pp.

Kéler, S. von (1969) 17. Ordnung Mallophaga (Federlinge und Haarlinge), in *Handbuch der Zoologie* (eds J.-G. Helmcke, D. Starck and H. Wermuth), **4**(2), Lfg. 10, 1–72.

Kim, K.C. (ed.) (1985) *Co-evolution of Parasitic Arthropods and Mammals*, Wiley, Chichester, 800 pp.

Zlotorzycka, J., Eichler, W.D. and Ludwig, H.W. (1974) Taxonomie und Biologie der Mallophagen und Läuse mitteleuropäischer Haus- und Nutztiere. *Parasitol. Schriftenreihe*, **22**, 160 pp.

See also Marshall (1981) under Predators, Parasitoids and Ectoparasitic Insects.

19. Hemiptera

Blackman, R.L. (1974) *Aphids*, Ginn, Aylesbury, 175 pp.

Blackman, R.L. and Eastop, V.F. (1984) *Aphids on the World's Crops*, Wiley, New York, 480 pp.

China, W.E. and Miller, N.C.E. (1959) Check-list and keys to the families and subfamilies of the Hemiptera-Heteroptera. *Bull. Br. Museum (Nat. Hist.), Entomol.*, **8**(1), 45 pp.

Claridge, M.F. (1985) Acoustic signals in the Homoptera: behaviour, taxonomy and evolution. *A Rev. Entomol.*, **30**, 297–317.

Cobben, R.H. (1968, 1978) Evolutionary trends in Heteroptera. I, II. *Mededel. Landbouwhoogeschool Wageningen*, **151**, 1–475; **78–5**: 1–407.

Dixon, A.F.G. (1985) *Aphid Ecology*, Blackie, Glasgow, 168 pp.

Duffels, J.P. and Van der Laan, P.A. (1985) *Catalogue of the Cicadoidea (Homoptera Auchenorrhyncha). 1956–1980*, Junk, Dordrecht, 414 pp.

Eastop, V.F. and Hille Ris Lambers, D. (1976) *Survey of the World's Aphids*, Junk, The Hague, 573 pp.

Evans, J.W. (1963) The phylogeny of the Homoptera. *A. Rev. Entomol.* **8**, 77–94.

Ferris, G.F. (1937–55) *An Atlas of the Scale Insects of North America*, Stanford University Press, Stanford, 6 Vols.

Goodchild, A.J.P. (1966) Evolution of the alimentary canal in the Hemiptera. *Biol. Rev.*, **41**, 97–140.

Hodkinson, I.D. (1974) The biology of the Psylloidea (Homoptera): a review. *Bull. Entomol. Res.*, **64**, 325–39.

Hodkinson, I.D. and White, I.M. (1979) Homoptera Psylloidea. *R. Entomol. Soc. Lond. Handbooks for the Identification of British Insects*, **2**(5a), 94 pp.

Jordan, K.H.C. (1972) 20. Heteroptera (Wanzen), in *Handbuch der Zoologie* (eds J.-G. Helmcke, D. Starck and H. Wermuth), **4**(2), Lfg. 16, 113 pp.

Kramer, S. (1950) The morphology and phylogeny of Auchenorrhynchous Homoptera (Insecta). *Illinois Biol. Monogr.*, **20**(4), 111 pp.

Lees, A.D. (1966) The control of polymorphism in aphids. *Adv. Insect Physiol.*, **3**, 207–77.

LeQuesne, W.J. (1960–9) Hemiptera Cicadomorpha, Hemiptera Fulgoromorpha. *R. Entomol. Soc. Lond. Handbooks for the Identification of British Insects*, **2**(2a), 1–64; **2**(2b), 65–148; **2**(3), 1–68.

Metcalf, Z.P. (1927–66) *General Catalogue of the Hemiptera*. (many parts, with contributions by W.D. Funkhouser, V. Wade, *et al.*; continued in Duffels and van der Laan, *op. cit.*).

Miller, D.R. and Kosztarab, M. (1979) Recent advances in the study of scale insects. *A. Rev. Entomol.*, **24**, 1–27.

Miller, N.C.E. (1971) *The Biology of the Heteroptera*, Classey, Hampton, Middlesex, 206 pp.

Mound, L.A. (1966) A revision of the British Aleyrodidae (Hemiptera: Homoptera). *Bull. Br. Museum (Nat. Hist.), Entomol.*, **17**, 397–428.

Mound, L.A. and Halsey, S.H. (1978) *Whitefly of the World. A Systematic Catalogue of the Aleyrodidae (Homoptera) with Host Plant and Natural Enemy Data*, British Museum (Natural History), London, 340 pp.

Nast, J. (1972) *Palaearctic Auchenorrhyncha (Homoptera). An Annotated Check List*, Polish Science Publications, Warsaw, 350 pp.

Nault, L.R. and Rodrigues, J.G. (eds) (1985) *The Leafhoppers and Planthoppers*, Wiley, Chichester, 518 pp.

Nielson, M.W. (1968) The leafhopper vectors of phytopathogenic viruses (Homoptera, Cicadellidae): taxonomy, biology and virus transmission. *Tech. Bull., US Dept. Agric.*, **1382**, 386 pp.

Oman, P.W. (1949) The Nearctic leafhoppers (Homoptera: Cicadellidae). A generic classification and check list. *Mem. Entomol. Soc. Washington*, **3**, 253 pp.

Parsons, M.C. (1964) The origin and development of the Hemipteran cranium. *Canadian J. Zool.*, **42**, 409–32.

Pesson, P. (1951) Ordre des Homoptères, in *Traité de Zoologie* (ed. P.P. Grassé), **10**(2), 1390–656.

Poisson, R. (1951) Ordre des Heteroptères, in *Traité de Zoologie* (ed. P.P. Grassé), **10**(2), 1657–803.

Ribaut, H. (1936, 1952) Homoptères Auchenorhynques. *Faune Fr.*, **31**, 228 pp.; **57**, 474 pp.

Ris Lambers, D.H. (1938–53) Contributions to a monograph of the Aphididae of Europe. I–V. *Temminckia*, **3**, 1–43; **4**, 1–134; **7**, 173–319; **8**, 182–323; **9**, 1–176.

Schuh, R.T. (1986) The influence of cladistics on Heteropteran classification. *A. Rev. Entomol.*, **31**, 67–93.

Slater, J.A. and Baranowski, R.M. (1978) *How to Know the True Bugs (Hemiptera-Heteroptera)*, Brown, Dubuque, Iowa, 256 pp.

Southwood, T.R.E. and Leston, D. (1959) *Land and Water Bugs of the British Isles*, Warne, London, 436 pp.

Stichel, W. (1955–62) *Illustrierte Bestimmungstabellen der Wanzen. II. Europa*, Erich Pröh, Berlin, 4 Vols.

Stroyan, H.L.G. (1977) Homoptera Aphidoidea (Chaitophoridae and Callaphididae). *R. Entomol. Soc. Lond. Handbooks for the Identification of British Insects*, **2**(4a), 1–130.

Strümpel, H. (1983) Homoptera (Pflanzensanger), in *Handbuch der Zoologie* (eds J.-G. Helmcke, D. Starck and H. Wermuth), **4**(2), Lfg. 28, 1–222.

Theron, J.G. (1958) Comparative studies on the morphology of male scale insects (Hemiptera: Coccoidea). *Ann. Univ. Stellenbosch*, **34A** (1), 1–71.

Van Emden, H.F. (ed.) (1972) *Aphid Technology*, Academic Press, London, 344 pp.

Weber, H. (1930) *Biologie der Hemipteren*, Springer, Berlin, 543 pp.

20. Thysanoptera

Ananthakrishnan, T.N. (1984) *Bioecology of Thrips*, Indira Publishing House, Michigan, 233 pp.

Davies, R.G. (1969) The skeletal musculature and its metamorphosis in *Limothrips cerealium* Haliday (Thysanoptera: Thripidae). *Trans. R. Entomol. Soc. Lond.*, **121**, 167–233.

Jacot-Guillarmod, C.F. (1970–8) Catalogue of the Thysanoptera of the World (Parts 1–5). *Ann. Cape Province Museum*, **7**, 1–216, 217–515, 517–976, 977–1255, 1257–556.

Lewis, T. (1975) *Thrips, Their Biology, Ecology and Economic Importance*, Academic Press, London, 350 pp.

Mound, L.A., Heming, B.S. and Palmer, J.M. (1980) Phylogenetic relationships between the families of recent Thysanoptera (Insecta). *Zool. J. Linn. Soc.*, **69**, 111–41.

Mound, L.A., Morison, G.D., Pitkin, B.R. and Palmer, J.M. (1977) Thysanoptera. *R. Entomol. Soc. Lond. Handbooks for the Identification of British Insects*, **1**(1), 79 pp.

Priesner, H. (1964) Ordnung Thysanoptera (Fransenflügler, Thripse). *Bestimmungsbücher zur Bodenfauna Europas*, Lfg. 2, 242 pp.

Priesner, H. (1968) Thysanoptera (Physapoda, Blasenfüsser), in *Handbuch der Zoologie* (eds J.-G. Helmcke, D. Starck and H. Wermuth), **4**(2), Lfg. 5, 32 pp.

Schliephake, G. and Klimt, K. (1979) Thysanoptera, Fransenflügler. *Tierwelt Deutschlands*, **66**, 477 pp.

Stannard, L.J. (1968) The Thrips, or Thysanoptera, of Illinois. *Bull. Illinois Nat. Hist. Surv.*, **29**(4), 552 pp.

21. Neuroptera

Aspöck, H., Aspöck, U. and Holzel, H. (1980) *Die Neuropteren Europas*, Goecke und Evers, Krefeld, Vol. 1, 495 pp.; Vol. 2, 355 pp.

Canard, M., Séméria, Y. and New, T.R. (eds) (1984) *Biology of Chrysopidae*, Junk, The Hague, 294 pp.

Carpenter, F.M. (1936) Revision of the Nearctic Raphidoidea (Recent and fossil). *Proc. Am. Acad. Arts Sci.*, **71**, 89–157.

Killington, F.J. (1930) *A Monograph of the British Neuroptera*, Ray Society, London, 2 Vols.

Wheeler, W.M. (1931) *Demons of the Dust*, Kegan Paul, London, 378 pp.

22. Coleoptera

Arnett, R.H. (1968) *The Beetles of the United States (A Manual for Identification)*, The American Entomological Institute, Ann Arbor, 1112 pp.

Balfour-Browne, F. (1940–58) *British Water Beetles*, Ray Society, London, 3 Vols.

Bertrand, H. (1972) *Larves et Nymphes des Coléoptères du Globe*, Imprimérie Paillart, Abbeville, 804 pp.

Böving, A.G. and Craighead, F.C. (1931) Larvae of Coleoptera. *Entomol. Americana*, **11**, 1–351.

Crowson, R.A. (1967) *The Natural Classification of the Families of Coleoptera*, Classey, Hampton, Middlesex, 1–187, 209–14.

Crowson, R.A. (1981) *The Biology of the Coleoptera*, Academic Press, London, 802 pp.

Evans, M.E.G. (1975) *The Life of Beetles*, Allen and Unwin, London, 232 pp.

Freude, H., Harde, K.W. and Lohse, G.-A. (1965–83) *Die Käfer Mitteleuropas*, Goecke und Evers, Krefeld, 11 Vols.

Harde, K.W. (1984) *A Field Guide in Colour to Beetles*, Octopus Books, London, 334 pp. (English edn ed. P.W. Hammond.)

Hodek, I. (1973) *Biology of Coccinellidae*, Junk, The Hague, 260 pp.

Horion, A. (1941–65) *Faunistik der mitteleuropäischen Käfer*, 10 Vols. (various publishers).

Jeannel, R. and Paulian, R. (1949) Coléoptères, in *Traité de Zoologie* (ed. P.P. Grassé), **9**, 771–1077.

Klausnitzer, B. (1978) *Ordnung Coleoptera (Larven)*, Junk, The Hague, 378 pp.

Lawrence, J.F. and Newton, A.F. (1982) Evolution and classification of beetles. *A. Rev. Ecol. Systemat.*, **13**, 261–90.

Lengerken, H. von (1954) *Die Brutfürsorge- und Brutpflegeinstinkte der Käfer*, Akademische Verlagsgesellschaft, Leipzig, 2nd edn, 383 pp.

Meixner, J. (1935) Coleopteroidea, in *Handbuch der Zoologie* (ed. W. Kükenthal), **4**(2), Lfg. 3–5: 1133–382.

Schenkling, S. (ed.) (1910→) *Coleopterorum Catalogus*, Junk, Berlin and 's-Gravenhage (in separate parts by various authors).

Thiele, H.U. (1977) *Carabid Beetles in their Environment. A Study in Habitat Selection by Adaptations in Physiology and Behaviour*, Springer, Berlin, 369 pp.

23. Strepsiptera

Bohart, R.M. (1941) A revision of the Strepsiptera with special reference to the species of North America. *Univ. California Publns, Entomol.*, **7**, 91–160.

Kinzelbach, R.K. (1969) Stylopoidea, in *Die Käfer Mitteleuropas* (eds H. Freude, K.W. Harde, and C.-A. Lohse), **8**, 139–59.

Kinzelbach, R.K. (1971) Strepsiptera (Fächerflügler), in *Handbuch der Zoologie* (eds J.-G. Helmcke, D. Stark and H. Wermuth), **4**(2), Lfg. 15, 1–73.

Kinzelbach, R.K. (1971) Morphologische Befunde an der Fächerflüglern und ihre phylogenetische Bedeutung (Insecta: Strepsiptera). *Zoologia, Stuttgart,* **119**, 1–256.

Ulrich, W. (1943) Die Mengeiden (Mengenillini) und die Phylogenie der Strepsipteren. *Zeitschr. Parasitenkunde,* **13**, 62–101.

24. Mecoptera

Byers, G.W. and Thornhill, R. (1983) Biology of the Mecoptera. *A. Rev. Entomol.,* **28**, 203–28.

Carpenter, F.M. (1931) Revision of the Nearctic Mecoptera. *Bull. Museum Comp. Zool. Harvard,* **72**, 205–77.

Hobby, B.M. and Killington, F.J. (1934) The feeding habits of British Mecoptera, with a synopsis of the British species. *Trans. Soc. Br. Entomol.,* **1**, 39–49.

Kaltenbach, A. (1978) Mecoptera (Schnabelhafte, Schnabeifliegen). In *Handbuch der Zoologie* (eds J.-G. Helmcke, D. Stark and H. Wermuth), **4**(2), Lfg. 25, 1–111.

Penny, N.D. (1975) Evolution of the extant Mecoptera. *J. Kansas Entomol. Soc.,* **48**, 331–50.

Penny, N.D. (1977) A systematic study of the family Boreidae (Mecoptera). *Kansas Univ. Sci. Bull.,* **51**, 141–217.

Potter, E.M. (1938) The internal anatomy of the order Mecoptera. *Trans. R. Entomol. Soc. Lond.,* **87**, 467–501.

Schlee, H.B. and Schlee, D. (1976) Bibliographie der rezenten und fossilen Mecoptera. *Stuttgarter Beitr. Naturkunde (A),* **282**, 1–76.

Webb, D.W., Penny, N.D. and Marlin, J.G. (1975) The Mecoptera, or scorpion flies, of Illinois. *Bull. Illinois Nat. Hist. Surv.,* **31**, 251–316.

25. Siphonaptera

Holland, G.P. (1949) The Siphonaptera of Canada. *Tech. Bull. Dept Agric. Canada,* **70**, 306 pp.

Holland, G.P. (1964) Evolution, classification and host relationships of Siphonaptera. *A. Rev. Entomol.,* **9**, 123–46.

Rothschild, M. (1975) Recent advances in our knowledge of the order Siphonaptera. *A. Rev. Entomol.,* **20**, 241–59.

Rothschild, M., Ford, B. and Hughes, M. (1970) Maturation of the male rabbit flea (*Spilopsyllus cuniculi*) and the Oriental rat flea (*Xenopsylla cheopis*): some effects of mammalian hormones on development and impregnation. *Trans. Zool. Soc. Lond.,* **32**, 105–88.

Rothschild, M. and Hopkins, G.H.E. (1953–71) *An Illustrated Catalogue of the Rothschild Collection of Fleas, etc.,* Vols. 1–5. British Museum (Natural History), London (continued as Traub *et al.* (1983)).

Rothschild, M., Schlein, Y. and Ito, S. (1986) *A Colour Atlas of Insect Tissues via the Flea,* Wolfe, London, 184 pp.

Smit, F.G.A.M. (1957) Siphonaptera. *R. Entomol. Soc. Handbooks for the Identification of British Insects,* **1**(16), 94 pp.

Snodgrass, R.E. (1946) The skeletal anatomy of fleas. (Siphonaptera). *Smithsonian Misc. Collns,* **104**(18), 94 pp.

Traub, R., Rothschild, M. and Haddow, J.F. (1983) *The Rothschild Collection of Fleas. The Ceratophyllidae: Key to Genera and Host Relationships, etc.,* Academic Press, London and Cambridge University Press, Cambridge, 288 pp.

26. Diptera

Buxton, P.A. (1955) *The Natural History of Tsetse Flies,* Lewis, London, 816 pp.

Cole, F.R. and Schlinger, E.I. (1969) *The Flies of Western North America,* University of California Press, Berkeley, 693 pp.

Colyer, C.N. and Hammond, C.O. (1968) *Flies of the British Isles,* Warne, London, 384 pp.

Crampton, G.C. Curran, C.H., Alexander, C.P. and Friend, R.B. (1942) Guide to the Insects of Connecticut. Part VI. The Diptera or true flies of Connecticut. First fascicle. *Bull. Connecticut Geol. Nat. Hist. Surv.,* **64**, 509 pp.

Curran, C.H. (1934) *The Families and Genera of North American Diptera,* The Author, New York, 512 pp.

Downes, J.A. (1958) The feeding habits of biting flies and their significance in classification. *A. Rev. Entomol.,* **3**, 249–66.

Griffiths, G.C.D. (1972) *The Phylogenetic Classification of Diptera Cyclorrhapha, with Special reference to the Structure of the male Postabdomen.* Junk, The Hague, 340 pp.

Griffiths, G.C.D. and Schweizerbart, E. (eds) (1980→) *Flies of the Nearctic Region,* (appearing in parts).

Hennig, W. (1938–52) *Die Larvenformen der Dipteren,* Akademie Verlag, Berlin, 3 Vols.

Hennig, W. (1973) Diptera (Zweiflügler), *Handbuch der Zoologie* (eds J.-G. Helmcke, D. Stark and H. Wermuth), **4**(2), Lfg. 20, 1–337.

Hoyt, G.P. (1952) The evolution of the mouthparts of adult Diptera. *Microentomology,* **17**, 61–125.

Lindner, E. (ed.) (1924→) *Die Fliegen der paläarktischen Region,* Schweitzerbartsch, Stuttgart (appearing in parts).

Lundbeck, W. (1907–27) *Diptera Danica,* Verlagsbuchhandlung, Copenhagen, Parts 1–7. (Incomplete).

McAlpine, J.F., Peterson, B.V., Shewell, G.E. *et al.* (1981→) Manual of Nearctic Diptera, Vol. 1. *Res. Branch, Agric. Canada, Monogr.,* **27**.

Norris, K.R. (1965) The bionomics of blowflies. *A. Rev. Entomol.,* **10**, 47–68.

Oldroyd, H. (1964) *The Natural History of Flies,* Weidenfeld and Nicolson, London, 324 pp.

Séguy, E. (1950) La biologie des Diptères. *Encyclopédie Entomol.,* **26**, 609 pp.

Snodgrass, R.E. (1944) The feeding apparatus of biting and sucking insects affecting man and animals. *Smithsonian Misc. Collns,* **104**, 1–113.

Soos, A. and Papp, L. (eds) (1984→) *Catalogue of Palaearctic Diptera.* Elsevier, Amsterdam. (Appearing in parts.)

Stone, A., Sabrosky, C.W., Wirth, W.W. *et al.* (1965) A catalog of the Diptera of America north of Mexico. *US Dept. Agric. Hbk. No.* **276**, 1696 pp.

Stubbs, A. and Chandler, P. (eds) (1978) *A Dipterist's Handbook*, Amateur Entomologist's Society, London, 255 pp.

Verrall, G.H. and Collin, J.E. (1901–61) *British Flies*, Gurney and Jackson, London and Cambridge University Press, Cambridge, Vols 5, 6 and 8.

27. Lepidoptera

Bourgogne, J. (1951) Lépidoptères, in *Traité de Zoologie* (ed. P.P. Grassé), **10**(1), 174–448.

Bradley, J.D., Tremewan, W.G. and Smith, A. (1973) *British Tortricoid Moths. Cochylidae and Tortricidae: Tortricinae*, Ray Society, London, 251 pp.

Brock, J.P. (1971) A contribution towards an understanding of the morphology and phylogeny of the ditrysian Lepidoptera. *J. Nat. Hist.*, **5**, 29–102.

Carter, D.J. (1984) *Pest Lepidoptera of Europe, with Special Reference to the British Isles*, Junk, Dordrecht, 432 pp.

Carter, D.J. and Hargreaves, B. (1986) *A Field Guide to Caterpillars of Butterflies and Moths in Britain and Europe*, Collins, London, 296 pp.

Common, I.F.B. (1975) Evolution and classification of the Lepidoptera. *A. Rev. Entomol.*, **20**, 183–203.

Dugdale, J.S. (1974) Female genital configuration in the classification of the Lepidoptera. *N.Z. J. Zool.*, **1**, 127–46.

Ehrlich, P.R. (1958) The comparative morphology, phylogeny and higher classification of the butterflies (Lepidoptera: Papilionoidea). *Kansas Univ. Sci. Bull.*, **39**, 305–70.

Ehrlich, P.R. and Ehrlich, A.H. (1961) *How to Know the Butterflies*, Brown, Duduque, Iowa, 262 pp.

Emmett, A.M. (ed.) (1980) *A Field Guide to the Smaller British Lepidoptera*, British Entomological and Natural History Society, London, 271 pp.

Forbes, W.T.M. (1923–60) Lepidoptera of New York and neighbouring states. *Mem. Cornell Univ. Agric. Exp. Stn,* **68**, 1–729; **274**, 1–263; **329**, 1–433; **371**, 1–188.

Fracker, J.B. (1915) The classification of Lepidopterous larvae. *Illinois Biol. Monogr.*, **2**, 1–169.

Gilbert, L.E. and Singer, M.C. (1961) Butterfly ecology. *A. Rev. Entomol.*, **6**, 365–97.

Goater, B. (1986) *British Pyralid Moths. A Guide to their Identification*, Harley Books, Colchester, 175 pp.

Hannemann, H.-J. (1977) Kleinschmetterlinge oder Microlepidoptera. *Tierwelt Deutschlands*, **63**, 11–273.

Heath, J. and Emmett, A.M. (1976→) *The Moths and Butterflies of Great Britain and Ireland*, Harley Books, Colchester (4 Vols to 1986).

Higgins, L.G. and Riley, N.D. (1970) *A Field Guide to the Butterflies of Europe*, Collins, London, 380 pp.

Hinton, H.E. (1946) On the homology and nomenclature of the setae of Lepidopterous larvae, with some notes on the phylogeny of the Lepidoptera. *Trans. R. Entomol. Soc. Lond.*, **97**, 1–37.

Kristensen, N.P. (1976) Remarks on the family-level phylogeny of butterflies (Insecta, Lepidoptera, Rhopalocera). *Zeitschr. Zool. Syst. Evolutionsforsch.,* **14**, 25–53.

Kristensen, N.P. (1984) Studies on the morphology and systematics of primitive Lepidoptera. *Steenstrupia*, **10**, 141–91.

Meyrick, E. (1928) *Revised Handbook of British Lepidoptera*, Watkins and Doncaster, London, 914 pp.

Mosher, E. (1916) A classification of the Lepidoptera based on characters of the pupa. *Bull. Illinois Lab. Nat. Hist.,* **12**, 15–159.

Robinson, R. (1971) *Lepidoptera Genetics*, Pergamon Press, Oxford, 687 pp.

Vane-Wright, R.I. and Ackery, P.R. (eds) (1984) *The Biology of Butterflies,* Academic Press, London, 429 pp.

28. Trichoptera

Fischer, F.C.J. (1960–73) *Trichopterorum Catalogus,* Nederlandse Entomologische Vereniging, Amsterdam, 15 Vols.

Hickin, N.E. (1967) *Caddis Larvae. Larvae of the British Trichoptera,* Hutchinson, London, 476 pp.

Macan, T.T. (1973) A key to the adults of the British Trichoptera. *Scient. Publns Br. Freshwat. Biol. Assoc.,* **28**, 1–151.

McKay, R.J. and Wiggins, G.B. (1979) Ecological diversity in Trichoptera. *A. Rev. Entomol.,* **24**, 185–208.

Malicky, H. (1971) Trichoptera (Köcherfliegen), in *Handbuch der Zoologie* (eds J.-G. Helmcke, D. Stark and H. Wermuth), **4**(2), Lfg. 21, 1–114.

Malicky, H. (1983) *Atlas of European Trichoptera,* Junk, Dordrecht, 298 pp.

Ross, H.H. (1944) The Caddis-flies or Trichoptera of Illinois. *Bull. Illinois Nat. Hist. Surv.,* **23**(1), 326 pp.

Ross, H.H. (1967) The evolution and past dispersal of the Trichoptera. *A. Rev. Entomol.,* **12**, 169–206.

Wiggins, G.B. (1977) *Larvae of the North American Caddis-fly Genera (Trichoptera),* University Press, Toronto, 401 pp.

29. Hymenoptera

Alford, D.V. (1975) *Bumblebees*, Davis-Poynter, London, 352 pp.

Bischoff, H. (1927) *Biologie der Hymenopteren*, Springer, Berlin.

Brian, M.V. (1977) *Ants*, Collins, London, 223 pp.

Brothers, D.J. (1975) Phylogeny and classification of the aculeate Hymenoptera, with special reference to Mutillidae. *Kansas Univ. Sci. Bull.,* **50**, 483–648.

Butler, C.G. (1974) *The World of the Honeybee*, Collins, London, 226 pp.

Clausen, C.P. (1940) *Entomophagous Insects*, McGraw-Hill, New York, 688 pp.

Dumpert, K. (1981) *The Social Biology of Ants*, Pitman, London, 304 pp.

Evans, H.E. (1966) *The Comparative Ethology and Evolution of the Sandwasps,* Comstock Publishing Associates, Cambridge, Massachusetts, 526 pp.

Evans, H.E. and West Eberhart, M.J. (1970) *The Wasps*, University of Michigan Press, Ann Arbor, 265 pp.

Frisch, K. von (1967) *The Dance Language and Orientation of Bees*, Harvard University Press, Cambridge, Massachusetts, 566 pp.

Heinrich, B. (1979) *Bumblebee Economics*, Harvard University Press, Cambridge, Massachusetts, 245 pp.

Königsmann, E. (1976–8) Das phylogenetische System der Hymenopteren, I–IV. *Dt. Entomol. Zeitschr. (N.F.)*, **23**, 253–79; **24**, 1–40; **25**, 1–55; **25**, 365–435.

Krombein, K.V., Hurd, P.D., Smith, D.R. and Burks, B.D. (1979–80) *Catalog of Hymenoptera in America North of Mexico*. Smithsonian Institution, Washington, 3 Vols.

Lindauer, M. (1964) *Communication among Social Bees*. Harvard University Press, Cambridge, Massachusetts, 143 pp.

Lorenz, H. and Kraus, M. (1957) Die Larvalsystematik der Blattwespen (Tenthredinoidea und Megalodontoidea). *Abh. Larvalsyst. Insekten*, **1**, 1–339.

Malyshev, S.I. (1968) *Genesis of the Hymenoptera and the Phases of their Evolution*, Methuen, London, 319 pp.

Michener, C.D. (1944) Comparative external morphology, phylogeny and a classification of the bees (Hymenoptera). *Bull. Am. Museum Nat. Hist.*, **82**, 157–326.

Michener, C.D. (1953) Comparative morphology and systematic studies of bee larvae with a key to the families of Hymenopteran larvae. *Kansas Univ. Sci. Bull.*, **35**, 987–1102.

Michener, C.D. (1974) *The Social Biology of Bees*, Harvard University Press, Cambridge, Massachusetts, 404 pp.

Richards, O.W. (1971) Biology of the social wasps. *Biol. Rev.*, **46**, 483–528.

Richards, O.W. (1977) Hymenoptera. Introduction and key to families. *R. Entomol. Soc. Lond. Handbooks for the Identification of British Insects*, **6**(1), 1–100 (revised edn).

Seeley, T. (1985) *Honeybee Ecology*, Princeton University Press, Princeton, 201 pp.

Snodgrass, R.E. (1956) *Anatomy of the Honey Bee*, Comstock Publishing Associates, Ithaca, New York, 334 pp.

Sudd, J.H. (1967) *An Introduction to the Behaviour of Ants*, Edward Arnold, London, 200 pp.

Wille, A. (1983) Biology of the stingless bees. *A. Rev. Entomol.*, **28**, 41–64.

See also references under Insect Parasitoids and Social Life.

5. EVOLUTIONARY RELATIONSHIPS OF INSECTS

Anderson, D.T. (1973) *Embryology and Phylogeny in Annelids and Arthropods*, Pergamon Press, London: 495 pp.

Boudreaux, H.B. (1979) *Arthropod Phylogeny with Special Reference to Insects*, Wiley–Interscience, New York, 320 pp.

Carpenter, F.M. (1976) Geological history and evolution of the insects. *Proc. 15th Int. Congr. Entomol.*, pp. 63–70.

Conway Morris, S. (1979) The Burgess Shale (Middle Cambrian) fauna. *A. Rev. Ecol. Systemat.*, **10**, 327–49.

Crowson, R.A., Rolfe, W.D.I., Smart, J. *et al.* (1967) Arthropoda: Chelicerata, Pycnogonida, Palaeisopus, Myriapoda and Insecta, in *The Fossil Record* (ed. W.B. Harland *et al.*), Geological Society, London, pp. 499–534.

Gupta, A.P. (ed.) (1979) *Arthropod Phylogeny*, Van Nostrand Reinhold, New York, 762 pp.

Hennig, W. (1981) *Insect Phylogeny*, Wiley, New York, 514 pp. (transl. and ed. A. Pont, with supplementary comments).

Hinton, H.E. (1958) The phylogeny of the Panorpoid orders. *A. Rev. Entomol.*, **3**, 151–206.

Kristensen, N.P. (1975) The phylogeny of hexapod 'orders'. A critical review of recent accounts. *Zeitschr. zool. Syst. Evolutionsforsch.*, **13**, 1–44.

Kristensen, N.P. (1981) Phylogeny of insect orders. *A. Rev. Entomol.*, **26**, 135–57.

Kukalova-Peck, J. (1978) Origin and evolution of insect wings, and their relation to metamorphosis, as documented by the fossil record. *J. Morphol.*, **156**, 53–125.

Larsson, S.G. (1978) *Baltic Amber. A Palaeobiological Study*, Brill, Leiden, 192 pp.

Laurentiaux, D. (1953) Classe des Insectes, in *Traité de Paléontologie* (ed. J. Piveteau), **3**, 397–527.

Lauterbach K.-E. (1980) Schlüsselereignisse in der Evolution des Grundplans der Mandibulata (Arthropoda). *Abh. naturwiss. Vereins Hamburg, N.F.*, **23**, 105–61.

Lyal, C.H.C. (1985) Phylogeny and classification of the Psocodea, with particular reference to the lice (Psocodea: Phthiraptera). *Systemat. Entomol.*, **10**, 145–65.

Manton, S.M. (1973) Arthropod phylogeny – a modern synthesis. *J. Zool.*, **171**, 111–30.

Manton, S.M. (1977) *The Arthropoda*, Oxford University Press, Oxford, 527 pp.

Rasnitsyn, A.P. (1981) A modified paranotal theory of insect wing origin. *J. Morphol.*, **168**, 331–8.

Rohdendorf, B.B. (ed.) (1962) *Treatise on Palaeontology. Mandibulata: Class Insecta*, Academia Nauk SSSR, Moscow, pp. 29–374 (in Russian).

Rolfe, W.D. (1985) Early terrestrial arthropods – a fragmentary record, in Evolution and environment in the late Silurian and early Devonian (eds W.G. Chaloner and J.D. Lawson). *Phil. Trans. R. Soc. B*, **309**, 207–18.

Snodgrass, R.E. (1952) *A Textbook of Arthropod Anatomy*, Comstock Publishing Associates, Ithaca, New York, 363 pp.

Weygoldt, P. (1986) Arthropod interrelationships – the phylogenetic–systematic approach. *Zeitschr. zool. Syst. Evolutionsforsch.*, **24**, 19–35.

Whalley, P. (1986) A review of the current fossil evidence of Lepidoptera in the Mesozoic. *Biol. J. Linn. Soc.*, **28**, 253–71.

Whalley, P. and Jarzembowski, E.A. (1981) A new assessment of *Rhyniella*, the earliest known insect, from the Devonian of Rhynie, Scotland. *Nature*, **291**, 317.

Wootton, R.J. (1981) Palaeozoic insects. *A. Rev. Entomol.*, **26**, 319–44.

6. SOME IMPORTANT MODES OF LIFE IN INSECTS

Insects and plants (general)

Ahmad, S. (1983) *Herbivorous Insects: Host-seeking Behaviour and Mechanisms,* Academic Press, New York, 264 pp.

Bell, W.J. and Cardé, R.T. (1984) *Chemical Ecology of Insects,* Chapman and Hall, London, 524 pp.

Chapman, R.F. and Bernays, E.A. (eds) (1978) Insects and host plant. *Entomol. Exp. Applicata,* **24,** 201–766.

Crawley, M.J. (1983) *Herbivory,* Blackwell, Oxford, 437 pp.

Edwards, P.J. and Wratten, S.D. (1983) *Ecology of Insect–Plant Relationships,* Edward Arnold, London, 60 pp.

Harborne, J.B. (1982) *Introduction to Ecological Biochemistry,* Academic Press, New York, 2nd edn, 278 pp.

Hedin, P.A. (ed.) (1983) Plant Resistance to Insects. *Am. Chem. Soc. Symp. Ser.,* **208,** 375 pp.

Hodkinson, I.D. and Hughes, M.K. (1982) *Insect Herbivory,* Chapman and Hall, London, 77 pp.

Juniper, B. and Southwood, T.R.E. (1986) *Insects and the Plant Surface.* Edward Arnold, London, 368 pp.

Miller, J.R. and Miller, T.A. (eds) (1986) *Insect–Plant Interrelations,* Springer, Berlin, 352 pp.

Prokopy, R.J. and Owens, E.D. (1983) Visual detection of plants by herbivorous insects. *A. Rev. Entomol.,* **28,** 337–64.

Rosenthal, G. and Jantzen, D. (1979) *Herbivores: their Interaction with Secondary Plant Metabolites,* Academic Press, New York, 718 pp.

Strong, D.R., Lawton, J.H. and Southwood, T.R.E. (1984) *Insects on Plants: Community Patterns and Mechanisms,* Blackwell, Oxford, 320 pp.

Van Emden, H.F. (ed.) (1973) Insect/plant relationships. *Symp. R. Entomol. Soc. Lond.,* **6,** 215 pp.

Visser, J.H. (1986) Host odor perception in phytophagous insects. *A. Rev. Entomol.,* **31,** 121–44.

Wallace, R. and Mansell, R. (eds) (1976) *Biochemical Interaction between Plants and Insects,* Plenum Press, New York, 425 pp.

Zwölfer, H. (1978) Mechanismen und Ergebnisse der Co-evolution von phytophagen und entomophagen Insekten und höhere Pflanzen. *Proc. 20th Phylogenetic Symp., Hamburg, 1975,* pp. 7–50.

Leaf-mining insects

Hering, E.M. (1951) *Biology of the Leaf-miners,* Junk, The Hague, 420 pp.

Hering, E.M. (1957) *Bestimmungstabellen der Blattminen von Europa einschliesslich des Mittelmeerbeckens und der Kanarischen Inseln,* Junk, 's-Gravenhage, Vol. 1. 648 pp.; Vol. 2, 534 pp; Vol. 3, 48 pp.

Needham, J.G., Frost, S.W. and Tothill, B.H. (1928) *Leaf-mining Insects,* Williams and Wilkins, Baltimore, 351 pp.

Spencer, K.A. (1973) *Agromyzidae (Diptera) of Economic Importance*, Junk, The Hague, 418 pp.

Insects and plant galls

Ananthakrishnan, T.N. (ed.) (1985) *The Biology of Gall Insects*, Edward Arnold, London, 362 pp.

Buhr, H. (1964) *Bestimmungstabellen der Gallen (Zoo- und Phytocecidien) an Pflanzen Mittel- und Nordeuropas,* Fischer, Jena, 2 Vols.

Felt, P.E. (1940) *Plant Galls and Gall Makers*, Comstock Publishing Associates, Ithaca, New York, 364 pp.

Mani, M.S. (1964) *The Ecology of Plant Galls*, Junk, The Hague, 400 pp.

Insects and flower pollination

Dafni, A. (1984) Mimicry and deception in pollination. *A. Rev. Ecol. Systematics,* **15**, 259–78.

Faegri, K. and van der Pijl, L. (1978) *The Principles of Pollination Ecology*, Pergamon Press, Oxford, 244 pp.

Free, J.B. (1970) *Insect Pollination of Crops*, Academic Press, New York, 544 pp.

Janzen, D.H. (1979) How to be a fig. *A. Rev. Ecol. Systematics*, **10**, 13–51.

Kevan, P.G. and Baker, H.G. (1983) Insects as flower visitors and pollinators. *A. Rev. Entomol.,* **28**, 407–33.

Kullenberg, B. (1961) Studies in *Ophrys* pollination. *Zool. Bidrag,* **34**, 1–340.

McGregor, S.E. (1976) Insect pollination of cultivated crop plants. *Agric. Handbook* **496**, ARS–USDA, Washington, DC, 411 pp.

Powell, J.A. and Mackie, R.A. (1966) Biological interrelationships of moths and *Yucca whipplei. Univ. California Publns. Entomol.,* **42**, 1–46.

Proctor, M. and Yeo, P. (1973) *The Pollination of Flowers*, Collins, London, 418 pp.

Real, L. (ed.) (1983) *Pollination Biology*, Academic Press, New York, 368 pp.

Richards, A.J. (ed.) (1978) *The Pollination of Flowers by Insects*, Academic Press, London, 213 pp.

Stebbins, G.L. (1970) Adaptive radiation of reproductive characteristics in Angiosperms. I. Pollination mechanisms. *A. Rev. Ecol. Systemat.,* **1**, 307–26.

Van der Pijl, L. and Dodson, C. (1966) *Orchid Flowers: Their Pollination and Evolution*, University of Miami Press, Florida, 214 pp.

Wiebes, J.T. (1979) The co-evolution of figs and their insect pollinators. *A. Rev. Ecol. Systemat.,* **10**, 1–12.

Insectivorous plants

Frank, J.H. and Lounibos, L.P. (eds) (1983) *Phytotelmata: Terrestrial Plants as Hosts for Aquatic Insect Communities*, Plexus, Medford, New Jersey, 293 pp.

Stack, A. (1980) *Carnivorous Plants*, MIT Press, Cambridge, Massachusetts, 240 pp.

Insects and micro-organisms

Batra, L.R. (ed.) (1979) *Insect–Fungus Symbiosis: Nutrition, Mutualism and Commensalism*, Wiley, New York, 276 pp.

Buchner, P. (1965) *Endosymbiosis of Animals with Plant Microorganisms*, Wiley–Interscience, New York, 909 pp.

Fuxa, J.R. and Tanada, Y. (1987) *Epizootiology of Insect Diseases*, Wiley, New York, 640 pp.

Houk, E.J. and Griffiths, G.W. (1980) Intracellular symbiotes of the Homoptera. *A. Rev. Entomol.*, **25**, 161–87.

Steinhaus, E.A. (1963) *Insect Pathology. An Advanced Treatise*, McGraw-Hill, New York, 2 Vols.

Wheeler, Q. and Blackwell, M. (eds) (1984) *Fungus–Insect Relationships. Perspectives in Ecology and Evolution*, Columbia University Press, New York, 514 pp.

Predators, parasitoids and ectoparasitic insects

Askew, R.R. (1971) *Parasitic Insects*, Heinemann, London, 316 pp.

Balduf, W.V. (1935) *The Bionomics of Entomophagous Coleoptera*, Swift, St Louis, 220 pp.

Balduf, W.V. (1939) *The Bionomics of Entomophagous Insects, Pt 2*. Swift, St Louis, 384 pp.

Brues, C.T. (1946) *Insect Dietary*, Harvard University Press, Cambridge, Massachusetts, 466 pp.

Clausen, C.P. (1940) *Entomophagous Insects*, McGraw-Hill, New York, 688 pp.

Doutt, R.L. (1959) The biology of parasitic Hymenoptera. *A. Rev. Entomol.*, **4**, 161–82.

Fisher, R.C. (1971) Aspects of the physiology of endoparasitic Hymenoptera. *Biol. Rev.*, **46**, 243–78.

Hocking, B. (1971) Blood sucking behaviour of terrestrial arthropods. *A. Rev. Entomol.*, **16**, 1–26.

Kim, K.C. (ed.) (1985) *Co-evolution of Parasitic Arthropods and Mammals*, Wiley, Chichester, 800 pp.

Marshall, A.G. (1981) *The Ecology of Ectoparasitic Insects*, Academic Press, 446 pp.

Price, P.W. (ed.) (1975) *Evolutionary Strategies of Parasitic Insects and Mites*, Plenum Press, New York, 224 pp.

Salt, G. (1970) *The Cellular Defence Reactions of Insects*, Cambridge University Press, Cambridge, 117 pp.

Thompson, S.N. (1986) Nutrition and in vitro culture of insect parasitoids. *A. Rev. Entomol.*, **31**, 197–219.

Vinson, S.B. (1976) Host selection by insect parasitoids. *A. Rev. Entomol.*, **21**, 109–33.

Vinson, S.B. and Iwantsch, G.F. (1981) Host suitability for insect parasitoids. *A. Rev. Entomol.*, **25**, 397–419.

Waage, J. (1979) The evolution of insect/vertebrate associations. *Biol. J. Linn. Soc.*, **12**, 187–224.

Waage, J. and Greathead, D. (eds) (1986) *Insect Parasitoids*, Academic Press, London, 390 pp.

Aquatic insects

Andersen, N.M. (1982) *The Semi-aquatic Bugs (Hemiptera, Gerromorpha). Phylogeny, Adaptations, Biogeography and Classification*, Scandinavian Science Press, Klempenbourg, 455 pp.

Anderson, N.H. and Sedell, J.R. (1979) Detritus processing by macro-invertebrates in stream ecosystems. *A. Rev. Entomol.*, **24**, 351–77.

Cheng, L. (1976) *Marine Insects*, Elsevier/North-Holland, New York, 585 pp.

Cummins, K.W. (1973) Trophic relations in aquatic insects. *A. Rev. Entomol.*, **18**, 183–206.

Hynes, H.B.N. (1970) *The Ecology of Running Waters*, University Press, Toronto, 555 pp.

Merritt, R.W. and Cummins, K.W. (1978) *An Introduction to the Aquatic Insects of North America*, Kendall Hunt, Dubuque, Iowa, 441 pp.

Pennak, R.W. (1978) *Freshwater Invertebrates of the United States*, Wiley, New York, 2nd edn, 803 pp.

Resh, V.H. and Rosenberg, D.M. (1984) *The Ecology of Aquatic Insects*, Praeger, New York, 638 pp.

Usinger, R.L. (ed.) (1956) *The Aquatic Insects of California*, University of California Press, Berkeley, 508 pp.

Wallace, J.B. and Merritt, R.W. (1980) Filter feeding ecology of aquatic insects. *A. Rev. Entomol.*, **25**, 103–32.

Wesenberg-Lund, G. (1943) *Biologie der Süsswasserinsekten*, Gyldendalske Boghandel, Copenhagen, 682 pp.

Protective coloration and mimicry

Blest, A.D. (1957) The function of eye spot patterns in Lepidoptera. *Behaviour*, **11**, 209–26.

Blum, M.S. (1978) *Chemical Defenses of Arthropods*, Academic Press, New York, 562 pp.

Carpenter, G.D.H. and Ford, E.B. (1933) *Mimicry*, Methuen, London, 134 pp.

Cott, H.B. (1940) *Adaptive Coloration in Animals*, Methuen, London, 508 pp.

De Ruiter, L. (1952) Some experiments on the camouflage of stick caterpillars. *Behaviour*, **4**, 222–32.

Duffey, S.S. (1981) Sequestration of plant natural products by insects. *A. Rev. Entomol.*, **25**, 447–77.

Edmunds, M. (1974) *Defence in Animals*, Longman, London, 358 pp.

Kettlewell, H.B.D. (1973) *The Evolution of Melanism*, Clarendon Press, Oxford, 424 pp.

Linsley, E.G., Eisner, T. and Klots, A.B. (1961) Mimetic assemblages of sibling species of Lycid beetles. *Evolution*, **15**, 15–29.

Rettenmeyer, C.W. (1970) Insect mimicry. *A. Rev. Entomol.*, **15**, 43–74.

Sheppard, P.M., Turner, J.R.G., Brown, K.S. *et al.* (1985) Genetics and the evolution of Muellerian mimicry in *Heliconius* butterflies. *Phil. Trans. R.*

Soc. B, **308**, 433–613.

Wickler, W. (1968) *Mimicry in Plants and Animals*, McGraw-Hill, New York, 225 pp.

Social insects

Alford, D.V. (1974) *Bumblebees*, Davis-Poynter, London, 352 pp.

Anderson,, M. (1984) The evolution of eusociality. *A. Rev. Ecol. Systemat.*, **15**, 165–89.

Breed, M.D., Michener, C.D. and Evans, H.E. (eds) (1982) *The Biology of Social Insects*, Westview Press, Colorado, 420 pp.

Brian, M.V. (1983) *Social Insects. Ecology and Behavioural Biology*, Chapman and Hall, London, 377 pp.

De Wilde, J. and Beetsma, J. (1982) The physiology of caste development in social insects. *Adv. Insect Physiol.*, **14**, 167–246.

Evans, H.E. and Eberhard, M.J.W. (1970) *The Wasps*, University of Michigan Press, Ann Arbor, 265 pp.

Free, J.B. (1987) *Pheronomes of Social Bees*. Chapman and Hall, London, 218 pp.

Free, J.B. and Butler, C.G. (1959) *Bumblebees*, Collins, London, 208 pp.

Frisch, K. von (1967) *The Dance Language and Orientation of Bees*, Harvard University Press, Cambridge, Massachusetts, 566 pp.

Hamilton, W.D. (1964) The genetical evolution of social behaviour. I, II. *J. Theor. Biol.*, **7**, 1–52.

Hamilton, W.D. (1972) Altruism and related phenomena, mainly in social insects. *A. Rev. Ecol. Systemat.*, **3**, 193–232.

Hermann, H. (ed.) (1979–82) *Social Insects*, Academic Press, New York, 4 Vols.

Howse, P.E. (1970) *Termites: A Study in Social Behaviour*, Hutchinson, London, 150 pp.

Krishna, K. and Weesner, F.M. (eds) (1969–70) *Biology of Termites*, Academic Press, New York, Vol. 1, 598 pp.; Vol. 2, 643 pp.

Lindauer, M. (1961) *Communication among Social Bees*, Harvard University Press, Cambridge, Massachusetts, revised edn, 173 pp.

Michener, C.D. (1974) *The Social Behaviour of the Bees: A Comparative Study*, Harvard University Press, Cambridge, Massachusetts, 404 pp.

Richards, O.W. (1971) Biology of the social wasps. *Biol. Rev.*, **46**, 483–528.

Schmidt, G.H. (ed.) (1974) *Sozialpolymorphismus bei Insekten*, Wissenschaftliche Verlagsgesellschaft, Stuttgart, 974 pp.

Schneirla, T.C. (1971) *Army Ants: A Study in Social Organization*, Freeman, San Francisco, 349 pp.

Spradbery, J.P. (1973) *Wasps: An Account of the Biology and Natural History of Solitary and Social Wasps*, Sidgwick and Jackson, London, 408 pp.

Wilson, E.O. (1971) *The Insect Societies*, Harvard University Press, Cambridge, Massachusetts, 548 pp.

7. THE BIOLOGY OF INSECT POPULATIONS

Andrewartha, H.G. and Birch, L.C. (1984) *The Ecological Web*, Chicago University Press, Chicago, 560 pp.

Baltensweiler, W., Benz, G., Bovey, P. and Delucchi, V. (1977) Dynamics of Larch Bud Moth populations. *A. Rev. Entomol.*, **22**, 79–100.

Begon, M. and Mortimer, M. (1986) *Population Ecology: A Unified Study of Animals and Plants*, Blackwell, Oxford, 2nd edn, 220 pp.

Clark, L.R., Geier, P.W., Hughes, R.D. and Morris, R.F. (1967) *The Ecology of Insect Populations in Theory and Practice*, Methuen, London, 232 pp.

Diehl, S.R. and Bush, G.L. (1984) An evolutionary and applied perspective of insect biotypes. *A. Rev. Entomol.*, **29**, 472–504.

Elton, C.S. (1966) *The Pattern of Animal Communities*, Chapman and Hall, London, 432 pp.

Ford, E.B. (1964) *Ecological Genetics*, Chapman and Hall, London, 335 pp.

Futuyma, D.J. and Peterson, S.C. (1985) Genetic variation in the use of resources by insects. *A. Rev. Entomol.*, **30**, 217–38.

Harcourt, D.G. (1964, 1971) Population dynamics of *Leptinotarsa decemlineata* (Say) in eastern Ontario. II, III. *Canadian Entomol.*, **96**, 1190–8; **103**, 1049–61.

Harcourt, D.G. (1969) The development and use of life tables in the study of natural insect populations. *A. Rev. Entomol.*, **14**, 175–96.

Hassell, M.P. (1976) *The Dynamics of Competition and Predation*, Edward Arnold, London, 68 pp.

Hassell, M.P. (1978) *The Dynamics of Arthropod Predator–Prey Systems*, University Press, Princeton, 237 pp.

Hassell, M.P. and Waage, J.K. (1984) Host–parasitoid population interactions. *A. Rev. Entomol.*, **29**, 89–114.

Huffaker, C.B. and Rabb, R.L. (eds) (1984) *Ecological Entomology*, Wiley, New York, 844 pp.

Lawton, J.H. (1983) Plant architecture and the diversity of phytophagous insects. *A. Rev. Entomol.*, **28**, 23–39.

Liss, W.J., Gut, L.J., Westgard, P.H. and Warren, C.E. (1986) Perspectives in arthropod community structure, organization, and development in agricultural crops. *A. Rev. Entomol.*, **31**, 455–78.

Morris, R.F. (1963) Predictive population equations based on key factors. *Mem. Entomol. Soc. Canada*, **32**, 16–21.

Morris, R.F. (ed.) (1963) The dynamics of epidemic spruce budworm populations. *Mem. Entomol. Soc. Canada*, **31**, 1–332.

Mound, L.A. and Waloff, N. (eds) (1978) Diversity of insect faunas. *Symp. R. Entomol. Soc. Lond.*, **9**, 1–204.

Nicholson, A.J. (1958) Dynamics of insect populations. *A. Rev. Entomol.*, **3**, 107–36.

Parsons, P.A. (1983) Ecobehavioral genetics: habitats and colonists. *A. Rev. Ecol. Systemat.*, **14**, 35–55.

Peters, T.M. and Barbosa, P. (1977) Influence of population density on size, fecundity and developmental rate of insects in culture. *A. Rev. Entomol.*, **22**, 431–50.

Pianka, E.R. (1970) On r and K selection. *Am. Naturalist*, **104**, 592–7.

Pielou, E.C. (1974) *Population and Community Ecology: Principles and Methods*, Gordon and Breach, New York, 424 pp.

Poole, R.W. (1974) *An Introduction to Quantitative Ecology*, McGraw-Hill, New York, 532 pp.

Price, P.W. (1984) *Insect Ecology*, Wiley, New York, 2nd edn, 600 pp.

Richards, O.W. and Waloff, N. (1954) Studies on the biology and population dynamics of British grasshoppers. *Anti-Locust Bull.*, **17**, 1–182.

Seber, G.E.F. (1982) *The Estimation of Animal Abundance*, Griffin, London, 2nd edn, 654 pp.

Shorrocks, B. (ed.) (1982) *Evolutionary Ecology*, Blackwell, Oxford, 418 pp.

Solomon, M.E. (1969) *Population Dynamics*, Edward Arnold, London, 60 pp.

Southwood, T.R.E. (ed.) (1968) Insect abundance. *Symp. R. Entomol. Soc. Lond.*, **4**, 1–160.

Southwood, T.R.E. (1975) *Ecological Methods*, Chapman and Hall, London, 2nd edn, 524 pp.

Southwood, T.R.E., Brown, V.K. and Reader, P.M. (1979) The relationship of plant and insect diversities in succession. *Biol. J. Linn. Soc.*, **12**, 327–48.

Strong, D.R., Simberloff, D., Abele, L.G. and Thistle, A.B. (eds) (1984) *Ecological Communities: Conceptual Issues and the Evidence*, Princeton University Press, Princeton, 613 pp.

Templeton, A.R. (1981) Mechanisms of speciation – a population genetic approach. *A. Rev. Ecol. Systemat.*, **12**, 23–48.

Varley, G.C., Gradwell, G.R. and Hassell, M.P. (1973) *Insect Population Ecology. An Analytical Approach*, Blackwell, Oxford, 212 pp.

Wingersky, P.J. (1978) Lotka–Volterra population models. *A. Rev. Ecol. Systemat.*, **9**, 189–218.

Wilson, E.O. and Bossert, W.H. (1971) *A Primer of Population Biology*, Sinauer, Stamford, Connecticut, 192 pp.

Young, A.M. (1982) *Population Biology of Tropical Insects*, Plenum Press, London, 511 pp.

8. BIOLOGY AND CONTROL OF INJURIOUS INSECTS

Insect pests of field crops

Alford, D.V. (1984) *A Colour Atlas of Fruit Pests. Their Recognition, Biology and Control*, Wolfe, London, 320 pp.

Annecke, D.P. and Moran, V.C. (1983) *Insects and Mites of Cultivated Plants in South Africa*, Butterworth, London, 383 pp.

Balachowsky, A.S. (1962→) *Entomologie appliquée à l'Agriculture*, Masson, Paris, 4 Vols.

Blackman, R.L. and Eastop, V.F. (1984) *Aphids on the World's Crops*, Wiley, New York, 466 pp.

Buczacki, S. and Harris, K. (1981) *Collins' Guide to Pests, Diseases and Disorders of Garden Plants*, Collins, London, 512 pp.

Carter, D.J. (1984) *Pest Lepidoptera of Europe with Special Reference to the British Isles*, Junk, Dordrecht, 432 pp.

Carter, W. (1973) *Insects in relation to Plant Disease*, Wiley, New York, 758 pp.

Davidson, R. and Lyon, W.F. (1979) *Insect Pests of Farm, Garden and Orchard*, Wiley, New York, 596 pp.

Edwards, C.A. and Heath, G.W. (1964) *The Principles of Agricultural Entomology*, Chapman and Hall, London, 418 pp.

Entwistle, P.F. (1972) *Pests of Cocoa*, Longman, London, 779 pp.

Ferro, D.N. (ed.) (1976) *New Zealand Insect Pests*, Lincoln University, Canterbury, New Zealand, 311 pp.

Grist, D.H. and Lever, R.J.A.W. (1969) *Pests of Rice*, Longman, London, 520 pp.

Harris, K.F. and Maramarosch, K. (1977) *Aphids as Virus Vectors*, Academic Press, New York, 559 pp.

Harris, K.F. and Maramarosch, K. (eds) (1980) *Vectors of Plant Pathogens*, Academic Press, New York, 467 pp.

Hill, D.S. (1983) *Agricultural Insect Pests of the Tropics and their Control*, Cambridge University Press, Cambridge, 2nd edn, 750 pp.

Hussey, N.W., Read, W.H. and Hesling, J.J. (1969) *The Pests of Protected Cultivation: The Biology and Control of Glasshouse and Mushroom Pests*, Edward Arnold, London, 404 pp.

Jones, F.G.W. and Jones, M.G. (1984) *Pests of Field Crops*, Edward Arnold, London, 3rd edn, 392 pp.

Kalshoven, L.G.E. (1981) *Pests of Crops in Indonesia*, Van Hoeve, Djakarta, 701 pp. (revised and transl. P.A. van der Laan).

Kitching, R.L. and Jones, R.E. (1981) *The Ecology of Pests: Some Australian Case Histories*, CSIRO, Melbourne, 254 pp.

Kranz, J., Schmutterer, H. and Koch, W. (eds) (1977) *Diseases, Pests and Weeds in Tropical Crops*, Parey, Hamburg, 666 pp.

Le Pelley, R.H. (1968) *Pests of Coffee*, Longman, London, 590 pp.

Maramarosch, K. and Harris, K.F. (eds) (1979) *Leafhopper Vectors and Plant Disease Agents*, Academic Press, London, 654 pp.

Metcalf, C.L. and Flint, W.P. (1951) *Destructive and Useful Insects*, McGraw-Hill, New York, 3rd edn, 584 pp.

Pearson, E.O. (1958) *The Insect Pests of Cotton in Tropical Africa*, Empire Cotton Growing Corporation, London, 355 pp.

Pfadt, R.E. (ed.) (1978) *Fundamentals of Applied Entomology*, Macmillan, New York, 798 pp.

Pirone, P.P. (1978) *Diseases and Pests of Ornamental Plants*, Wiley, New York, 566 pp.

Pruthi, H.S. (1969) *Textbook on Agricultural Entomology*, Indian Council of Agricultural Research, New Delhi, 977 pp.

Singh, S.R., Van Emden, H.F. and Taylor, T.A. (eds) (1978) *Pests of Grain Legumes: Ecology and Control*, Academic Press, London, 454 pp.

Uvarov, B.P. (1966, 1977) *Grasshoppers and Locusts*, Cambridge University Press, Cambridge, Vol. 1, 481 pp.; Vol. 2, 597 pp.

Vasantharaj David, B. and Kumaraswami, T. (1975) *Elements of Economic Entomology*, Popular Book Depot, Madras, 508 pp.

Williams, J.R., Metcalfe, J.R., Montgomery, R.W. and Mathes, R. (eds) (1939) *Pests of Sugar Cane*, Elsevier, Amsterdam, 568 pp.

Insect pests of forestry, timber and stored products

Anderson, J.F. and Kaya, H.K. (1976) *Perspectives in Forest Entomology*, Wiley, New York, 435 pp.

Beeson, C.F.C. (1941) *The Ecology and Control of the Forest Insects of India and th· Neighbouring Countries*, Vasant Press, Dehra Dun, 767 pp.

Berryman, A.A. (1986) *Forest Insects: Principles of Practice of Population Management*, Plenum Press, New York, 294 pp.

Bevan, D. (1987) Forest Insects, *Forestry Commission Hbk*, **1**: 153 pp.

Browne, F.G. (1968) *Pests and Diseases of Forest Plantation Trees*, Oxford University Press, Oxford, 1330 pp.

Coulson, R.N. and Witter, J.A. (1984) *Forest Entomology: Ecology and Management*, Wiley, New York, 669 pp.

Gray, B. (1972) Economic tropical forest entomology. *A. Rev. Entomol.*, **17**, 313–54.

Harris, W.V. (1971) *Termites: Their Recognition and Control*, Longman, London, 2nd edn, 187 pp.

Hicken, N.E. (1972) *The Woodworm Problem*, Hutchinson, London, 2nd edn, 123 pp.

Hickin, N.E. (1975) *The Insect Factor in Wood Decay: An Account of Wood-boring Insects with Particular Reference to Timber Indoors*, Associated Business Programmes, London, 3rd edn, 383 pp. (revised and ed. R. Edwards).

Hickin, N.E. (1985) *Pest Animals in Buildings*, Godwin, London, 385 pp.

Hinton, H.E. (1945) *A Monograph of the Beetles Associated with Stored Products*, British Museum (Natural History), London, 443 pp.

Munro, J.W. (1966) *Pests of Stored Products*, Hutchinson, London, 234 pp.

Schwenke, W. (ed.) (1972→) *Die Forstschädlinge Europas*, Parey, Hamburg, 5 Vols.

Insect pests of medical and veterinary importance

Bruce-Chwatt, L.J. (1985) *Essential Malariology*, Heinemann, London, 2nd edn, 452 pp.

Busvine, J.R. (1980) *Insects and Hygiene*, Chapman and Hall, London, 3rd edn, 565 pp.

Buxton, P.A. (1947) *The Louse*, Edward Arnold, London, 2nd edn, 164 pp.

Buxton, P.A. (1955) *The Natural History of Tsetse Flies*, Lewis, London, 816 pp.

Clements, A.N. (1963) *The Physiology of Mosquitoes*, Pergamon Press, Oxford, 393 pp.

Davies, H. (1977) *Tsetse Flies in Nigeria*, Oxford University Press, Ibadan, 340 pp.

Defoliart, G.R., Grimstad, P.R. and Watts, D.M. (1987) Advances in mosquito-borne arbovirus/vector research. *A. Rev. Entomol.*, **32**, 479–505.

Ford, J. (1971) *The Role of Trypanosomiases in African Ecology: A Study of the Tsetse Fly Problem*, Clarendon Press, Oxford, 568 pp.

Friend, W.G. and Smith, J.J.B. (1977) Factors affecting feeding by bloodsucking insects. *A. Rev. Entomol.*, **22**, 309–31.

Furman, D.P. and Catts, E.P. (1983) *Manual of Medical Entomology*, Cambridge University Press, Cambridge, 4th edn, 224 pp.

Glasgow, J.P. (1963) *The Distribution and Abundance of Tsetse*, Pergamon Press, Oxford, 252 pp.

Greenberg, B. (1971) *Flies and Disease*, Princeton University Press, Princeton, 2 Vols.

Harrison, G. (1978) *Mosquitoes, Malaria and Man*, Dutton, New York, 314 pp.

Harwood, R.F. and James, M.T. (1979) *Entomology in Human and Animal Health*, Macmillan, New York, 7th edn, 548 pp.

Horsfall, W.R. (1972) *Mosquitoes: Their Bionomics and Relation to Disease*, Hafner, New York, 723 pp.

Kettle, D.S. (1984) *Medical and Veterinary Entomology*, Croom Helm, Beckenham, 664 pp.

Laird, M. (ed.) (1977) *Tsetse: the Future for Biological Methods in Integrated Control*, International Development Research Centre, Ottawa, 220 pp.

Laird, M. (ed.) (1981) *Blackflies: the Future for Biological Methods in Integrated Control*, Academic Press, London, 399 pp.

Laird, M. and Miles, J.W. (1983, 1985) *Integrated Mosquito Control: Methodologies*, Academic Press, London, Vol. 1, 388 pp.; Vol. 2, 444 pp.

Levine, M.I. and Lockey, R.F. (1981) *Monograph on Insect Allergy*, Typecraft, Pittsburgh, 84 pp.

Lewis, D.J. (1974) The biology of Phlebotomidae in relation to leishmaniasis. *A. Rev. Entomol.*, **19**, 363–84.

Mattingley, P.F. (1969) *The Biology of Mosquito-borne Disease*, Allen and Unwin, London, 184 pp.

Muirhead-Thomson, R.C. (1968) *Ecology of Insect Vector Populations*, Academic Press, London, 174 pp.

Muirhead-Thomson, R.C. (1982) *Behaviour Patterns of Bloodsucking Flies*, Pergamon Press, Oxford, 240 pp.

Mulligan, H.W. (ed.) (1970) *The African Trypanosomiases*, Allen and Unwin, London, 903 pp.

Rogers, D.J. and Randolph, S.E. (1985) Population ecology of tsetse. *A. Rev. Entomol.*, **30**, 197–216.

Service, M.W. (1976) *Mosquito Ecology: Field Sampling Methods*, Applied Science Publishers, London, 583 pp.

Smith, K.G.V. (ed.) (1973) *Insects of Medical Importance*, British Museum (Natural History), London, 560 pp.

Smith, K.G.V. (1986) *A Manual of Forensic Entomology*, British Museum (Natural History), London, 256 pp.

Soulsby, E.J.L. (1971) *Helminths, Arthropods and Protozoa of Domesticated Animals*. Baillière, Tindall and Cassell, London, 6th edn, 824 pp.

Washino, R.K. and Tempelis, C.H. (1983) Mosquito host bloodmeal identification: methodology and data analysis. *A. Rev. Entomol.*, **28**, 179–201.

Williams, R.E., Hall, R.D., Broce, A.E. and Scholl, P.J. (1985) *Livestock Entomology*, Wiley, New York, 348 pp.

Yuill, T.M. (1986) The ecology of tropical arthropod borne viruses. *A. Rev. Ecol. Systemat.*, **17**, 189–219.

Zeledón, R. and Rabinovich, J.E. (1981) Chagas' disease: an ecological appraisal with special emphasis on its insect vectors. *A. Rev. Entomol.*, **26**, 202–33.

Zumpt, F. (1965) *Myiasis in Man and Animals in the Old World*, Butterworth, London, 267 pp.

Insect pest control (general)

Conway, G.R. (ed.) (1984) *Pest and Pathogen Strategies*, Wiley, Chichester, 512 pp.

Flint, M.L. and van den Bosch, R. (1982) *Introduction to Integrated Pest Management*, Plenum Press, New York, 256 pp.

Huffaker, C.B. (ed.) (1980) *New Technology of Pest Control*, Wiley, New York, 500 pp.

Knipling, E.F. (1979) The basic principles of insect population suppression and management. *USDA Agric. Hbk.*, **512**, 659 pp.

Kumar, R. (1984) *Insect Pest Control with Special Reference to West Africa*, Edward Arnold, London, 320 pp.

Martin, H. and Woodcock, D. (1983) *The Scientific Principles of Plant Protection*, Edward Arnold, London, 496 pp.

Matthews, G.A. (1984) *Pest Management*, Longman, London, 285 pp.

Metcalf, R.L. and Luckman, W.H. (1982) *Introduction to Insect Pest Management*, Wiley, New York, 577 pp.

Pimentel, D. (1981) *CRC Handbook of Pest Management in Agriculture*, CRC Press, Boca Raton, Florida, 3 Vols.

Youdeowei, A. and Service, M.W. (1983) *Pest and Vector Management in the Tropics*, Longman, London, 320 pp.

Insecticidal control

Brown, A.W.A. (1978) *Ecology of Pesticides*, Wiley, New York, 525 pp.

Caswell, R., Debold, K.J. and Gilbert, L.S. (eds) (1981) *The Pesticide Handbook*, Entomological Society of America, Hyattsville, 29th edn, 300 pp.

Coats, J.R. (1982) *Insecticide Mode of Action*, Academic Press, New York, 488 pp.

Corbett, J.R., Wright, K. and Baillie, A.C. (1984) *The Biochemical Mode of Action of Pesticides*, Academic Press, New York, 2nd edn, 392 pp.

CPCR (1987) *Crop Protection Chemicals Reference*, Wiley, New York, 3rd edn, 2000 pp.

Doll, R. (ed.) (1979) Long term hazards from environmental chemicals. *Phil. Trans. R. Soc. B*, **205**, 197 pp.

Elliott, M., Janes, N.F. and Potter, C. (1978) The future of pyrethroids in insect control. *A. Rev. Entomol.*, **23**, 443–70.

Hutson, D.H. and Roberts, T.R. (eds) (1986) *Insecticides*, Wiley, Chichester, 400 pp.

Mallis, A. (1981) *Handbook of Pest Control*, Entomological Society of America, Hyattsville, 6th edn, 1200 pp.

Matsumura, F. (1985) *Toxicology of Insecticides*, Plenum Press, New York, 2nd edn, 650 pp.

Matthews, G.A. (1978) *Pesticide Application Methods*, Longman, London, 480 pp.

Metcalf, R.L. (1980) Changing role of insecticides in crop protection. *A. Rev. Entomol.*, **25**, 219–56.

Perring, F.H. and Mellanby, K. (1977) *Ecological Effects of Pesticides*, Academic Press, London, 300 pp.

Ware, G.W. (1982) *Pesticides: Theory and Application*, Freeman, San Francisco, 308 pp.

Wilkinson, C.F. (ed.) (1976) *Insecticide Biochemistry and Physiology*, Heyden, London, 740 pp.

Worthing, C.R. and Walker, S.B. (eds) (1984) *The Pesticide Manual*, British Crop Protection Council, 7th edn, 695 pp.

Non-insecticidal control methods

Burges, H.D. (ed.) (1981) *Microbial Control of Pests and Plant Diseases 1970–1980*, Academic Press, New York, 949 pp.

Burges, H.D. and Hussey, N.W. (1971) *Microbial Control of Insects and Mites*, Academic Press, New York, 861 pp.

Caltagirone, L.E. (1981) Landmark examples in classical biological control. *A. Rev. Entomol.*, **26**, 213–32.

Clausen, C.P. (ed.) (1978) Introduced parasites and predators of arthropod pests and weeds: a world review. *Agric. Hbk US Dept. Agric.*, No. 480, 545 pp.

Coppel, H.C. and Mertins, J.W. (1977) *Biological Insect Pest Suppression*, Springer, Heidelberg, 320 pp.

Curtis, C.F. (1985) Genetic control of insect pests: growth industry or lead balloon? *Biol. J. Linn. Soc.*, **26**, 359–74.

Davidson, G. (1974) *Genetic Control of Insect Pests*, Academic Press, London, 158 pp.

Debach, P. (1964) *Biological Control of Insect Pests and Weeds*, Reinhold, New York, 844 pp.

Ferron, P. (1978) Biological control of insect pests by entomogenous fungi. *A. Rev. Entomol.*, **23**, 409–42.

Henry, J.E. (1982) Natural and applied control of insects by Protozoa. *A. Rev. Entomol.*, **26**, 49–73.

Hoy, M. and Herzog, D.C. (eds) (1985) *Biological Control in Agricultural IMP Systems*, Academic Press, New York, 600 pp.

Huffaker, C.B. and Messenger, P.S. (eds) (1976) *Theory and Practice of Biological Control*, Academic Press, New York, 788 pp.

Hussey, N.W. and Scopes, N. (eds) (1985) *Biological Pest Control: the Glasshouse Experience*, Mallard Book Services, Poole, 240 pp.

Kalmakoff, J. and Longworth, J.F. (1980) Microbial control of insect pests. *DSIR (N.Z.) Bull.*, **228**, 1–101.

Kogan, M. (ed.) (1987) *Ecological Theory and Integrated Pest Management Practice*, Wiley, New York, 382 pp.

Kydonieus, A.F. and Beroza, M. (1982) *Insect Suppression with Controlled Release Pheromone Systems*, CRC Press, Boca Raton, Florida, Vol. 1, 274 pp.; Vol. 2, 312 pp.

Maramorosch, K. and Sherman, K.E. (eds) (1985) *Viral Insecticides for Biological Control*, Academic Press, New York, 809 pp.

Maxwell, F.G. and Jennings, P.R. (eds) (1980) *Breeding Plants Resistant to Insects*, Entomological Society of America, College Park, Maryland, 683 pp.

Metcalf, R.L. and Luckman, W.H. (eds) (1982) *Introduction to Insect Pest Management*, Wiley, New York, 592 pp.

Mitchell, E.R. (ed.) (1981) *Management of Insect Pests with Semiochemicals*, Plenum Press, New York, 528 pp.

Nordland, D.A., Jones, R.L. and Lewis, W.J. (eds) (1981) *Semiochemicals: Their Role in Pest Control*, Wiley, New York, 306 pp.

Pal, R. and Whitten, M.J. (eds) (1974) *Use of Genetics in Insect Control*, Elsevier, Amsterdam, 241 pp.

Poinar, G.O. and Thomas, G.M. (1984) *Laboratory Guide to Insect Pathogens and Parasites*, Plenum Press, New York, 408 pp.

Quraishi, M.S. (1977) *Biochemical Insect Control*, Wiley, New York, 280 pp.

Steiner, W.W.M., Tabachnik, W.J., Rai, K.S. and Narrang, S. (eds) (1982) *Recent Developments in the Genetics of Insect Disease Vectors*, Stipes Publishing, Champaign, 665 pp.

INDEX

Generic and specific names are in italics. Synonyms are indicated by a cross-reference (e.g. *Calandra see Sitophilus*). Page numbers in **bold** type denote illustrations.